D1615412

Trees of the British Isles

Trees of the British Isles

Edited by Barry Tebbs

Orbis · London

Acknowledgements

Contributing authors Penny Anderson · Susyn Andrews · Stephen Blackmore · Lesley Caudry · William Condry · Pam Forey · Esmond Harris · Jeanette Harris · Charles Hilton · Chris Humphries · Charlie Jarvis · Terry Jennings · Sabina Knees · Scott Leathart · John Lewis · John Mason · Bob Press · Ian Richardson · Keith Rushforth · Peter Schofield · William Seymour · Robert A Spicer · Ken Stott · David Sutton · Hugh Synage · Brian Taylor · Barry Tebbs · Roy Vickery · John Waters · Gerald Wilkinson

Photo credits Penny Anderson 22(T): S Andrews 199(TR): Heather Angel 10, 16, 20, 22(B), 23, 25(B), 28, 31, 33(M,BR), 36, 37(B), 38(T), 39(M,B), 46-7, 49, 51(B), 57(T), 58(T,B), 60, 61(B), 64(T,B), 65, 66, 69(T,B), 71, 72, 73, 74(T, 76(BR), 77, 82(T), 85(T,M), 88, 89, 90(M), 94, 95(T,M), 97, 99, 100, 101, 104(M,B), 106(T,B), 107(T), 108, 109(B), 112, 117, 119, 120(B), 123, 134, 135(B), 138, 139, 142(T), 143, 144(M,B), 145(T,M), 146, 147(M), 150(B), 153(T,B), 154, 155, 157, 158, 159, 162, 163(M), 167, 168(M,B), 169, 170(B), 171, 173(M), 174, 175, 177(M), 178, 179(B), 180(M), 181, 187(B), 188, 191(B), 192, 193(T,B), 196, 197(T), 201(T,M), 206, 207, 208, 210, 211(T,BR), 215, 218(T,M), 219(BL), 225, 226(BR), 230, 231, 232, 236(T), 243, 244(B), 248(M), 257(T), 261: Aquila Photographics/A Cooper 70(B): DI McEwan 38(B), 42: J Roberts 205(T): Sawford & Castle 120-1: A-Z Collection 13, 15(B), 18(TR), 40, 41(M), 74(T), 75, 76(BL), 93(T,M), 130, 132, 163(B), 199(B), 200, 202, 205(B), 219(M), 220, 221, 222(T), 224(T), 233(T), 234, 236(B), 337(B), 238, 244(T), 245(T), 251(B), 256(B): Ian Beames 62: Daisy Benth 198: Theo Bergstrom 43(T,B), 44(T,B): Frank Blackburn 22(LM): Michael Chinery 259: Bruce Coleman Ltd/J Burton 6, 56, 186; B Coleman 237(M); E Crichton 52(T,B), 70(T), 78(B), 151, 160(B), 222(BR), 233(B), 248(B), 258; N Fox-Davies 102, 224(M); M Freeman 47(L); L Lee Rue 111 242(B); H Reinhard 140, 191(T); R Wilmshurst 126: William Condry 177(B): David Corke 141(M): Eric Crichton Photos 103, 114, 116, 129(L,R), 216(B): Adrian Davies 18(BL), 185(B): Martin Dorhn 110: Vaughan Fleming 9(R), 226(BL), 260(T): Format Publishing Services 34(T), 35(M): Bob Gibbons Photography/R Fletcher 257(T); B Gibbons 33(BL), 63(B), 83, 84(M), 90(B), 148(B), 179(M), 211(BL), 246, 256(T): Brian Hawkes 166: Ken Hoy 26(L,R), 27(L,R): George Hyde 170(T), 173(B), 182(R), 187(M). 195(M), 209, 247, 248(T), 253(M): Institute of Geological Sciences 107(B): EA Janes 164: Ian Jones-Parry 189(T): Martin King & Mike Read/G Dore 30; M King 80(T), 229 (T); M King & M Read 70; M Read 32(B): Stewart Lane 12: Scott Leathart 98(B): John Mason 9(TL), 61(T), 153(M), 160(T), 163(B), 204(T), 216(M), 242(T): Richard Mills 39(T), 251(T), 253(T): Pat Morris 68(T,M,B), 85(B), 95(B), 105, 109(M), 142 (BL), 182(L), 229(B): NHPA/J & M Bain 50(B); R Bilharry 22(UM); NA Callow 25(M), 58(M), 63(M); GJ Cambridge 1: GJ Cambridge & J & M Bain 145(B), 176(B), 183, 194; R & C Foord 190; B Hawkes 195(B); EA Janes 37(T), 41(T), 80(B), 125(B), 133, 135(T), 172, 176(T), 228; LH Newman 223; KG Preston-Mafham 165(M); M Savonius 51(T), 67, 165(B), 203, 217: Nature Photographers Ltd/SC Bisserot 86, 87(T), 127, 222(BL), 240; FV Blackburn 2, 8, 25(T), 32(T), 148(T), 161(T), 204(B); B Burbidge 82(B), 96, 98(T), 260(B); K Carlson 14(M); A Cleave 180(B), 197(B); AK Davies 11; JV & GR Harrison 147(B); A Mitchell 54, 128; CK Mylne 180(T), 185(T); M Oates 84(B); C Palmer 15(T), 149; T Schilling 47(R), 92(M); R Tidman 35(T): Maurice Nimmo 30, 68, 184, 235: Premaphotos Wildlife/KG Preston-Mafham 63(T), 131, 189(B), 201(B): Presstige Pictures/R Jones 250; T Tilford 252: John Robinson 15(M), 45(M), 57(M), 118, 150(T), 156: Keith Rushforth 34(B), 48: Harry Smith Collection 18(TL), 29, 50(T), 76(T), 78(T), 87(B), 199(TL), 219(BL), 245(B), 249, 254: K Stott 121(M,B): DA Sutton 17(T,UM,LM,B), 18(BR); MJ Thomas 91, 92(T); UNHA/A Goodger 241; G Rankin 218(B): Victoria & Albert Museum 45(T): Wildlife Services/M Leach 161(B): Gerald Wilkinson 14(B), 118, 125(T), 126, 136, 137(M,B), 141(B), 142(BR), 165(T), 214.

Artists' credits Russell Barnett 35, 44: Eugene Fleury 53(map): The Garden Studio/Bob Bampton 9, 57, 108, 109, 134(M), 136, 137, 189, 190, 199, 227, 230, 231, 241, 242; Kristen Jakob 72, 74(TR); Patti Pearce 21, 24; Liz Pepperell 179: Will Giles 77: Groom & Pickerill/Helen Senior 126, 161, 223, 224, 236, 237, 247, 259, 260: The Hayward Art Group 38, 61, 99, 100(TL), 101, 115(B), 124(c/u), 134(B), 139(c/u), 138, 140, 152(c/u), 167(thorns), 183, 197, 207(c/u), 216: Linden Artists/Tim Hayward 30-1; David More 13, 14, 19, 33, 53(trees), 59, 64, 65, 66, 70, 74(TL), 76, 80-1, 84, 86-7, 88, 90, 93, 95, 97, 98, 100(TR), 102, 104, 107, 115(T), 117, 120, 124(trees), 127, 129, 131, 132, 134(T), 139(trees), 141, 144, 147, 150, 152(trees), 155, 156, 158, 162, 165, 167(trees), 171, 173, 174, 177, 182, 185, 187, 193, 195, 204, 205, 207(trees), 210, 211, 215, 219, 221, 226, 229, 239, 245, 250, 251, 253, 255(trees), 261: Paul Nesbitt 33(line): Sandra Pond 39, 41, 42(L), 45, 58, 68, 234, 255(c/u), 256, 257: Bob Press 219(line): Colin Salmon 42(M), 48: Gerard Thomas 30: Colin Walton 14.

Material in this book previously appeared in *The Living Countryside*
© 1981, 1982, 1983, 1984 Eaglemoss Publications Limited and Orbis Publishing Limited.

First published in Great Britain by Orbis Publishing Limited, London 1984
© Orbis Publishing Limited 1984

Printed in Italy by Imago Publishing Limited

ISBN 0 85613 624 7 (hardcover)
ISBN 0 85613 633 6 (paperback)

Contents

Introducing trees

Mankind has been aware of trees since the very beginning of conscious thought. As we evolved, so our perception of trees altered. At first, the sheer bulk of a tree was worthy of note only as a large feature of the landscape, perhaps to be recognised when falling or being blown down as a phenomenon of no little danger. Later still, it was realised that trees would burn under certain circumstances, and that this fire could be utilised. From here, it was but a short step to using more wood to keep a fire going and, eventually, to start a fire. From this first use of wood, our awareness of it as a material grew. Trees became transformed into simple boats, devices to roll heavy articles over, and other things. Trees were also seen as a source of a valuable construction material. Timber is, of course, still very much in use today, and other tree products, such as rubber, paper, and the fruits and seeds of certain trees, are an essential part of our daily life.

Different woods have long been used for different purposes. The classic example of this is the beech, which is so highly prized for furniture construction that towns have prospered due to the nearness of large quantities of beech woodland. Other trees also have distinct uses; willows in particular being used both for making wattles and baskets, and also that most typically English weapon, the cricket bat! Some trees, such as hornbeam, box and spindle, produce woods of great hardness. These were used wherever durable wood was required. Other wood is simply decorative, making fine furniture and inlays.

Trees have also become objects to be appreciated for their grace, beauty and splendour of form. There are now many more species of trees growing in these islands than the 35 or so native species. These introduced trees have been imported in some cases simply for their timber, but many others, such as the superb cedars and larches, elegant trees such as the walnuts, and flowering species such as magnolia and oriental cherry, are here to please the eye. Our most useful street tree, the London plane is, surprisingly, also an introduction.

With a growing appreciation of the aesthetic attractions of trees has come a similar growth in the knowledge of their biology. We now know that both the largest, and the oldest, organisms on earth are trees–the Californian redwood, and the bristle-cone pine respectively. We can classify trees, and we can unravel their physiology and biochemistry. We understand how trees grow, and to what diseases they are prone. It enables us to know, for instance, why one small beetle has virtually removed the country's population of English elms.

The following pages provide a full account of the most popular trees and shrubs to be seen in the British Isles. Starting with the classification, ecology and uses of trees, the book then describes the lifestyles, habitats and appearance of over 130 species.

Opposite: A deciduous woodland scene–an oakwood in spring.

Britain's trees classified

The botanical names of trees tell us a great deal about how different species, and groups of species, are related to each other, and they also help us understand how trees have evolved from ancestral species over millions of years.

Above: The diversity of trees is clear enough even from a distance – the broad-leaved species in the foreground here look quite different from the upright conifers planted behind. Close to, a look at the leaves, flowers and fruits reveals more significant differences, both between conifers and broad-leaved trees and between different species in each group. These similarities and differences are recognised in our modern system of tree classification.

Plants are vital to man's needs. He has always relied on them to supply him with food and they have long provided him with timber for building and burning, and for a whole range of products, including paper, drugs, chemicals, oils and so on. The list is almost endless.

Because of their importance, man must early on have learned to name different plants so that he could recognise them quickly and distinguish them from one another. He would also have learned to classify plants as herbs, shrubs or trees and then he would have begun to group together plants that seemed similar under some general name, such as 'rose' or 'oak'.

This rudimentary grouping together of plants was the beginning of classification – a process that is essential when we think of just how many different plants there are in the world: for flowering plants and gymnosperms (conifers) the number is probably greater than 300,000 species.

However, the naming of trees was for long a haphazard affair. For example, the English, the sessile and the holm oaks were all correctly regarded as being closely related to each other because they all bear similar fruits – acorns. Hence, they were all called oaks. On the other hand, the sweet chestnut and the horse chestnut were also thought to be closely related because of their fruits. Yet today they are classified as belonging to quite different families.

Obviously, common names are not accurate enough for scientific purposes, and they are also too parochial for the international scientific community. To get round this problem Latin was adopted for naming trees (and all other plants and animals) since it was familiar to most scientists and understood by people of different nationalities. And the naming was given scientific precision by a set of rules that made it possible to fix the names of all living organisms.

Scientific classification These rules were first laid down in the 18th century by the Swedish botanist, Carl von Linné (more often called Linnaeus). He invented the principle of using two Latin words to name a species. The first is the generic name (genus) which, when combined with the second specific (species) name, gives a unique identity to each species and a clue to its relationships. Closely related species are given the same generic name but different specific names. For example, the Norway spruce is *Picea abies* and the closely related Colorado spruce is *Picea pungens*. All the species with the same generic name are said to belong to the same genus (plural genera), in this case *Picea*.

The process of classification does not end with all the different species being placed in the appropriate genera. In a similar manner, groups of genera can be combined into a higher category called a family, which in turn can be combined into even higher groups called orders, and so on to give a hierarchy of groups. To understand more about this hierarchy, it helps to look at evolution.

Evolution To justify the hierarchical system of classification, biologists assume that all the diverse organisms we see today evolved from a single common ancestor millions of years ago by a series of divisions. At each division, new species were formed which had characters different from those of their parents. Today, we have many different species showing varying degrees of relationship between each other, more closely related species having more recent ancestors than

Left: Sitka spruce (*Picea sitchensis*) with young female cones. Though similar to the Scots pine (*Pinus sylvestris*), shown right, in that both are conifers, the Sitka spruce is clearly very different in its leaves. Sitka spruce leaves are short, stiff and attached singly to the shoot, while on a pine they are usually much longer, more flexible and attached to the shoot in bundles, in this case pairs. The cones, both young and mature, are also noticeably different.

A close look at the beech family

How do we decide which two among the oak, the sweet chestnut and the beech are most closely related to one another? All are classified in the same family because they have many characters in common —the flowers are catkins, the fruit consists of one or more seeds partly or wholly enclosed in a casing, and so on. However, a closer look at the characters shows that the sweet chestnut and the beech have more characters in common with each other than either have with the oak. The branching diagrams show that the sweet chestnut and the beech have five characters in common (1, 4, 5, 6 and 7), whereas the oak and beech have only two in common (1 and 2) and the oak and the sweet chestnut also have only two in common (1 and 3). Therefore, the branching diagram on the far left best fits the facts and so is the one accepted as nearest the truth.

Oak   Sweet chestnut   Beech

Above: An examination of the flowers and fruits of the three species shows many of the characters listed in the table, particularly points 3, 4, 5 and 8.

Table of characters

		A	B	C
1	Male flowers in catkins	A	B	C
2	Male flowers flexuous	A	B	C
3	Male flowers spike-like	A	B	
4	Fruit cupules 4-lobed		B	C
5	Seeds enclosed in fruits		B	C
6	2–3 seeds in the fruits		B	C
7	Seeds angular		B	C
8	Fruits cup-like	A		
9	1 seed in fruits	A		
10	Seeds round	A		
11	Male catkins rigid		B	
12	Male catkins hang in clusters			C

A   Oak   B   Sweet chestnut   C   Beech

Below: Of the three possible branching diagrams that can be drawn for the oak, sweet chestnut and beech, the one on the far left fits the table best.

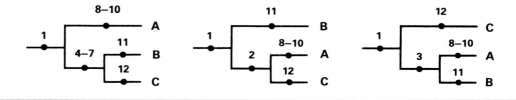

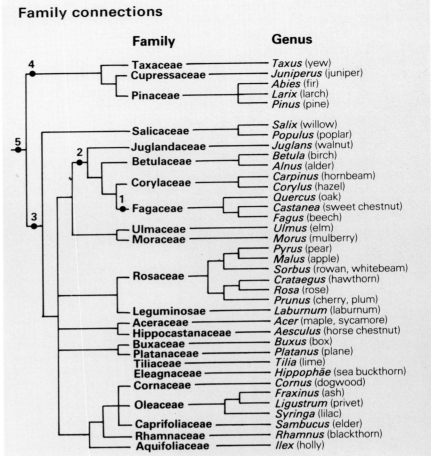

Family connections

| Family | Genus |

those that are more distantly related.

All this can be represented on what is known as a branching diagram or (rather confusingly in this case) as a tree diagram. Species with primitive characters appear close to the central 'trunk' of the tree while those with more recently evolved characters appear higher up in the branches.

Characters and relationships To see how a tree diagram works, consider the beech family. The diagram shows that it contains three British genera: oak, sweet chestnut and beech. All are classified as being in the same family because they have so many characters in common. But of these three, which two are more closely related to each other? To decide this, we can look at each tree's characters. If two species share the same characters, it can be assumed that they came from an ancestor not shared by the third species. In this case, the beech and the sweet chestnut have more characters in common with each other than either have with the oak, therefore it can be assumed that they inherited these features from a common ancestor not shared by the oak. Hence the forking pattern shown in the tree diagram (point 1).

It is possible to recognise groups of families. Thus the beech family (Fagaceae) can be combined with the hazel family (Corylaceae), the birch family (Betulaceae) and the walnut family (Juglandaceae) because they all bear catkins. This large group of trees forms a

super-order, the Hammelidinae (point 2).

Other groups can be identified among all the other families of broad-leaved trees, though the reasons are often obscure to the layman. For example, the rose family (Rosaceae) and the legume family (Leguminosae) are combined because the seeds lack an endosperm (a separate food store), the leaves bear stipules, and so on. Eventually all the broadleaved families combine to form the subclass Angiospermae (point 3).

Branching diagrams can also be drawn for conifer trees. The largest genus here is the pines, *Pinus*, characterised most obviously by the fact that their needles are modified branches occurring in bunches of two, three or five. The pines, larches and firs form a large family, the Pinaceae, which, with the other conifer families, forms the subclass Pinidae (point 3). The Pinidae and the Angiospermae join to form the class Pinitae (point 5), which then forms a larger group with all the other green plants.

Disagreements With so much information to be considered, it is not surprising that there are major disagreements among biologists about how species should be classified: some biologists now think that evolutionary ideas of relationships cannot be included in a classification scheme. The arguments rage on, and there has not been such bad temper in biology since 130 years ago, when Darwin first enunciated his theory of evolution.

Above: A table of the more common British trees and shrubs, showing how the different genera are grouped in families, and how these in turn are related to each other. This type of diagram is called a branching diagram or a tree diagram. It can be taken to represent more than just the relationship between genera and families. Since biologists assume that species closely related to each other shared a recent common ancestor, it follows that a tree diagram can be taken to represent the course of evolution of trees to our modern diversity of species.

Above left: The Rosaceae is a huge family numbering some 2000 species, including the hawthorn and other familiar trees. All members are distinguished principally by details of flower structure, but in the case of the hawthorn the relationship is clearly seen in the fruits (shown here) which, superficially, are distinctly hip-like in shape.

Tree design

A close look at the shapes of trees reveal some superb adaptations that allow them to become the largest organisms ever seen on this Earth.

From a very early age we are familiar with the fundamental design of a tree. Ask a young child to draw one and he or she will show a trunk and, somewhere above, branches and leaves. No other type of plant makes such an impact on us. Partly, this is due to the permanence of many specimens, but it is mainly their sheer size that impresses us.

Large size (usually at least 6m/20ft), along with a stout single stem at the base of the structure and leaf-bearing branches, are all features shared by almost every species of tree in the world. They must give trees important advantages over other plants, otherwise trees

would never have survived and flourished in the wild. But what are these advantages, and why are trees designed the way they are?

Size and strategy A tree has a distinct advantage over smaller plants. It can over-shadow them, filtering out the useful wave-lengths in sunlight that all plants need for photosynthesis, so that very few other species can compete directly underneath. A corollary to this is that once trees become established in a favourable climate they are unlikely to be displaced by any other plants. It is not surprising, therefore, that most of Britain was covered by forest before man began clearing it – trees being the end product of natural plant succession.

The great height attained by some trees, however, presents considerable problems. Imagine what would happen if an herbaceous plant normally 30cm (1ft) high were the height of a tree – say, 30m (100ft) – yet were made of the same herbaceous materials. Because the height is increased by a factor of 100 the weight of this giant plant would be a million times greater than the normal herb. The materials which are quite strong enough to support a plant the size of a buttercup would be totally inadequate to support something the size of a tree. The sheer weight of the plant would cause it to collapse.

Trees partly overcome this problem by the

Above: Broad-leaved trees such as this sycamore have most of their leaves on the tips of their branches to catch as much sunlight as possible. For a tree to produce leaves inside its canopy tends to be a waste of valuable material because these leaves would receive much less sunlight and so produce less food.

Girth and age
The girth of a trunk gives a good indication of the age of a tree, though the results may be misleading for some quick-growing species or specimens that are very young, very old, diseased or overcrowded. Measure the girth (circumference) of the trunk at a height of 1.5m (5ft) above the ground. The answer will be 2.5cm (1in) for every year of the tree's age. Thus a tree with a girth of 2.5m (8ft) will be about 100 years old.

Tree shapes: natural and man-made

Man's interference in his environment has led to several tree shapes quite different from the normal broad-leaved or conifer design. By cutting back trees to ground level he produced the coppice shape and to a height above ground level, the pollard. Fastigiate and most weeping forms are both mutations that would not normally survive in the wild but are propagated by man.

pollarded
(beech)

coppiced
(hazel)

weeping
(weeping beech)

broad-leaved
(oak)

fastigiate
(Lombardy poplar)

coniferous
(larch)

Opposite: Tall, straight-trunked beeches line the road at Savernake Forest, Wiltshire.

Below: The tapering shape of a tree trunk (such as this trunk of an old sweet chestnut tree) means that it is widest at its base. This is the best shape for resisting the sometimes considerable forces exerted on a tree by the wind.

way in which the cells in their trunk, branches and roots are constructed. As these cells die, various materials are laid down in them to strengthen the cell wall and so produce the material we call wood, a material that is not present in herbaceous plants.

Another way in which trees solve this problem is by having relatively thicker, straighter trunks than herbaceous plants—in exactly the same way as an elephant's legs are relatively much thicker and straighter than those of a mouse.

Importance of branches How does a tree manage to support enough leaves to manufacture the foods it needs yet, at the same time, keep the amount of materials needed for this to a minimum? The problem is solved by the tree's branching pattern.

Imagine two extreme designs of tree. In one, all the leaves are connected to just one single stem that twists its way through every part of the leaf canopy. The advantage of this design is that it keeps to a minimum the total length of stem material needed. But the stem has to perform two functions: as well as supporting the leaves it has to transport fluids between them and the roots. And, as a plumbing system, this design of a tree is totally impracticable because, for a tree with, say, 100,000 leaves, the stem would have to be enormously long. (Incidentally, trees with unbranched stems do exist. They are palms, which overcome the disadvantages of this design by having few, very large, divided leaves.)

The other extreme design is where every leaf has its own stem arising directly from the ground. This would be a very efficient pluming system, because the average distance from a leaf to the ground is much less than in the first design, but it would be very wasteful of stem material. Such a design is, however, found among some small herbaceous plants and a few shrubs.

The actual design of a typical tree is a compromise between these two extremes, in which a single trunk from the base branches repeatedly until the ultimate twigs bear the leaves. This design is a remarkably good compromise between the two extreme examples given above because it makes the most of the advantages while minimising the disadvantages of each example. Branching makes the best use of stem materials and it also provides an efficient means of transporting fluids to and from the leaves.

Leaf sizes and shapes

As air flows over the leaf surface it is slowed down and, just above the surface, forms a layer of still air—the boundary layer—which insulates the leaf and may overheat it. That is why large leaves like those of a sweet chestnut heat up more than small leaves such as a hornbeam's on a sunny day. Some trees evade this problem by adopting different leaf shapes such as lobing in the case of the sycamore or compound leaves like those of an ash. Both shapes reduce the build-up of the boundary layer over the leaf surface.

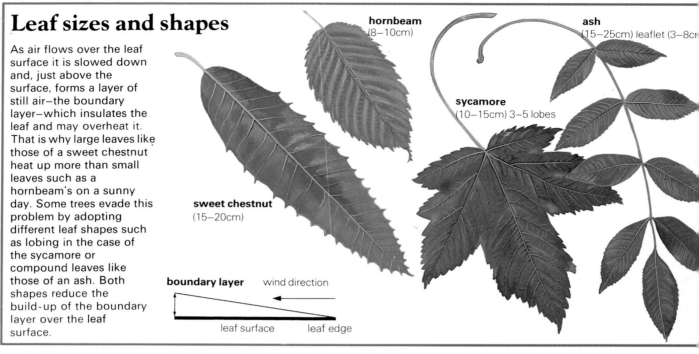

hornbeam
(8–10cm)

ash
(15–25cm) leaflet (3–8cm

sycamore
(10–15cm) 3–5 lobes

sweet chestnut
(15–20cm)

boundary layer   wind direction

leaf surface   leaf edge

Left: Holly is one of the few European broad-leaved trees that are evergreen. To protect themselves from excess water loss during the winter, the leaves are covered with a thick waxy cuticle on the upper surface. The vast majority of broad-leaved trees, however, lose their leaves entirely to avoid the rigours of winter.

Branching angles Given that it is good design for a tree to have branches, does it make any difference at what angle these branches split away from each other? Without going into details here, it seems that it does. Engineers have researched the problem in connection with the amounts of materials needed for various construction designs, and they have discovered that a branching angle of 90° requires the least amount of materials (wood, in the case of a tree). Furthermore, scientists looking at blood vessels have discovered that the flow of blood is most efficient when smaller vessels branch off from main vessels at right-angles.

Yet, despite this, there exist trees with very narrow branching angles, resulting in a narrow columnar shape known as fastigiate. An example is the Lombardy poplar, a tree that probably arose as a spontaneous mutation of the ordinary black poplar. Without man's intervention such a freak would never have survived in the wild.

Weeping trees seem to be the opposite of fastigiate trees. Yet most have a normal branching angle. Their shape arises from the fact that the new wood grows too fast for the tree to be able to support its weight.

Small leaves The final major design criterion concerns the leaves. A large tree may have as many as a quarter of a million leaves, which are mostly orientated to catch as much light as possible. To this end they are arranged to form a mosaic with remarkably little overlapping between adjacent leaves. On most species the leaves are fairly small, usually less than 10cm (4in) across. Even those with larger leaves, such as the horse chestnut, tend to have the leaf lobed or divided into separate leaflets. The leaf is also thin, thus exposing the largest surface area for a minimum waste of leaf material. But the main design question is why

Leaf variations

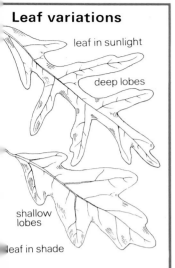

leaf in sunlight

deep lobes

shallow lobes

leaf in shade

The boundary layer effect is one reason why an oak leaf growing in the sun is more deeply lobed than one in shade.

Above right: The shape of a tree varies greatly with habitat. In an open habitat such as the Scottish Highlands, Scots pine matures to form its characteristic flat-topped crown. However, in the confined space of a plantation (see right) a Scots pine takes on a very different shape: much more upright and narrow. Notice also that the plantation trees have lost the foliage on their lower branches.

Below right: The shapes of trees also vary greatly with age. The young Scots pine shown here has a quite different outline to either of the two mature specimens shown above. It has a much broader, conical shape than the plantation tree, and it lacks the flat-topped crown on the tree growing in an open habitat.

Opposite left: The weather can have a great effect on the shape of a tree. Branches can be broken by winds or lightning, and trees subjected to frequent gales can become stunted. Prevailing winds can also have their effect, causing the tree to develop on the leeward side only, so that it appears to lean with the wind – as shown by this elm growing near the north Cornwall coast.

have a large number of small leaves, rather than just one giant leaf?

Keeping cool The small size of leaves may, in part, be explained by the fact that on a sunny day a leaf absorbs much more heat than it can lose. On a hot day, even in this country, the temperature of a leaf can reach a lethal limit. The problem is made worse by the existence of a layer of still air – called the boundary layer – immediately above the leaf surface that insulates the leaf and prevents it from cooling. The larger the leaf the thicker this boundary layer becomes, so more numerous and smaller leaves, lobing and dividing into leaflets are all methods of keeping leaves cool.

There is another reason for having small leaves. In Britain, most of our broad-leaved trees are deciduous. Yet large leaves require disproportionately large veins, large leaf stalks, and a thick blade – all for exactly the same reason as a tree needs a thick trunk. To lose large leaves after just one season would mean a massive loss of hard-won material.

Small leaves with a lighter construction are far more efficient for deciduous trees. Really large tree leaves are restricted mostly to evergreen species of the humid tropics.

Design and evolution The gradual evolution of trees to their present design has, of course, been a process of natural selection. Natural selection has favoured particular designs over others, less suitable ones becoming rare or dying out altogether: those species best able to survive the rigours of their environment to produce offspring are more likely to be represented in later generations.

So today we see a very successful group of plants that have colonized a large part of the Earth's surface, and have produced the largest and also the longest-lived individuals in the world.

Bark

Bark–whether it be rough and fissured as on an oak, or smooth as on a beech–performs the same function in all trees: that of protecting the delicate living tissue in the trunk from the weather and from attack by animals and diseases.

Even the most casual visitor to a public garden will have noticed the immense variation in the barks of trees. The smooth, brilliant white bark of the Himalayan birch and the glossy, reddish-brown, peeling bark of the Tibetan cherry make these two of our most attractive ornamental trees. Among our more familiar species, the sweet chestnut has a

Below: The rich reddish-brown trunk of the sweet chestnut, combined with the spirally arranged ridges found on many older specimens, make this species one of the few common trees in Britain that can be identified by bark alone.

strikingly spiralled bark, while that of the Scots pine is a rich brown and falls away from the tree in flakes. To us, the bark of a tree is often a very useful aid to identification, particularly in winter when many trees have lost their leaves. For the tree, however, the bark performs a vital function in protecting it from extremes of weather and against the attacks of a variety of agents, from bacteria and fungi to rabbits and deer.

How bark functions Bark consists of a living inner layer of tissue (the phloem) and an outer dead layer. The phloem plays a vital role in transporting sugars down from the leaves, where they are manufactured by photosynthesis, to the roots and other parts. The outer layer of bark is waterproof and so protects the underlying tissues from drying out. In parts of the world where seasonal fires are a potential hazard some trees have extra-thick barks to insulate the living tissue from the heat. The best known of these is the cork oak from the Mediterranean region, the bark of which has thermal insulating properties rivalling those of glass fibre. Furthermore, the presence of air spaces makes the material light and compressible. Combine this with its waterproof qualities and you have the ideal material for sealing bottles–cork. The cork oak is not often seen in British parks, but its hybrid with the Turkey oak, called Lucombe's oak, appears much more frequently, especially in the West Country.

Bark is also a tree's first line of defence against attacks by bacteria, fungi, insects and larger animals such as deer and rabbits. In most cases it repels these attacks effectively, though large herbivores may destroy so much of a tree's bark in winter when other food sources are scarce that the trunk is completely encircled by the damage. When this happens the tree inevitably dies.

To provide extra protection against this possibility, trees with thin barks higher up often have much thicker barks near the base. This may be seen on both silver birch and Scots pine.

Bark formation Bark is formed by the activity of a special sort of cambium (the wet, green tissue lying just underneath the bark). Known as the bark cambium, this layer plus the corky cells it creates are together known as the periderm. In the young tree, the periderm first arises in the outer tissues of a shoot and can be seen as a colour change, usually from green to grey. The colour change is caused by the presence of waterproof waxes and other materials in the walls of the bark cells.

In some species, such as beech and hornbeam, the periderm thus created can last for many years, slowly increasing in size by cell division as the tree's girth expands. In the majority of trees, however, the first periderm is soon followed by others arising from progressively deeper layers of the stem. With the formation of each periderm, the tissue layers lying outside it are cut off from their

source of water and nutrients, and so die.

Different bark types As the branches and trunks increase in girth resulting from cell division in the cambium, the bark must also increase in size. Thus new layers of bark are continually created within the stem. The number of layers of cork cells produced by the periderm and the depths at which they occur in the stem vary considerably and determine the thickness of the bark. A thin bark, such as that of *Stewartia* species, is smooth while a thick bark, such as that of English oak or black walnut, is rough and fissured.

In some trees the older layers of bark readily peel away or break off. This can be seen in the paper-bark maple and various species of strawberry tree. If the layers remain firmly attached, as in wellingtonia and coast redwood, then a thick bark builds up, which is only gradually worn away. Persistent barks often become deeply fissured because the older, dead, layers on the outside are unable to grow to keep pace with the expanding trunk.

In some species the periderm can completely encircle the stem and, if the outer bark falls away, then whole cylinders of bark can be discarded. Traveller's joy, honeysuckle and paper birch all have such barks. In the case of paper birch, large sheets of its bark were used by certain North American Indians in the building of their canoes.

In other trees the periderm is much more localised, arising one beneath another like overlapping scales. The resulting bark is therefore shed as discrete, irregularly shaped pieces. In Britain, the most familiar examples of this type of bark are those of yew and London plane.

Lenticels for air In common with herbaceous plants, the stem of a young tree contains structures known as stomata through which the stem cells obtain oxygen and lose carbon dioxide. When the stem loses its original epidermis it also loses its stomata and their job is taken over by small lens-shaped pores in the bark called lenticels.

Most woody plants have lenticels on their stems, though they can vary from being microscopically small to 1cm ($\frac{1}{2}$in) or more in diameter. In some species, such as birches, the

Above: In some species the first layer of bark laid down by the young tree quickly grows to build up a thick layer of corky tissue. On a young Dutch elm (a hybrid between the smooth-leaved elm and the wych elm) this corky tissue splits as the tree grows, forming corky 'wings' around the young shoots. These can be seen on the branches in the picture shown here.

lenticels enlarge with age.

Other features Along with lenticels, some trees also have spines on their branches or trunks. Hawthorns have spines formed from small branches, though at up to 1.5cm ($\frac{5}{8}$in) long they are insignificant compared with the branched thorns of some honey locusts, which can grow to a length of 10cm (4 in). The more familiar locust tree, or false acacia, has spiny stipules on its younger branches. These were originally at the bases of the leaves.

Occasionally trees produce masses of shoots directly from the bark. These arise from buds that, for most of the time, lie dormant within the trunk. This is a particular feature of the common lime, which often has large tufts of leafy shoots sprouting from its bark. Dormant buds can be very important to the tree as a means of regeneration after a forest fire, damage by lightning or even heavy pruning. The Judas tree is unusual in that it frequently produces bunches of flowers directly from its bark.

Bark products While some trees are grown for their ornamental barks, other trees have barks that are of considerable commercial importance to us. One of the most familiar bark products is latex, which is secreted by specialised cells arising in the phloem. By making incisions in the bark of certain trees the latex can be extracted and converted into products such as rubber and the gum of chewing gum. Few trees growing in Britain

Three bark types

Thick barks, such as that of the black walnut (right), are often rough and deeply fissured into small plates.

The London plane (right) has a thin bark that falls away in plates, reflecting the arrangement of the periderm layers underneath.

Some trees, such as wellingtonia (right), develop a thick, fibrous bark that is only very gradually worn away.

yield latex, but one such is the fig.

Some trees are tapped for the sugary sap carried in their phloem. The sugar maple, for example, yields maple syrup while in southern Europe several species of pine are tapped for their resin. Certain wines are flavoured with resin from the Aleppo pine. Other resin products from pines include rosin and turpentine.

Another very important source of bark products are materials produced by the tree inside the bark cells themselves, mostly as a form of chemical defence against animals and other potential attackers. An example is tannin, high levels of which are found in the barks of oak trees, making them important in the tanning of hides for leather.

Finally, a few barks are used as a source of aromatic products. Perhaps the best known of these is the spice cinnamon, which is the inner bark of a tree from south-east Asia. The scent myrrh is also extracted from the bark of a tree, in this case by tapping the bark and extracting the myrrh from the resin.

Above: The paper-bark maple is now widely planted in parks and gardens for its beautiful reddish-brown bark which peels away in strips.

Above right: The deeply fissured lower part of a white poplar's trunk contrasts with the much smoother bark higher up. Notice the conspicuous rows of lenticels on the upper half of the tree.

Right: Père David's maple, one of a group of snake-bark maples with distinctive silvery-white lines running down their olive-green barks.

Below: A close-up view of the bark of a Scots pine shows it to consist of a series of overlapping scales.

Barks in Britain

NATIVE

Some of the more distinctive barks of our native (naturalised in the case of sycamore) trees.

1 Silver birch
(*Betula pendula*).
2 Common beech
(*Fagus sylvatica*).
3 Strawberry tree
(*Arbutus unedo*).
4 English oak
(*Quercus robur*).
5 Hornbeam
(*Carpinus betulus*).
6 Crack willow
(*Salix fragilis*).
7 Yew
(*Taxus baccata*).
8 Scots pine
(*Pinus sylvestris*).
9 Sycamore
(*Acer pseudoplatanus*).
10 Common ash
(*Fraxinus excelsior*).
11 Rowan
(*Sorbus aucuparia*).

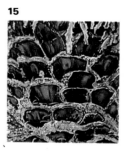

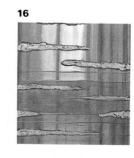

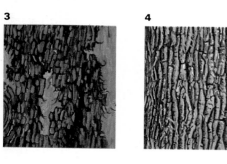

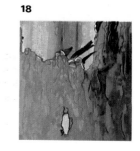

INTRODUCED

Many of the most attractive barks seen in Britain are on trees introduced here from abroad, in some cases being brought over particularly for the ornamental qualities of their barks.

12 Silver lime
(*Tilia tomentosa*).
13 White-barked Himalayan birch
(*Betula jacquemontii*).
14 Tasmanian blue gum
(*Eucalyptus globus*).
15 Chusan palm
(*Trachycarpus fortunei*).
16 Tibetan cherry
(*Prunus serrula*).
17 Monkey puzzle
(*Araucaria araucana*).
18 Chinese stewartia
(*Stewartia sinensis*).
19 Caucasian elm
(*Zelkova carpinifolia*).
20 Persian ironwood
(*Parottia persica*).
21 Tree of heaven
(*Ailanthus altissima*).
22 False acacia
(*Robinia pseudoacacia*).

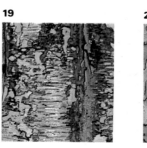

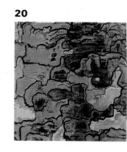

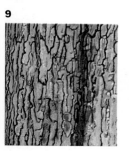

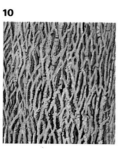

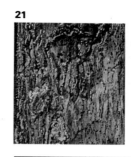

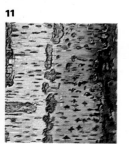

Honey locust
(*Gleditsia triacanthos*), an introduced tree from the USA, is unique in having thorns up to 10cm (4in) long sprouting from the trunk.

Conifer plantations

Conifer plantations are not all dark, lifeless rows
of silent trees. In well-managed forests,
blocks of trees – from the newly planted to the
mature – create a patchwork of mini habitats
in which a variety of wildlife finds refuge.

Devoted naturalists tend to decry the role of conifer woods, regarding them as little more than uniform carpets of alien species planted without any consideration for landscape and so dense that they blot out sound and light. To put conifers in context, it is probably more realistic to compare them to modern agriculture than to deciduous woodland. They will never be as rich as the more natural deciduous woods, but they are an intensive, economic way of using land. The plantations are monocultures like the farmer's wheat and silage crops; the rides and fire-breaks function like hedgerows and lanes.

When compared to agricultural land conifer plantations often appear in a more favour-

Stages in a plantation

A forester's plantation often contains blocks of trees at different stages of growth. The illustration shows six main stages.

KEY

1 A piece of newly-dug land, with narrow trenches down the hill and drainage channels across, ready to be planted.

2 Five-year-old pines planted three years ago.

3 A fire-break through a block of ten-year-old spruces.

4 After about 20 years some trees are felled to allow others to grow bigger. The felled wood is stacked at the roadside.

5 Small plants can establish themselves at the edges of rides. Fire beaters and a water tank are nearby in case of fire, and a rabbit fence protects the young trees.

6 A 70-year-old plantation ready to be felled. This is done in large sections over about ten years.

Left: Conifers cover 7% of the land in Britain, and almost 5% in Ireland. Most pine plantations are managed on a 60-80 year cycle. Even when the canopy is at its most dense—after 10-12 years—birds can nest in the thick branches. Thereafter the trees are felled at intervals of about five years and the felled areas are quickly colonised by the grasses, bracken and flowers that grow at the edges of the more permanent rides.

able light. But to say this is not to advocate the planting up of good quality agricultural land, much less downland, species-rich meadow, remnants of lowland heath or deciduous woodland. Such a policy could only be to the detriment of wildlife. However on poor, often upland soils, where the land only supports scrub, the planting of conifers provides a welcome habitat for a number of plants and animals.

Initial disadvantages Why can a coniferous plantation never be as rich as a good native broadleaved wood? To start with, the trees in each conifer block are uniform in age and evergreen, unless larch is the main species. In addition to consisting mainly of alien species, they are planted at regular intervals, and so are of the same height and provide the same density of cover. This planting policy is designed for ease of felling and thinning. There are no old trees to provide nesting holes for birds and roosts for bats and no broadleaved species to provide the quantity and variety of invertebrate life on which predators can feed.

Once the canopy layer is established (after 10-15 years in a pine wood) there are no undershrubs, very little cover for nesting at ground level, few flowers for insect pollinators, or fruit for voles, mice and birds. The lack of light when the conifers are at their most dense ensures that apart from fungi there is little ground flora. Without the ground flora and its seeds, herbivorous small mammals and invertebrates are reduced in number. This in turn restricts predators, such as ground beetles, shrews, weasels and birds like the robin and great tit. The accumulation and slow decay of pine and larch needles can make the soil acidic. Acid soil is inhospitable to various soil organisms such as worms and bacteria and to many flowering plants. Finally, most plantations contain little or no dead wood, a habitat which in deciduous woodland can contain up to a third of the species present, including beetles,

ants, bees, wasps and woodlice.

Diversity of habitats With what appears to be so many negative aspects, it is hardly surprising that some people object to coniferous plantations. But in large plantations divided into many compartments or blocks the habitat diversity is often considerable. The felled areas allow opportunists like the foxglove, and on sandy soils possibly heather and bell heather, to move in. As the new trees grow up these plants will disappear to be replaced by wavy-hair grass or perhaps broad buckler fern after the trees are thinned.

The power line tracts, fire-breaks and rides allow light to penetrate at the margins and here a variety of plants is often found together with butterflies, hoverflies and bees. On sandy soils, such as in parts of Sherwood Forest in Nottinghamshire, sand spurrey, pill sedge and various grasses are to be found. Where limestone chippings have been used for forest roads or when the plantation is on chalk or limestone, then many species associated with limestone grassland persist at the edges of the dark wall of conifers.

Apart from these opportunist species, if the planting policy provides stable areas which are not disturbed, for instance rides, heathland plants can flourish. The clubmosses might find room among grassy or rocky edges. Indeed, in lowland areas, the forests are becoming increasingly important for this group of plants as their natural heath and moorland habitats are in decline.

Temporary visitors Animal life in the plantations can be more varied than the plant life. As the forest matures, the animal population changes. At first the exclusion of grazing animals, which would otherwise eat the young trees, allows the growth of a thick wall of grasses to develop. This attracts short-tailed field voles, whose runs and holes soon riddle the grassy tussocks. In turn the voles provide food for the magnificent short-eared owl. Spiders, beetles and other invertebrates prefer the damp, dark conditions at the base of the

Above: Rosebay willowherb grows in profusion between Scots pine and birch trees in this 9-year-old plantation on Arnfield Moor in the Peak District. As the trees grow taller they will gradually shade out the willowherb until only a few hardy grasses remain.

Right: Pine martens have benefitted from the spread of coniferous plantations, particularly in Scotland. They are extremely agile tree climbers and feed mainly on rodents and small birds.

Left: You have to look hard at the canopy of conifer trees to spot the goldcrest's nest, usually suspended from a branch. Goldcrests, like pine martens, have increased in number with recent afforestation.

grass tussocks under the litter and so predatory shrews and foxes as well as insectivorous birds, such as tree pipits, grasshopper warblers and linnets, are often seen in the plantation.

As the trees grow into a dense thicket, these birds decrease and their place is taken by wrens, willow warblers and hedge sparrows which choose the thickets for nesting. Once the trees reach 3-4m (10-13ft), thrushes, blackbirds and chaffinches begin to nest. At this stage the lower branches of the trees are removed–a process called brashing–to prevent knots forming in the wood and reduce the risk of fire. Animals needing a dense undergrowth such as voles are forced out.

Above: This fungus, *Boletus variegatus*, (not edible) is one of many that can grow in the shade of dense conifers.

The taller trees, however, provide nesting sites for jays, crows and magpies. It is at this stage that the canopies of mature trees can become an important breeding site for goldcrests. Coal-tits, which do not compete very successfully with other tits in deciduous woods, find refuge in these older plantations. Squirrels are able to find suitable branches to build their dreys, and it is the red squirrel in particular which is associated with pine plantations.

Changes in bird population Once the trees are thinned, after about 20 years, many of the song birds seem to leave. The trees are usually thinned every five years and so the canopy is less dense from this stage onwards. The tall trees are still used as roosts by owls and you can often find their pellets scattered around on the ground beneath. Both the long-eared owl, a bird of northern Britain, and the sparrowhawk, whose numbers are now increasing, prefer to nest in the old pines that survive in woods which are not commercially managed. The increase in pine woods has played an important part in the recovery of populations of what were once quite common species. These include birds such as the siskin and crossbill (which feed on the pine seeds) as well as mammals like the pine marten.

The Forestry Commission has made particular efforts to protect and manage the herds of deer in the new forests. In Scotland these are mostly red deer but in England there are fallow, roe and more locally muntjac deer as well. Culling of the herds is necessary to keep them to a manageable size and so prevent too much damage to trees. Such management also includes mowing the rides and retaining open glades within the planted areas to provide the deer with grass.

Planning ahead Coniferous plantations are a monoculture and, like all monocultures, they are susceptible to devastation by pests particularly large numbers of a single species; moth larvae are often the worst offenders in coniferous plantations. It has been suggested that by providing a more varied habitat, the forest managers could use wildlife to reduce the possibility of such outbreaks. In Germany wood ants have been introduced into plantations to control caterpillars and leaf-eating bugs. Studies at Thetford Chase indicate that visiting flocks of tits may take as much as 20% of certain moth pupae and larvae in winter from the coniferous trees, but they need to be supported by the provision of more deciduous trees to help them feed broods in summer.

Although coniferous plantations can never be as rich as the more natural broadleaved woods, nonetheless they do provide what are, occasionally, important reservoirs of wildlife. And, if managed thoughtfully, the forests could not only help to maintain the diversity of species in Britain but even enable the wildlife they do support to contribute to the success of this particular form of economical land use.

Above: The lack of a well established shrub layer in this Forest of Dean oak wood in Gloucestershire means that bracken can flourish in the field layer. Holes in the trunk of the holly tree offer birds nesting sites.

Deciduous woodlands

A wood can be rather like a four-storey house – with mosses at the bottom, two storeys of flowers, ferns and shrubs, and an attic made up by the canopy of foliage.

What chiefly distinguishes woodland from other habitats such as grassland or heather moor is that it has a dimension which they lack – that of height. This provides a series of habitats for many species of wildlife, ranged one above the other from ground level up to 20 or 30m (65 or 100ft). So a useful way of looking at a wood is to think of it as consisting of various layers of vegetation; and of these, four are usually recognised.

At the lowest level is the ground layer – the very small plants, chiefly mosses, which grow on the floor of the wood. Next comes the field layer (or herb layer) – the wild flowers and the ferns. Above them grows the shrub layer (or under-storey), of which hazel is a typical species. And high over the rest of the wood are the upper boughs and twigs of mature oaks, ashes, beeches and others which form the tree layer (canopy).

You don't need to look at many woods before you realise that there are great differences between them. Some may have all four layers well developed. Others, and they are more usual, may be lacking in one or more layers. Why are there these differences? Often there is no single answer. In ecology it is always necessary to be on the look-out for multiple causes, especially in so complex a site as a woodland. And because practically every British woodland exists to serve a human purpose, the presence or absence of any of the four layers is often due to man's interference rather than to natural causes.

Here and there, even in a quite natural woodland, you may find an absence or near absence of one or other layer. This often happens if the tree layer is particularly dense with summer leaves that suppress the layers below by cutting them off from the light they need. So the only type of wood which can have all four well-developed layers is one where plenty of light comes down through the tree layer even at the height of summer. In ashwoods, for instance, the divided, pinnate leaves of the ash allow much more light to filter through them than do the leaves of most other large trees. Pure ashwood, however, is not found in many areas. A more common type of wood is a mixture of ash and oak. In such a wood, provided the oaks are not too many or too close, especially if there are a few clearings and a variety of trees of different ages, you will probably find all four layers better developed than in most other woods.

Tree layer The upper branches and twigs of a tree are structured to expose the maximum number of leaves to the light. Since many of the young leaves, especially of oaks, are highly palatable and nutritious for insects, the canopy becomes the scene of immense activity in spring and early summer. Phenomenal numbers of caterpillars, mainly of mottled umber, winter and green tortrix moths, begin to eat the leaves as soon as the buds open. And the caterpillars in turn are taken in large

numbers by tits, warblers, finches, redstarts, pied flycatchers, starlings and many other birds which are feeding hungry broods of nestlings. In years of caterpillar plagues a wood's entire tree layer may be stripped of its leaves and the shrub layer may also be devastated. In such years an unusual amount of light gets down to the field layer. However, once the caterpillars have pupated, starved to death or been eaten, a replacement flush of leaves appears on the trees. Another group of insects active in the tree layer in spring produces oak apples, marble galls, artichoke galls and many others.

In winter the highest twigs are searched for tiny forms of animal life by sharp-eyed small birds such as the tits, nuthatch and lesser spotted woodpecker. But the most obvious birds of the tree layer are those large species which come in spring to build their nests there – the heron, rook carrion crow, buzzard, sparrowhawk and several others. Many birds also use the tree tops for perching by day, and for roosting after dark.

Shrub layer This complex zone consists of shrubs, the lower branches of mature trees and saplings which, if they survive, will grow up to take their place in the tree layer. Some shrubs and young trees can tolerate quite a lot of shade; others survive only in clearings or where the big trees stand well apart. For hundreds of years, until the early 20th century, the shrub layer was very important in the life of rural Britain. This dense jungle of hazel, hawthorn, ash, hornbeam, sweet chestnut, willow and many other species was completely cut down (coppiced) at regular intervals to produce the sticks and poles that were in such demand in the farming countryside.

For two or three years after coppicing the ground was carpeted with wild flowers encouraged by the light suddenly let into the wood. There was also a great increase in butterflies, bees, beetles and other insects that revelled in the fragrance and the sunshine. But in another two years all this changed. New tall stems shot up from the cut stumps and the shrub layer again became impenetrable. The flowers began to die out, but there were more small birds; warblers, thrushes and, in the south of England, nightingales, all used the shrubs for nesting. But growth continued and in about three more years the coppiced shrubs grew into a dense mass of tall poles unsuitable for any of these birds. Then the shrubs were felled once more and the cycle began again.

Today most of the old coppices have been destroyed or are neglected. However, in many woodland nature reserves the old coppice system is being restored for the benefit of wild flowers, insects, birds and other creatures and the cut wood is used for fencing and woodburning stoves and fires.

Field layer While the wild flowers of the field layer are at their best in clearings or in the dappled sunlight under ash trees, those beneath the closed canopy of beech woods are

The main layers
Although there are four main woodland layers it is unusual to find all four fully developed in the same wood. The illustration below shows what the various layers might look like in a lime-rich mixed beech and ash wood. Enough light filters down for a thin field layer to develop. Normally there is little or no field layer in pure beechwoods because the canopy is so dense. Each woodland layer offers different feeding, nesting and sheltering sites for wildlife.

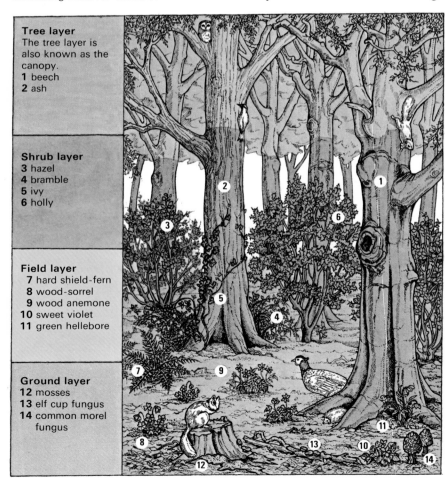

Tree layer
The tree layer is also known as the canopy.
1 beech
2 ash

Shrub layer
3 hazel
4 bramble
5 ivy
6 holly

Field layer
7 hard shield-fern
8 wood-sorrel
9 wood anemone
10 sweet violet
11 green hellebore

Ground layer
12 mosses
13 elf cup fungus
14 common morel fungus

Right: Small invertebrates and insects are pecked out from the cracks in the bark of a tree by the agile tree creeper. The eggs of the mottled umber moth make up part of this bird's winter food supply. The tree creeper's favourite nest site is behind loose bark.

Right: The mottled umber caterpillar is one of the main defoliators of oak trees. As the oak leaf buds open the eggs of the mottled umber moth hatch into caterpillars which start to devour the leaves.

Below: This wood of coppiced hazel allows a dense field layer of wood sorrel to flower before the hazel starts to leaf. The wood sorrel is nourished by the leaf mould of the ground layer.

few. But even in these shady places there are peculiar plants which, lacking chlorophyll, manage to do without the process of photosynthesis by which nearly all other plants take carbon dioxide from the air. Instead these plants, called saprophytes, take their food from dead organic matter as many fungi do. The bird's-nest orchid is the best known of the beechwood saprophytes. Also tolerant of shade are the ferns which, in some woods, are abundant.

The field layer is the world of the wood mice, bank voles and shrews which dwell among the thick cover. Here, too, live hedgehogs, rabbits, hares and their predators the fox, stoat and (mainly in Wales) the polecat. Among birds which hide their nests in the field layer are woodcock, pheasant and, in clearings, the nightjar. Among typical butterflies of the field layer are the speckled wood, green-veined white and several of the fritillaries.

Ground layer This is the domain of the shade-tolerant, earth-carpeting mosses, many of which also cover fallen logs and the cut stumps of trees. But mosses are not in every wood. They need almost all-the-year-round moisture and so are commonest in the west and north of Britain, especially in upland woods where rainfall is high and mists are frequent. In drier lowland woods the ground may only be covered by drifts of dead leaves which shelter whole populations of small creatures. Many fungi also inhabit the ground layer. Their underground threads often grow in close association with the root-tips of trees, to the advantage of both fungus and tree. They send up their fruiting bodies – toadstools – mostly in autumn, bringing attractive shapes and colours to the woodland floor.

While it is useful to think of a woodland as built up in several layers, in nature these layers never actually occur in such distinct compartments as shown in diagrams. Also many invertebrates and birds, and mammals such as squirrels and bats, move freely from one layer to another. Even a few plants – ivy, traveller's-joy, honeysuckle and polypody fern, for instance – belong to all layers. So do tree trunks: different mosses, lichens and invertebrates are found on different sections of the trunk from ground level up to the tree crown.

The vitality of a woodland depends on a powerful flow of life-giving substances circulating through all the layers with every plant and animal playing a part by its life and death. For a healthy woodland, though made up of various layers, is really one successful, ever-changing community. For example, a plant provides sustenance for an insect which, in turn, is food for a bird that then falls victim to a larger predator. Plants take nutritive substances from the soil to the tree-tops and return it again in falling leaves and twigs, and the food-chains circulate organic material through all the woodland layers.

Woodland through the year

Deciduous woodland changes its appearance dramatically as the year progresses. The seasons are well-marked, each one presenting the woodland in a new light and each with new problems for the plants and animals which live there to solve.

Below: A deciduous forest clearly reflects the external and internal influences of each of the different seasons. The differences are obvious, even in this small glade ringed by beeches, holly and hornbeam and dissected by a small stream. The new young leaves of spring are just appearing (left), but by the middle of summer they form a shady canopy which allows very little light through (right).

Each of the four seasons—spring, summer, autumn, and winter—has a special quality and tempo of its own. Whilst the changing seasons can be observed in almost any part of the countryside—hedgerows and meadows, for instance—nowhere are they reflected more dramatically or graphically than in a deciduous woodland. A photographic record, like the one here which depicts the same scene (a beech and hornbeam glade) at different times of the year, illustrates this clearly.

Spring In the spring, the light has a translucent quality that will not be equalled all year. In the small forest glade, this light brings changes. The ring of beeches and hornbeams—deciduous trees that have been bare all winter

—now appear bright green with new leaf. Each bud breaks to reveal a miniature chemical factory which will spend the entire spring and summer producing food in the form of sugar from water and carbon dioxide, powered by the new season's sunlight. Another tree also begins to show an increase in activity although this cannot be measured by the amount of new green leaf produced. This is the evergreen holly, a tree with thickly cuticled leaves which prevent excessive water loss in winter. Holly will also be producing new leaves, but on new branches that will begin growing once the leaves have restored themselves to full activity.

Summer The season moves on in the glade and, with the coming of summer, a subtle change has occurred. The light airiness of spring, which allowed a brief flowering of grasses and other herbaceous plants, is dimmed as the leaf canopy now becomes fully formed. Both beech and hornbeam have entire leaves which overlap sufficiently to cast quite a considerable shade. The glade is now a cool, restful place, with only the holly able to grow in the limited light. Holly is a typical under-storey plant, existing very well under even very dense canopy. In the canopy itself the leaves of both species of trees are actively producing vast quantities of simple sugars which are further built up to form the food reserves of the tree. These are used to promote new growth, and also to form and ripen the

gradually enlarging seeds which will have been produced by the pollination of the flowers that appeared as the leaves formed.

Autumn In autumn, the light imperceptibly changes again. The glade is still shady, and the weather still fine, but the sun is now lower in the sky and less effective in powering photosynthesis, and drifts of leaves begin to litter the ground. The leaves that have produced so much food for the trees throughout the spring and summer now are shed. The hornbeams and beeches begin to close down for the winter. Each leaf is lost by the formation of a brittle abscission layer at the end of the leaf stalk nearest to the stem. Before this waterproof seal is complete, vital components such as the green pigment chlorophyll and other associated substances are translocated out of the leaf to be stored over winter in the main body of the tree. In return, many waste products are 'dumped' in the leaf, producing the rich autumn leaves. Finally the abscission layer is complete, and the leaf falls. The fruits so typical of autumn – the beech mast and the three-lobed hornbeam fruit – also drop with the leaves. Only the holly still has unripe fruits. It has a very long flowering season – from May to August – and it does not join in the general autumnal fruit production.

Winter The autumn leaves now form a dense carpet on the woodland floor, and the stage is set for the final change of the year to occur. With all the useful products removed to places of storage within the main body of the tree, many waste products shed, and the buds for next year's flowers and leaves formed, sealed and wrapped in protective bud-scales, the tree metabolism slows gradually until a state of near-dormancy sets in. Winter is always the time of most risk for plants. Water often becomes unavailable – locked into the soil as frost – so the profligate consumption of the summer months is impossible, and hence the evolution of the deciduous system in trees such as hornbeam and beech. Holly prevents excess water loss by the possession of a thick waxy cuticle on the leaves and sunken stomatal pores, which significantly decrease the water loss due to transpiration.

Other climatic factors combine to make winter a testing time, the time when weak individuals are tested to the utmost, and weeded out. Strong gales rip through forests, testing the entire fabric of the tree. Beeches in particular are shallow rooted, and a savage local squall can pull out even a large tree. Only those that are best protected, both by position and strength of root, survive. As the turn of the year approaches, the carpet of leaves is overlaid by one of snow, subtly softening and changing the landscape. The holly, meanwhile, has its red berries ripening with the approach of Christmas. It has come through the seasons seemingly very little changed, and deserves the praise of the carol, 'the first tree in the greenwood, it is the holly.'

Below: The seasons progress in the beech/hornbeam glade: autumn leaves carpet the ground and the trees look suddenly bare (left), while in winter there is a carpet of a different and harsher kind – snow (right).

Trees and fungi

From late summer onwards, fungal fruiting bodies of many shapes and sizes can be seen in our woodlands, apparently sprouting up overnight (see opposite). Many of these mushrooms are a seasonal sign of a symbiotic relationship between certain fungi and trees that continues underground all through the year.

Below: A group of fly agarics surrounding a birch tree—their favourite habitat. The red caps flecked with white (the remains of the volva which once enclosed the whole fruiting body) make this fungus one of the most easily recognised species. Fly agarics are highly poisonous and should never be eaten—nor, indeed, should any wild fungus unless you are absolutely sure that you have identified it correctly and you know it is edible.

n their non-reproductive state, fungi exist s fine thread-like cells called hyphae. Every o often these hyphae throw up spore-bearing rgans—the familiar mushrooms, also known s fruiting bodies or sporocarps. Most of the ime, however, the fungus exists only as yphae buried within a food source for, nlike green plants, fungi cannot photo-ynthesise and have to obtain their food eady-made from other sources. Many feed n decaying organic matter, some are para-itic, while others exist in partnership with iving hosts.

A large number of fungi found on forest oors fall into the last of these groups: they btain their food from living trees. The yphae of these fungi grow through the soil nd colonize the short, fine roots of nearby rees. The fungus covers each root with a heath of tissue and the hyphae penetrate etween the root cells. This association etween fungus and tree is called a mycor-hiza and the fungus is said to be a mycorrhi-al fungus.

Both the tree and the fungus benefit from his close relationship. The fungus is able to bsorb nourishment, in the form of sugars, rom the tree. The tree, on the other hand, as its root-hair formation suppressed by the ungus and relies on the latter to absorb ater and essential minerals from the soil. s the fungus grows out into the surrounding oil, it becomes capable of collecting water nd minerals from a much greater volume of oil than the tree ever could on its own.

Mycorrhizal relationships are formed with nany woody plant families, including the eech, birch, lime and pine families. Among he fungi that form mycorrhizas, many are on-specific, that is they can be found in ssociation with several different species of ree, while others are confined to a par-icular genus of trees.

Amanitas and milk-caps Among the most videly distributed of fungal groups is the enus *Amanita*. These usually have white ills and spores, with a central stalk whose ase is typically enclosed within a sac called he volva. This volva once enveloped the porocarp when it was very small and still developing.

Two commonly seen fungi in this genus are the blusher (*Amanita rubescens*) and fly agaric (*A. muscaria*). The former is found in many types of woodland. The fruiting body is rosy-brown and the cap is covered in grey warts, the remnants of the volva. Fly agaric is the archetypal toadstool; it appears in large numbers in broad-leaved woods, especially birch.

Another fungus commonly found in birch woods is the ugly milk-cap (*Lactarius turpis*). The milk-caps are so-called because they ooze a white, latex-like liquid if broken. The ugly milk-cap is a dark olive-brown colour. A more attractive member of this genus is the peppery milk-cap (*Lactarius piperatus*). This is one of the most frequently encountered fungi in broad-leaved woods. Its cap, which may reach a diameter of 15cm (6in), is milky white and the gills are also white or yellowish. The white stalk is squat and cylindrical.

Forming a mycorrhiza

To form a mycorrhiza, the fungus envelops the tree root in a sheath and sends thread-like hyphae to form a 'Hartig net' in between the root cells so that nutrients can be exchanged. The mycorrhiza on the right is formed by a Basidiomycete, a large group to which most familiar fungi belong; on the left is one formed by an Ascomycete.

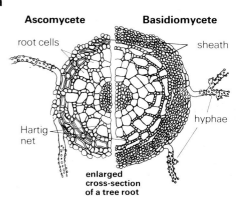

Ascomycete   Basidiomycete
root cells   sheath
Hartig net   hyphae
enlarged cross-section of a tree root

Below: The larch bolete is very common in autumn under larches, its yellow to rust-coloured cap being covered with a distinctive pale lemon slime.

The liquid that oozes out when the flesh or gills are damaged is white and has a strongly peppery taste.

Boletes and russulas Birch woods are the home for the brown birch bolete (*Leccinum scabrum*). The boletes all have a central stalk topped by a fleshy cap whose lower surface consists not of gills but of a vast number of pores and fine tubules through which the spores are released. Many boletes possess a fine network of marks known as a reticulum at the tops of their stalks.

The best-known bolete is the penny bun or cep (*Boletus edulis*). To those who enjoy eating fungi, this species is a delight because it has an exquisite flavour and can be eaten raw or cooked. It has a convex cap which becomes flattened with age, while at the same time the pores change in colour from white to olive. The cap can vary from pale ochre to dark chestnut and the stalk, which may be squat or tapered, is a lighter colour. This fungus can be found in broad-leaved and coniferous woods.

A group of colourful fungi also found in

Mycorrhizal associations

Below: **Slippery Jack** (*Suillus luteus*). Found only in conifer woods, usually beneath Scots pine. A bolete. Height to 10cm (4in). Common and edible.

Below: **The sickener** (*Russula emetica*). A common species in coniferous woods, with a distinctive red cap and white stalk. Height to 9cm (3½in). Poisonous.

Below: **Bay bolete** (*Boletus badius*). A common coniferous species whose lemon pores turn blue when bruised. Height to 15cm (6in). Edible.

Above: **Summer truffle** (*Tuber aestivum*). A rare fungus found buried close to beech trees on calcareous soils. Up to 7cm (3in) across. Edible.

both broad-leaved and coniferous woods is the russulas. The common yellow russula (*Russula ochroleuca*), whose cap may be yellow, ochre or greenish-yellow, is found in a wide range of different woods, while two other species in this group are confined to beechwoods. These are the beechwood sickener (*R. mairei*), a poisonous fungus whose cap varies from red to white, and the geranium-scented russula (*R. fellea*), which has a straw-coloured cap and smells of geraniums.

Coniferous fungi Most coniferous forests in Britain are commercial plantations which appear to be uniform, monotonous stands of just a few species. However, diversity is often provided by the variety of mycorrhizal fungi found in such forests.

Several of the species mentioned above occur in both broad-leaved and coniferous woods. On the other hand, some are confined solely to coniferous habitats. One such is slippery Jack (*Suillus luteus*), which is particularly associated with Scots pine. It is an edible bolete with a chestnut-coloured cap covered in brown slime. The stalk is a pale straw colour and has a large white to cream ring around it that darkens to sepia.

Another edible bolete found in coniferous woods is the bay bolete (*Boletus badius*). As its common name suggests, the colour of its cap varies from bay (reddish-brown) to dark brick-red. When young, the cap is downy but it soon becomes smooth with age.

A bolete with a specific conifer host is the larch bolete (*Suillus grevillei*), which is found only in association with larch trees. The sickener (*Russula emetica*), however, is invariably seen in almost any coniferous wood during autumn. This scarlet-capped russula is poisonous.

Coniferous milk-caps The milk-caps are another common group in coniferous forests.

The curry-scented milk-cap (*Lactarius camphoratus*) is usually associated with pines, though it also occurs in deciduous woods. When dried, the reddish-brown fruiting body develops a strong scent reminiscent of curry. For this reason it is used in Germany as a food flavouring.

The rufous milk-cap (*Lactarius rufus*), which is found in pine and spruce forests, is a reddish-brown fungus with brittle, pale brown gills. It exudes a white latex which, at first, has a mild taste and then, after about a minute, becomes very hot and acrid. Unlike most mycorrhizal fungi, which appear from late summer to late autumn, this species can be seen as early in the year as June.

Above: Rufous milk-caps growing on the floor of a coniferous wood. The shape of the cap, with its depressed centre and exposed gills, is typical of many milk-caps. Notice also the white latex being extruded from the gills— hence this group's name.

Below: The fruiting bodies of some mycorrhizal fungi, showing the trees under which they are most likely to be seen growing. All appear mainly from late summer through the autumn.

Below: **Brown roll-rim** (*Paxillus involutus*). Found in coniferous and deciduous woods. The gills flush chestnut on bruising. Height to 8cm (3in). Poisonous.

Right: **Brown birch bolete** (*Leccinum scabrum*). Common in birch woods. Its pores bruise to an ochre colour. Height to 20cm (8in). Not poisonous.

Right: *Leccinum carpin*. A rare bolete usually found under hornbeam or hazel, but sometimes under oak. Height to 9cm (3½in). Not poisonous.

Below: **Gas-works fungus** (*Tricholoma sulphureum*). Found in all types of wood. The flesh emits a smell similar to coal gas. Height 5cm (2in). Inedible.

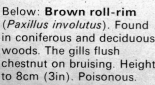

Trees and disease

Trees can live to a greater age than almost any other plant – sometimes to a thousand years or more. Yet even they succumb to decay and, eventually, death as one of many possible fungal diseases takes hold and attacks the heartwood.

The chance of a tree seedling reaching maturity is extremely remote: only one in a thousand survives the first year and only one in ten thousand lives long enough to bear seed. Furthermore, a young tree faces adverse conditions such as wind, drought and fire, competition from other plants and damage from fungi and animals.

Despite all this, trees 100 or 200 years old are fairly common, but specimens older than that become increasingly rare. Various factors influence the age to which a tree might live. Hardness of wood, speed of growth and favourable conditions and habitat all play their part, as do the different ages at which different species mature. Birches, for example,

Above: Few species of trees regularly produce individuals that live for more than a few hundred years. In Britain the two exceptions to this are oaks (such as the Hollow Oak in Windsor Great Park shown here), which often exceed 500 years, and yews, which may live for 1000 years.

Right: This bracket-shaped fruit body is an outward sign that the heartwood of the birch tree is being attacked by the heart rot fungus.

reach maturity at about 50 years old, beeches mature at twice that age and oaks at 150 years old. (Maturity is said to be the time when a tree stops increasing in height and its annual increase in girth becomes minimal, though without actually ceasing.)

Once a tree reaches maturity the presence of lignin and antiseptic chemicals in the heartwood protects it from decay for perhaps hundreds of years. Eventually, however, spores of fungi force an entry into the tree through a wound of some sort – where a branch has broken off perhaps, or where an insect has attacked the sapwood. Once that happens, the tree becomes diseased and goes into a gradual decline which can end only with its death.

Beech bark disease An example of a fungus that attacks in this way is beech bark disease (*Nectria coccinea*). The initial stage of the disease is closely linked to the tree being attacked by beech scale (*Cryptococcus fagi*), a minute sucking insect that attacks only beech.

A serious infestation of scale can, on its own, weaken a tree but greater damage is caused by the fact that the wounds inflicted by the insect on the bark open a path through which beech bark disease can enter the tree. As the fungus gains hold, small patches of bark die; if peeled away, a distinct orange line can be seen at the junction between the dead wood and the live wood. Sometimes sap flows from the infected areas and, as the attack progresses, the leaves turn yellow and the foliage in the crown of the tree becomes sparse. A severely affected tree dies within a few years.

Honey fungus Not all diseases are specific to one species of tree. Honey fungus (*Armillariella mellea*) attacks a wide range of hosts and even species that are resistant to

attack, such as oak, can be killed indirectly by honey fungus weakening the roots so much that the tree is blown over during a gale. Nor does honey fungus need an insect to allow it entry to the tree.

The fungus gains its name from the colour of its toadstools, but it exists largely as a mass of microscopically fine hyphae growing within the roots and stumps. Beneath the bark the hyphae are abundant enough to form a creamy-white fungal mass called a mycelium, which is clearly visible and looks rather like a thin sheet of paper spread over the inner wood. Sometimes the hyphae aggregate into thin black strands which either develop beneath the bark or spread out through the soil to infect host trees near by.

Sooty bark One disease has become a major killer only since the very hot summer of 1976, and that is sooty bark disease of sycamore (*Cryptostroma corticale*). At present it is limited to a area within a radius of about 300km (200 miles) of London.

This disease, which causes a dark, dry patch to appear just under the outer bark, has spread under the effect of two factors. The major factor is the weather – warm summers favour severe attacks while cool weather acts as a natural control. The other factor is more local in its effect. The grey squirrel feeds on the fungus and it also strips bark from sycamore trees, thus spreading the disease.

Heart rot The familiar bracket fungi so often seen on the boles of birch trees in summer and autumn are the outgrowths of a serious disease that will eventually kill the tree. This disease is heart rot fungus (*Piptoporus betulinus*) and it attacks birches already damaged in some way.

The fruit body (ie, the bracket fungus) has a pale brown upper surface with white flesh that

Sooty bark of sycamore

This disease attacks sycamore trees, causing a dry sooty layer, olive to brownish-black in colour, to appear just beneath the outer bark. This sooty layer consists of spores which disperse to expose a greyish layer. This in turn eventually turns black. Shown here are infected bark (far left) and healthy bark (near left).

Beech bark disease

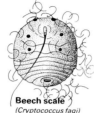

Beech scale
(Cryptococcus fagi)

Beech bark disease enters through wounds caused by beech scale, a tiny insect (left) covered with a dense white waxy secretion. Healthy bark and an infected patch are shown mid and far left, respectively.

Below left: Heart rot in a felled oak. As the heartwood rots away it becomes no longer capable of supporting the tree, which is then susceptible to being blown over during a gale.

Right: The toadstools of honey fungus vary greatly in size and shape, but they can be distinguished by their honey-brown colour. They can often be seen in clumps at the foot of trees from summer to early winter.

Below: Honey fungus is sometimes known as the bootlace fungus, a reference to one of its most characteristic features – the thin black strands called rhizomorphs that grow through the soil to spread the disease.

is soft at first and then becomes corky. Pores on the underside release numerous minute spores – too small to be seen except as a fine dust – that disperse to infect further hosts. Eventually the wood of an attacked birch turns reddish-brown and breaks up into dry rectangular blocks, each separated by thin sheets of white mycelium. In the final stages of the disease, branches and even trunks of the affected tree are liable to snap without warning.

Tree nurseries

Most trees growing in Britain today—from urban park or garden trees to the vast acres of Forestry Commission plantations—originated in a tree nursery, where young plants are raised and tended to give them the best possible start in life.

which in turn leads to stronger-growing, healthier young plants.

In the case of forestry planting, however, using nursery stock does have disadvantages. Planting large areas can be extremely expensive. Also, by breeding nursery trees for certain qualities, the nurseryman may breed out other characteristics which are desirable for the well-being of the wildlife the plantation is expected to support.

Nursery stocks There are a variety of different ways in which a nurseryman cultivates his stock, depending on the species of tree and its ultimate purpose. The principal types are seedlings, transplants, whips and feathers, and standards.

Seedlings are raised from seed in a specially prepared seed-bed, usually for one or two years, though sometimes for three. They are not usually planted directly into a forest because they lack sufficient food reserves and a well-enough developed root system to enable them to survive in the hostile environment of a forest site.

The most popular stock for planting out into forests is transplants—seedlings that have been sown and replanted elsewhere to produce a plant with a sturdier root system. The act of transplanting severs the seedling's roots, which causes the plant to grow more roots and also slows down its growth of foliage to redress the balance. This produces a sturdier plant that has greater food reserves and is more likely to survive in a forest. Another advantage of transplanting is that it allows the nurseryman to correct the spacing between plants.

By growing on seedlings or transplants for a further year or two, the nurseryman can produce whips, which are long thin branchless plants about 1m (3ft) tall, or feathers,

The job of a tree nursery is simply to produce large numbers of young trees, either by growing them from seed or by propagating them. A few of the larger private nurseries stock hundreds, or even thousands, of different species but most produce a fairly limited range to suit the demands of their customers. For example, Forestry Commission or other forestry-orientated nurseries produce only the type of tree required by the forestry industry—mainly small conifer transplants. On the other hand, Local Authority nurseries and private wholesalers confine themselves mainly to the more popular ornamentals seen in private gardens, parks and landscaping schemes.

Pros and cons There are several advantages in planting nursery-raised stock. The nurseryman can choose his stock for particular qualities and he can protect it from the unwelcome attentions of birds and animals, and from pests and diseases. When breeding trees, he can select superior individuals to improve the genetic quality of the next generation. He can also grow the trees in straight lines, making them easier to care for and weed,

Above: The Hillier nurseries near Winchester stock more trees, of a greater number of species and varieties, than any other nursery in the world—roughly 1¼ million specimens of about 8000 species and varieties. Formed more than 100 years ago, the nurseries together cover about 180 hectares (450 acres) and have a staff of 250.
Most of their sales are to Local Authorities and development corporations, though they also have several retail outlets and a mail-order system.

Right: A young pendulous form of swamp cypress—too young as yet to show its weeping habit. This tree will eventually be sold for an amenity planting.

which are usually taller than whips and have small side-branches along the stem. Both types of tree are used mainly for landscape and ornamental plantings. Standards are larger plants, about 2.5-3.5m (8-11ft) tall, with a clear stem up to 2m (6ft) high and a branched head.

Methods of cultivation Much nursery stock is raised from seed. The method is relatively cheap and quick, but there are disadvantages. The quality of the seed may be uncertain and the crop has a variable appearance; this may be an advantage in forestry, where some variability in appearance helps to break up the monotony, but is not usually desirable when planting an avenue.

There is also the problem of dormancy. The seeds of a few species, such as birch, will germinate immediately after ripening, but most undergo a period of dormancy first, waiting until the spring before they germinate. Nursery-sown seed has to be specially treated to simulate the change of seasons and induce germination.

As well as raising trees from seed, there is a whole range of vegetative techniques for propagation. A well-known method is to take cuttings. There are two types of cutting: hardwood and softwood. Hardwood cuttings are taken of mature shoots during the autumn or early spring when the cutting is not putting on foliage and so is best able to grow new roots. Softwood cuttings are taken from shoots that are not yet mature. They are taken in the summer when the cutting is in leaf. Taking softwood cuttings is not a common technique for propagating trees.

Other techniques include layering, grafting and budding. In layering, the shoot of a tree is bent down to the ground and covered with soil. After a year or two, the shoot forms roots beneath the soil and it can be severed from the parent to form a new plant. Grafting and budding cover a range of techniques in which a small segment of tree called the scion, complete with bud, is attached to another tree, the rootstock, so that the cambium in the two parts is joined. (The cambium is the layer of cells between the inner wood and the bark where growth occurs.) Since the scion is attached, via the cambium joint, to the roots of the rootstock, it makes new growth.

Modern methods One recently developed technique for propagating plants has just started to be used for trees. The method is called micropropagation. Small groups of cells, or even a single cell, are taken from part of a plant, often the bud. They are grown in test-tubes on a mixture of hormones, fungicides, sugars and agar (a type of jelly) in a laboratory. The cells multiply, forming shoots and roots. The most difficult part of the operation is to transfer the plant from the aseptic conditions of the test-tube to a normal growing medium. Provided this can be done, it is possible to develop several thousand new plants from one cutting within a year.

Above: Rows of year-old rowans (with compound leaves) and maples. Trees of this age and shape—one-or two-year olds with long slender stems and no side branches—are called whips. Along with feathered trees, which are similar but have side branches, they are often grown by Local Authority nurseries for landscaping and amenity purposes. They are also commonly grown by wholesale nurseries for sale to the public in garden centres and other outlets.

Right: Young cherry trees being secured to stakes for support. Instead of laboriously tying the two together, the nurseryman here is using a machine that fires plastic clips around the tree and stake, performing the operation in a fraction of the time. This allows him to stake great numbers of trees very fast. If a large nursery, containing perhaps many thousands of young trees, is to be economically viable, such labour-saving devices are essential.

Whip and tongue grafting

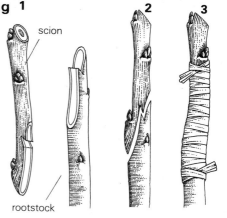

Of the many techniques of grafting available to the tree nurseryman, one of the most commonly used is whip and tongue grafting. The top of the rootstock is sliced off at an angle and the same angle of cut is made to the scion (**1**). (Notches are sometimes included in the cut to allow the two halves to interlock.) The scion and rootstock are then joined (**2**) and bound with tape (**3**).

scion

rootstock

Forestry

Roughly eight percent of Britain is covered by
forests. The type of species planted depends on
whether they are in an upland or lowland location.

Right: A young hardwood and conifer plantation at Ashridge in Hertfordshire. Conifers are quite often planted among slow-growing trees, such as beech, because their faster growth encourages the growth of the hardwood trees upwards towards the light.

Opposite: Dense growth of conifers at Delshangie Wood, Glenurquhart Forest in Scotland. The aftermath of clearfelling resembles a battlefield: a chaos of stumps, branches and churned up soil. Yet within a year replanting starts, and in a few years no trace of the destruction will be visible.

In prehistoric times, some two-thirds of the British Isles was covered in forests. Over the centuries the figure has dwindled to about 4%, and for the best part of this century re-afforestation has been the main concern of foresters. The Forestry Commission was established after the First World War to ensure new planting, and since 1945 it has worked in partnership with private woodland owners. There are now over two million hectares of woodland, and the Forestry Commission plans to double this by the 21st century.

The forester's first requirement is a suitable site. However, with our huge population in a group of relatively small islands, such land is at a premium. Agriculture and towns claim the better sites and soils, so the land available for forestry is usually in upland areas: places where trees once grew before sheep farming put an end to natural tree regeneration, and where the soil became progressively impoverished by over-grazing.

An early problem for foresters was to find tree species that were hardy enough to tolerate harsh, exposed conditions and relatively infertile soils, and at the same time produce enough useful timber. Scrub oak, silver birch and, in northern areas, Scots pine, were three of the most common native species, but they could not provide timber in sufficient quantities and of large enough size. So foresters looked to Continental Europe and north-west America and found two trees that seemed ideal: the Norway spruce and Sitka spruce. These two species are still the ones planted most today.

Seedlings Re-afforestation starts in the forest nursery, which is usually a flat, sheltered site where the soil is easily worked. A rotovator prepares the seedbeds in spring and the tiny seeds are broadcast sown, then covered with fine gravel, and finally netting to keep off birds, particularly finches. A year later, when the seeds are a few inches high, they are lifted and transplanted in neat lines in another part of the nursery. The soil is well fertilised to encourage the transplants to develop strong, fibrous root systems which will stand them in good stead when they are moved to the planting sites in 18 months to two years time.

Preparing the site Before the new trees arrive, the new forest site itself needs considerable preparation. More often than not the land is badly drained, something that must be remedied since trees do not like standing half the year in water. Nor do they

Below: A dense growth of young larch leafing out in May in the New Forest. Even if it seems difficult to identify a larch plantation from a distance, there is no problem in winter, for the larch is our only conifer to shed its needles in autumn. Larches are highly valued for their quick growth and resilient timber.

Above: The interior of a larch plantation. Larch plantations can support a greater variety of wildlife than most other conifers; their delicate needles and deciduous habit allow more light to enter the forest.

British forestry

animals. Within the fence trees may be threatened by smothering weeds such as grass and bracken. These weeds are cut away by hand sickles or by tractor-driven swipes run up between the rows. Weeding is easy and fast because the trees are planted in straight lines.

As the trees grow taller and their lower branches begin to meet those of their immediate neighbours, competing vegetation is suppressed and the forester can then leave his trees alone for 12-15 years – apart from maintaining fences, keeping a close lookout for insect and fungal pests and fire (the biggest danger of all). Given good luck, the trees grow with increasing vigour each year, and new long leading shoots give ready evidence of their well-being. As the individual plants compete for light they draw one another upwards, and at the same time give each other protection.

After 15-20 years the forester cuts out those trees which will impede the growth of the better trees. A given area of land can support only a certain volume of timber, either in many small trees or fewer, larger specimens. Since these upland trees are being produced for the sawmills (the thinnings go to the pulpmills), the final crop trees must have space enough to permit ample development during the 60 or so years they are growing.

like the hard, impervious layer, or pan, often found near the surface of degraded soils. This layer prevents tree roots from penetrating deep enough to reach growth-supporting nutrients and stops the trees acquiring the stability they need to be able to stand for decades.

Forest ploughs hauled by tractors dig deep down, breaking the pan and providing a channel for excess water. They turn up a continuous slice of sub-soil that smothers the surrounding heather and grasses. The young trees are planted with the help of special planting spades. The transplants are heeled into notches cut in the soil at 2m (6ft) intervals. One man can plant at a rate of about 1200 plants per day. With spacing to allow for access rides, about 2500 trees are planted per hectare.

Protection Young trees need protection; in new plantations the main threat to their survival comes from sheep, rabbits, and, in many places, deer. The whole plantation is enclosed with durable fences of appropriate patterns which exclude these

Lowland sites Not all the forestry planting sites are in the uplands: sheltered valleys and lowland sites are also available, and here a wider choice of tree species can be made. However, conifers are usually planted because they grow much faster than deciduous hardwood trees, and it is softwood that the market wants. Douglas fir, larch and Corsican pine (much of Thetford Forest in East Anglia is Corsican pine, a more rapid producer of timber than our native Scots pine) are species most commonly planted in the better, sheltered places. As the soil is of higher quality, these species can be planted without deep ploughing, but they still require the same protection from animals, weeds and fire.

Hardwood forests The long-established hardwood forests are found in lowland Britain and they are mainly of oak or beech.

Left: A temporary sawmill which has been set up in a larch forest. The trees are sawn into manageable lengths for the sawmills and pulp or chipboard factories.

Their management poses quite different problems from those found in coniferous plantations. Most hardwood forests are managed to maintain the forest cover in perpetuity, at the same time producing a permanent and regular supply of timber. Little or no planting is done, and the stock of trees is maintained by natural seedlings. The result is woodland that contains trees of all ages and sizes. The problem for the forester is to keep the age classes in reasonable equilibrium. He does this by removing a portion of each age class whenever mature trees are felled for the market, thus opening the tree canopy sufficiently to allow a crop of natural seedlings to grow in the sunlight. A great deal of skill, patience and experience is required and if, as sometimes happens, there are no natural seedlings – oak and beech seed rather infrequently – the forester may have to plant groups of saplings to fill the gaps. As small sized hardwood timber is difficult to sell, the forester may plant conifers on the forest edges and in the larger gaps caused by wind blow or perhaps disease. These trees give an earlier return on some of the investment and provide protection for the sensitive young hardwoods.

Harvesting the crop The harvesting of the tree crop is a noisy end to decades of patient husbandry. Chain saws buzz and the trees come crashing down to be cut into manageable log lengths. Tractors grind slowly over the roughened, stump-ridden ground as they drag the logs to the ride-side where hydraulic grabs lift them on to huge lorries that carry them away to the sawmills and the pulp and chipboard factories.

The problem for the forester is to predict the requirements of the timber trade in 60-100 years time, while at the same time growing an economically viable crop.

Above: A forest fire sweeping through a pine plantation. These fires are not only an economic disaster, they can be catastrophic to wildlife as well.

Right: A mature Scots pine tree being felled in the New Forest. This species is our only native pine tree. The valuable timber is used for telegraph poles, furniture, fencing posts and many other purposes.

The history of a Scots pine

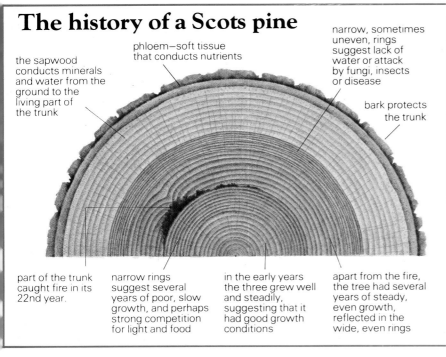

the sapwood conducts minerals and water from the ground to the living part of the trunk

phloem—soft tissue that conducts nutrients

narrow, sometimes uneven, rings suggest lack of water or attack by fungi, insects or disease

bark protects the trunk

part of the trunk caught fire in its 22nd year.

narrow rings suggest several years of poor, slow growth, and perhaps strong competition for light and food

in the early years the three grew well and steadily, suggesting that it had good growth conditions

apart from the fire, the tree had several years of steady, even growth, reflected in the wide, even rings

Above: Felled Scots pine trees. You can 'read' a cross section of one of the boles (left) for a detailed, accurate history of the tree in each year of its life. The width of the rings varies from one side of the trunk to another, reflecting exposure to varied conditions, such as continuous wind from one direction. Wide rings indicate rapid growth.

Timber

Timber is the most valuable of all our natural resources. From fuel and building materials to tools, furniture and paper, we use timber for so many different purposes that it is almost impossible to imagine life without it.

Below: Logs of beech after felling. Along with oak, beech is the most commonly used hardwood in Europe. Its combination of strength and lightness makes it ideal for furniture and a range of domestic products, such as handles and spoons.

Although all parts of a tree have their uses, commercially its most important part by far is its wood. Of all the timber felled in the world, about half is used for fuel in the form of logs or charcoal, much of it in the tropics and the Third World countries. The rest is used as timber or processed wood – plywood, chipboard and pulp.

A quick look at the wooden items found in a house soon shows that wood is not a uniform material but extremely variable, differing in pattern, colour and hardness. The most basic difference is between the wood of conifers, such as pines and cedars, which is called 'softwood', and that of the flowering trees (beech, oak and so forth), which is called 'hardwood'. However, these terms are confusing since they refer only in the most general way to the strength and durability of the two groups. For example, the softest, lightest wood is the 'hardwood' balsa, along with certain true 'softwoods', such as spruce.

Wood structure When looked at in cross-section, a tree trunk contains several different layers. On the outside is the protective bark; inside is the food-conducting phloem; inside that is a thin layer of cambium where the trunk forms new cells; then comes the water-conducting wood, the xylem, and in the centre is dead xylem, the heartwood.

For timber, the most important parts of a tree are the xylem and the heartwood. The xylem contains several types of cell, occurring

Cutting a log

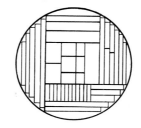

Above: There are many ways of sawing up a log. In this method, called 'round the log', each of the four sides is worked in turn to give a variety of planks, and the centre is then cut up for structural timber.

Left: A plantation of Douglas firs in the Forest of Dean. This wood is much used for building.

Below: Piles of peeled conifer logs ready for pulping in the Alice Holt Forest, Hampshire.

Structure and growth rings

The xylem of a hardwood contains vessels to conduct water and minerals, fibres to provide support and parenchyma to store food. In some species, such as oak, the vessels formed in the spring are larger, making the wood paler than at other times of the year—hence the appearance of annual growth rings. Other hardwoods, such as beech, show no such differences in their cells through the year. However, they do lay down different materials into the wood during the summer, so growth rings are still recognisable.

Softwoods also possess parenchyma, but the function of the vessels and fibres is combined in the tracheids, which perform a combined conducting and supporting role. Softwoods also show growth rings because the tracheids laid down in the summer have a smaller diameter and thicker walls than those produced in the spring.

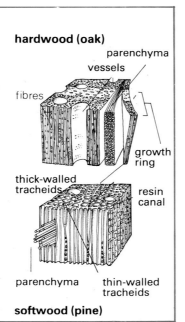

hardwood (oak)

parenchyma

vessels

fibres

growth ring

thick-walled tracheids

resin canal

parenchyma

thin-walled tracheids

softwood (pine)

in varying amounts in different species of tree. The differences between hardwoods and softwoods are due to the fact that they contain different types of cells.

In hardwoods, the most important component is the vessels, which consist of tubular cells placed end to end to act as a passage for minerals and water. Surrounding these in most hardwoods are fibre cells—long, thin, tapered cells with extremely thick walls, which provide the vessels with a supporting matrix. The variation in hardness between the different hardwoods is due mainly to the properties of these two groups of cells. In balsa, for example, the fibre cells have thin walls and the vessels are large and closely spaced. On the other hand, ebony, which is one of the hardest and heaviest woods, has thick-walled fibre cells with small, widely spaced vessels, which are often made harder by extremely tough deposits of gum in the middle of the cells.

Most species of hardwood trees have a third component called wood parenchyma. These are thin-walled cells that store food materials. They are arranged in vertical stacks that radiate from the centre of the wood outwards in lines known as medullary rays. These are responsible for the characteristic grain patterns of certain polished woods.

Softwoods have a quite different structure. They lack separate vessels and fibres, instead having tracheid cells that perform a combined conducting and supporting role. They also have parenchyma. Both sets of cells have channels to allow resin to flow.

Heart of the matter The cells in the xylem have a limited life span. Over a period of years their walls become impregnated with a substance called lignin, which makes them become gradually harder and rigid. Eventually, the cells become blocked with lignin, die and become a part of the tree's heartwood. Since the cells retain the same shape in death as they had in life, the structure of the heartwood is the same as that of the xylem.

There are considerable differences in colour and hardiness between the heartwood and the xylem due to the presence, in varying degrees, of gums and resins produced in the cells. In the most prized timbers, such as ebony, the heartwood is almost black from the presence of hard resins and gums, which also make this wood extremely hardy.

Timber for building The different uses to which timber may be put are determined by its characteristics—its grain pattern, density, colour, hardiness and so on. For example, balsa is ideal for making model aeroplanes because of its lightness, whereas heavy woods —teak, ebony and box—are more suitable for furniture-making. Cedar wood is often used for the outside of houses because of its attractive appearance and resistance to rot. Elm is useful for lock gates and the bottoms of barges because it does not rot easily under water, while the lightness and toughness of beech

Commercial woods

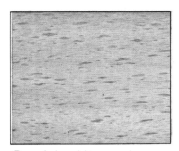

Beech is white or pale brown with a straight grain and characteristic flecks.

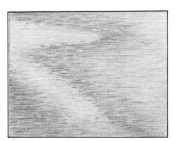

Ash is white and straight-grained with conspicuous growth rings.

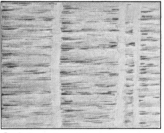

Oak is pale yellow-brown and straight-grained with a coarse texture.

Olive is pale to medium brown with dark markings and an irregular grain.

Cedar is a pale brown wood with a strong characteristic fragrance.

makes it a good choice for the roofing frames of houses.

However, before any wood can be used in building or furniture manufacture it has to be dried in controlled conditions. Fresh wood contains water (which is why logs crackle in a fire) and, as it dries, it shrinks, warps and cracks. Obviously, this cannot be allowed to happen to wood that has been incorporated into a building or a piece of furniture, so it is dried out before being used. This used to be done by leaving the logs or cut planks out in the open, but nowadays they are seasoned in humidity-controlled kilns to produce a large quantity of workable timber in the fastest possible time.

Processed wood The last 20 years or so have seen marked changes in the pattern of timber use. The value of timber has increased so much that the appearance of an end product is now often more important than the materials that go into its manufacture. A familiar example is chipboard which, when coated with a plastic laminate, is used for kitchen work surfaces and utility units in the home.

The advantage of chipboard is that it can be made from all sorts of wood, particularly trees too small to be cut into planks, and it can be made to any size and be manufactured by machines.

Plywood is a combination material of a different sort. Thin sheets of wood are glued together with the grain of each layer lying at right-angles to the grains of the layers immediately above and below. The 'ply number' – such as 3-ply or 6-ply – refers to the number of sheets. Plywood is much stronger than a plank of wood of the same thickness and the arrangement of its sheets makes it resistant to warping.

Timber for pulping Today, vast quantities of wood are pulped for paper. To give just one example, a top-selling national newspaper will consume up to 15,000 trees in a single edition.

Wood pulp is produced either mechanically or chemically. In the former process sections of logs are gradually pulped on a revolving grindstone and the fibres removed by water. In chemical pulping, the logs are chipped into pieces and then digested in either soda, calcium or magnesium sulphate or sodium sulphite. The resulting slurry is then beaten and chopped in a huge cylinder equipped with a rotating set of knives. China clay or starch is added to fill in pores in the wood fibres and give weight to the paper, and dyes and resins are added to reduce absorbency.

The mixture is then pumped into a paper-rolling machine, where it is passed through a series of rollers that squeeze the pulp into paper. Finally, after being dried, the paper is passed through chilled rollers to give it a finish. Fine-quality papers may be glazed with China clay or some other material to give them a glossy finish.

Products from pulp

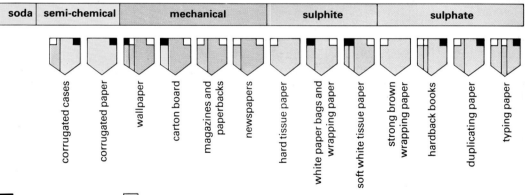

soda	semi-chemical	mechanical			sulphite	sulphate	
corrugated cases	corrugated paper	wallpaper	carton board	magazines and paperbacks	newspapers	hard tissue paper	white paper bags and wrapping paper	soft white tissue paper	strong brown wrapping paper	hardback books	duplicating paper	typing paper

■ hardwood ☐ softwood

Above: The chart shows the different treatments given to pulped woods to achieve different products. For example, carton board is mainly produced mechanically out of softwood, although a proportion is manufactured from soda-treated hardwood. Half of all the softwood timber cultivated in the northern hemisphere goes for pulping.

Left: A pulp mill in the Highland Region, with piles of timber cut into chips ready for processing.

Furniture woods

Despite recent advances in new materials, much of our furniture is still made from solid timber, whether home-grown wood such as beech or teak from the tropics.

Throughout the world and for thousands of years people have recognised the fact that wood is the perfect natural material for furniture, combining as it does an ability to be cut, carved, planed, glued, turned, bent, coloured and polished with a choice of patterning, weight, durability and hardness.

Which woods are used in furniture making has always been influenced by availability— hence the traditional popularity of oak in Britain. During the 17th century various foreign hardwoods began to be imported into Britain and have contributed greatly to the development of furniture styles. The most important of these was mahogany, which increased in popularity with the abolition in 1733 of the import tax on exotic woods. This heralded the 'Golden Age of Cabinet Making', with names such as Chippendale, Adam, Hepplewhite and Sheraton, who all combined the new wood with French trends towards daintiness in furniture design.

Since those days the increasing pressure on the world's resources of timber has led to constraints over the types of wood used in furniture. Some that were once widely available are now increasingly rare. A dramatic example is the furniture wood ramin, supplies of which were first exported from South-

Above and below: Some furniture is still made in small workshops, such as that of chair-maker Stewart Linford in the centre of the Chiltern Hills in Buckinghamshire. In the above picture, yew wood that has been steam-treated is being bent for the back of a chair, and below, the final product is being given a coat of sealer.

east Asia and Indonesia during the 1950s but are now in jeopardy only 25 years after the discovery of the wood by the Western world.

Today three main categories of furniture are produced: 'utility' furniture, constructed from processed wood such as chipboard, plywood and blockboard and finished with a plastic or timber veneer; solid furniture, reflected in the current fashion for pine and teak; and the increasingly popular 'reproduction' market.

Imports and home-grown Most of our furniture wood is now imported, despite the apparent abundance of trees in some parts of Britain and several major reafforestation schemes. Both large manufacturers and the numerous small-scale workshops employ buyers to scour the British countryside for suitable logs, but this represents only a small fraction of the furniture wood used in Britain. The rest comes mainly from Continental Europe and North America.

British sources of furniture woods include our native and long-naturalised timber trees— oak, beech, ash and elm. Other, rarer, trees such as walnut, sweet chestnut and yew are much sought after. A high proportion of the best British furniture timber is used nowadays as veneers in high-quality reproduction pieces.

Imported logs are checked rigorously for disease. Dutch elm disease was introduced into Britain in the bark of imported logs, causing the present disastrous epidemic, and

elm, oak and sweet chestnut are now not allowed into this country unless their bark has been removed, for fear of introducing further diseases.

Some temperate-zone woods are imported for use in solid furniture, for example, American white oak may sometimes feature in modern fitted kitchens. Pine, which is so often seen in solid furniture is mostly imported from Sweden or the USSR. Tropical woods are used for both solid furniture and for veneers. The most common examples are teak (mostly from Burma and Thailand), mahogany (the best comes from Brazil), afrormosia (from West Africa) and rosewood (mostly from India and Central America). Most of our man-made timber boards contain foreign woods and, indeed, are manufactured abroad.

Hardwoods for different uses Each type of timber has its own particular properties and characteristics, both mechanical and aesthetic, which make it suitable for certain uses. The underlying reason for these differences is in the wood's structure – the types, sizes and arrangement of cells in the heartwood. Trees such as oak, elm and beech, which are all hardwoods, have a xylem consisting primarily of fibres and water-conducting vessels. The hardness of the wood is related to the fibre content, and the straightness of its grain is determined by the straightness of the fibres. The vessels mainly determine the texture of the wood: woods with wide vessels are said to have a coarse texture.

For example, oak has numerous fibres and wide vessels, so it is both hard and coarse, making it difficult to work. Birch and beech, however, have narrow vessels and are fine-textured woods. Beech has become increasingly popular over the years because its straight grain and hardness make it easy to

The parts of a chair

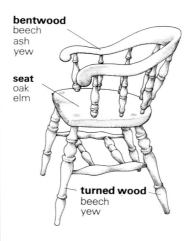

bentwood
beech
ash
yew

seat
oak
elm

turned wood
beech
yew

The range of properties offered by different timbers is exploited by using more than one wood in a piece of furniture. In a typical Windsor chair – a type of chair in which the parts are socketed together – beech or yew is used for the turned parts. These are fitted into an elm or oak seat, both tough woods that can withstand the force needed to bang them in. Flexible beech, ash or yew is used for the bentwood back. Stewart Linford's Windsor chairs (above right) have an elm seat with both the legs and the back of yew.

Below: Planks of elm are slowly dried for up to two years before being finally dried in a kiln. During the last ten years our elm population has been devastated by Dutch elm disease. Fortunately, however, only the sapwood is attacked. The heartwood remains unaffected and can still be used for furniture making.

work and it turns, bends and polishes well.

That some woods such as oak are difficult to work is reflected in certain characteristic styles and uses with which they are associated. Oak construction tends to be rough and massive, with carving in bold relief. Elm is likewise difficult to work, being coarse with a wild and wavy grain. With the development of sophisticated and more efficient drying techniques it is now being used successfully in solid furniture. In the past, however, it had only rough outdoor applications, such as farm

component of man-made boards used in utility furniture.

Veneered furniture Many decorative woods are scarce and therefore limited to being used for veneering – the technique of glueing a thin layer of an attractive wood on to a backing of relatively plain but strong wood or board. Veneer woods chosen for their attractive appearance include cherry, walnut, sweet chestnut, yew and many foreign timbers, particularly mahogany and rosewood. Even teak, which was once widely used for solid laboratory furniture because of its resistance to acid and heat, is now often used simply as a veneer in such applications.

Other woods are used in veneers for marquetry and inlaying. The former is the assembling of a pattern from thin leaves of wood; the latter is the filling-in of a recessed design cut into a background of solid wood. Holly and whitebeam are used for this, as are tulipwood (from Brazil and Burma) and satinwood (of which there are two types, one from the West Indies and the other from Sri Lanka). Strongly coloured woods are often used, ebony being the obvious example.

Hidden woods The complete opposite to veneering is the use of woods that do not need to be attractive because they are used in the parts of furniture that remain hidden. Both home- and foreign-produced timbers are used. Birch, being tough yet easy to work, is ideal for the frames of upholstered chairs. An example of a foreign wood is virola from central America, which is light and takes a smooth finish, and so is used for the sides of drawers.

Above: The abolition of a tax on foreign woods brought about the Golden Age of Cabinet Making in the mid 18th century. This mahogany cabinet is thought to have been designed by the furniture maker, William Vile, in 1760.

Left: The wild wavy grain of elm is used to great effect in this table top.

buildings, wharves and coffins, where its great durability was more important than an accurate finish.

Softwoods for furniture The structure of softwoods – woods of coniferous origin – is quite different from that of hardwoods. The role of the fibres and water-conducting vessels is combined in one type of cell, called a tracheid. In general, the structure of a softwood tends to make it weaker, and so less useful in furniture making, than a hardwood. An exception to this, however, is pine, reflected in the resurgence of pine furniture in recent years – a phenomenon that reflects the current awareness of the attractiveness and value of natural wood. The subtle variations in colour and the presence of knots add interest and warmth that is lacking in artificial laminates.

Softwoods are, however, a very important

Veneering

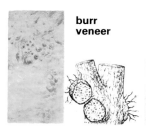

burr veneer

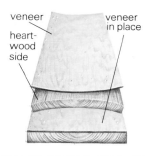

veneer

heart-wood side

veneer in place

The most sought-after veneers are cut from the lumpy outgrowths (burrs) of a tree trunk such as walnut.

Most veneers are laid as a single sheet on to the heartwood side of the backing to prevent warping (left). For best-quality work two sheets are laid cross-grain to each other – called counter veneering (right).

sliced veneer

Sliced veneers are taken by cutting across the whole width of a half-log. The wood shown here is rosewood.

rotary-cut veneer

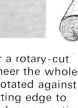

For a rotary-cut veneer the whole log is rotated against a cutting edge to produce a continuous sheet – here of maple.

veneer

Tree gardens

If you want to see exotic trees then the place to find them is in a specialised 'tree garden' called an arboretum. Britain has dozens of arboreta, from the Isles of Scilly to as far north as Wester Ross in Scotland, many boasting rare species from the distant corners of the world.

An arboretum is primarily a place where trees, and associated plants such as shrubs, are collected so that they can be examined, compared and, not least, simply enjoyed. Some arboreta contain just a score or two of species, whereas the biggest, Hillier's Arboretum in Hampshire, has a collection of nearly 10,000 species, varieties and cultivars.

An arboretum is quite different from a garden. For a start, most arboreta are very much larger than any garden, sometimes covering several square miles. Such an area obviously cannot be maintained to the neatness of a garden, and there is usually little need to do so. Trees are generally able to maintain themselves, and shrub layers help greatly in keeping weeds under control. Arboreta are, therefore, much less formal in appearance than a well-kept garden.

The function of arboreta The most significant function of an arboretum is as a repository for different tree species – a place where living specimens can be studied and compared. Many rare and endangered tree species are grown in British arboreta, a role that is becoming increasingly important as more and more natural forests and plant communities are destroyed. An extreme example of this concerns the tree *Franklinia alatemalia*, which has been extinct in the wild since 1790 but can still be seen growing in arboreta (it was native to the state of Georgia

Above: Some arboreta specialise in particular groups of trees, oaks or birches, for example. The Winkworth Arboretum, near Godalming in Surrey, has a notable collection of maples (*Acer* spp.). The best time to see them is in October when they show their autumn colours.

Right and far right: Many British arboreta have a wide range of unusual and exotic trees.
On the near right is the famous pagoda tree (*Sophora japonica*) at Kew Gardens. This tree was planted in 1753, which makes it one of Kew's oldest trees and the first pagoda tree to be planted in Britain. It is still flourishing, despite its need for supports.
On the far right is a group of Chusan palms (*Trachycarpus fortunei*) at Borde Hill gardens in Sussex. This species is one of the few palms to grow well in Britain.

in the USA).

The importance of this role can be seen when it is considered how many of our drugs, foods and other items are obtained from plants, trees included, yet few endangered trees have so far been tested for their potential.

Tree testing Another important function carried out in the larger arboreta is to test the hardiness, growth characteristics and speed of growth of newly introduced tree species. In this way botanists can determine which trees have forestry or amenity potential in this country.

Once it has been decided that a species shows promise, samples from different parts of its native range are tested to discover whether trees from any particular locality offer a significant advantage. For example, the Sitka spruce was first discovered to have great potential as a source of timber in Britain after being tested in an arboretum. Subsequent tests showed that Sitka spruces from north-western United States grow fastest in Britain, but that they are susceptible to frost damage here. On the other hand, specimens from Alaska, the far north of the tree's native range, were found to grow too slowly here. The best specimens came from British Columbia in Canada; they grew fast but were also hardy enough to survive frosts.

Arboreta also play an active role in plant breeding, first to discover parent trees that might make useful hybrid offspring, and also to compare the qualities of hybrid trees with those of pure species.

Arboreta for pleasure To the general public, the most important role of an arboretum is as a place of beauty and amenity. Even to someone who has little knowledge of trees, an arboretum can be an inspiring place at any time of year. In spring there is the brilliant fresh green of young leaves emerging; in summer there are the spectacular flowers of trees such as the sweet chestnut and laburnum to be enjoyed, followed in the autumn by the reds, browns and yellows of the dying leaves. Even in winter an arboretum is still worth visiting, for there are likely to be evergreen trees, both coniferous and broad-leaved, to be appreciated. With deciduous trees, winter is the best time of year for studying their barks and habit of growth.

History of arboreta Historically, the development of arboreta in Britain has been closely linked to the introduction of foreign tree species. There are about 35 species of trees native in Britain. Along with some new species introduced here by the Romans (such as the walnut and possibly the sycamore), these were the only trees found in Britain until the 16th century.

From 1500 onwards new species began to be brought back to Britain as explorers opened up new lands. At first these introductions were on a small scale, but they gradually increased over the following few centuries. By the middle of the 18th century enough new trees had been introduced to make the establishment of an arboretum an

attractive idea. The Kew arboretum dates from this time.

Initially, arboreta were simply gardens with a collection of trees in them. They only developed their own distinct style separate from gardens during the early part of the 19th century, when a whole range of new species from western North America suddenly started to appear in this country.

The boom in new trees began with the botanist-explorer David Douglas, who brought back many notable species, for example, the Douglas fir and the Sitka spruce.

During the 1850s, Douglas's work was followed up by a group of Scottish land-owners who called themselves the Oregon Association. They sent botanists out to the west coast of North America, the new species they brought back being planted by the land-owners as so-called 'policy' woods. These are mixed plantings, established both for pleasure and to test their forestry potential, and are often seen close to the castles of Scottish landowners. The Oregon Association was responsible for the introduction of the western hemlock and Lawson's cypress.

The work of this Association began a craze for planting private arboreta, helped by a flood of new material that has arrived in this country during the last hundred years, par-ticularly from the Far East.

Arboreta today Even today, most arboreta are still private establishments, with their own

independent means of support. However, they have been badly hit during the last 30 years by the combined effects of inflation and excessive taxation, and their numbers are declining.

Of the rest, some notable arboreta are financed by Local Governments, universities or charitable trusts, particularly the National Trust–for example, Stourhead in Wiltshire and Bodnant in Powys are both National Trust properties. Most of the remaining arboreta, however, are funded by Central Government. These include the Royal Bot-anic Gardens, several Forestry Commission arboreta and the gardens in Windsor Great Park, which are run by the Crown Estate.

Above: One of the functions of arboreta is to carry out scientific research. Here, different methods of treating tree-wounds caused by the removal of branches are being tested on a Swedish whitebeam (*Sorbus intermedia*).

Opposite: The pink horse chestnut is often planted in parks and arboreta.

Below: Some of the larger arboreta that are open (if only occasionally) to the public.

Gazetteer of British and Irish arboreta

1 Royal Botanic Garden, Kew, Surrey. The foremost botanic garden in Britain; numerous rare species.
2 Savill and Valley Gardens, Windsor Great Park, Berks.
3 Royal Horticultural Society, Wisley, Surrey. A number of good collections.
4 Winkworth Arboretum, Godalming, Surrey.
5 National Pinetum, Bedgebury, Kent. Very wide range of conifers.
6 Wakehurst Place, Ardingly, Surrey.
7 Borde Hill, near Haywards Heath, Sussex.
8 Highdown, Goring, Sussex.
9 Hillier Arboretum, Amptfield, Hants. Largest collection of specimens in the temperate world.
10 Exbury Gardens, near Fawley, Hants.
11 Bicton Gardens, East Budleigh, Devon.
12 Trewithin, Cornwall.
13 Tresco Abbey, Isles of Scilly. Many tender trees, particularly from the

southern hemisphere.
14 Stourhead, near Mere, Wiltshire.
15 Bath Botanic Gardens, Avon. Small collection of unusual trees.
16 Westonbirt Arboretum, near Tetbury, Glos. A large and splendid arboretum.
17 Cambridge University Botanic Garden, Cambridge.
18 Hergest Croft, Kington, Herefordshire.
19 Powys Castle, Welshpool, Powys. Some very tall trees.
20 Bodnant, Gwynedd.
21 Castle Howard, Yorkshire.
22 Thorpe Perrow, Bedale, Yorkshire.
23 Dawyck, Stobo, Peeblesshire.
24 Royal Botanic Garden, Edinburgh. A notable collection.
25 Younger Botanic Garden, Benmore, Strathclyde.
26 Castlewellian, Newcastle, Co. Down.
27 National Botanic Garden, Glasnevin, Dublin.
28 Powerscourt, Co. Wicklow.
29 Birr Castle, Co. Offaly. Enormous collection.

Exotic trees

The British Isles are graced with a greater variety of foreign trees than just about any other country in the world. Some are grown here in plantations for their timber but most have been introduced for their decorative flowers, bark or foliage.

A walk through our parks and gardens soon shows that there is a great wealth of different trees in the British Isles, but it would be a mistake to think that they are all native to this country. In fact, we have only 35 indigenous species; the vast majority of our cultivated trees – some 1700 different species in all – were introduced here from other countries throughout the temperate world. The sweet chestnut, for example, comes from southern Europe, the tulip tree forms natural stands in the deep, rich soils or river valleys in western North America, while the maidenhair tree originates in China. Of these 1700 introductions about 600 can be commonly seen in parks and gardens, the remainder being more or less confined to private collections and botanic gardens.

First arrivals It is generally agreed that the Romans first introduced some of our most familiar exotics, such as the mulberry, sweet chestnut and walnut. Evidence that they did introduce some species comes from the discovery of the seeds of the stone pine – a native of Italy – in the refuse heaps of Roman encampments in Britain.

The next major step forward in the cultivation of exotic trees was probably during the 17th century, with the establishment of the Oxford Botanic Garden and the Chelsea Physic Garden. The most noteworthy introduction of this time was the common larch which was to become, a century later, an important forestry tree. The great pioneer in the cultivation of this tree was the Duke of Atholl, who planted it extensively on his country estate in Perthshire. His son was also

Above: Many of our most ornamental exotics come from the Far East, such as this Japanese maple. Several cultivars of it are grown in Britain. The one shown here, 'Septemlobum', is a small tree planted for its delicate foliage and blaze of autumn colour.

Right: Only a few exotics have managed to become naturalised in this country, the most successful being the sycamore, a species from southern Europe brought over by the Romans.

interested in forestry and was nicknamed 'the planter', for it is said that during his lifetime he planted 27 million larches.

In 1804 the Horticultural Society (now the Royal Horticultural Society) was founded and, in 1824, it commissioned the great botanist-explorer, David Douglas, to collect plants from western North America, until then a little-known region. Douglas was responsible for such introductions as the Sitka spruce, noble fir and Douglas fir.

The latter part of the 19th century and the early 20th century saw many trees being brought over here from western China, a region with an extremely rich flora. Many plant collectors of this time were employed by nurseries. One such nursery was Veitch and Son, who were fortunate enough to have working for them a most prolific collector called Ernest Wilson. His prettiest introduction is probably the dove tree or handkerchief tree.

Forestry introductions There are few countries in the world today where exotic trees play a more important role than they do in Britain, and the most important of these roles is in forestry. In 1966 Britain had more than 3 million acres of land under forest, managed as a timber crop. For commercial timber production a tree needs to be fast growing and have a long, straight trunk, both qualities found mainly in softwoods. There is only one such species native to Britain, the Scots pine, and due to the present emphasis on high-volume production it has been necessary to look elsewhere for suitable species.

Above: Many introduced species grow best along the west coast of Britain, where the Gulf Stream keeps the climate mild from Cornwall up to Scotland. In these areas exotic subtropical trees from the Southern Hemisphere can be grown, and one of the most famous gardens for such trees is at Tresco in the Isles of Scilly. Here, tree ferns from New Zealand and Australian eucalypts thrive alongside acacias from South Africa. Palms from various tropical countries both north and south of the equator also grow here, such as this Chusan palm from southern China.

Left: In commercial forestry, the Sitka spruce is our most widely planted conifer, being well adapted to the cool, humid climate of northern and western Britain—the sites of most of our forestry plantations. In 1965, the area under Sitka spruce totalled about 255,000ha (612,000 acres).

The most commonly grown forestry tree in Britain is the Sitka spruce. Another much favoured conifer is the closely related Norway spruce, and both the common and the Japanese larch are also widely planted.

Amenity trees The ever-increasing spread of our towns and cities has brought with it a greater awareness of the amenity value of trees. Few of our own native species are used in urban planning, however, because of their low tolerance of air pollution. But there are many exotic trees that can survive these trying conditions, the best example being the London plane. This hybrid between the western and the oriental planes is widely planted as a street tree in southern Britain, where it can grow to a height of 30m (100ft) and live for up to 300 years.

The false acacia from North America also has much to offer as a town or city tree. In June its racemes of white, pea-like flowers contrast elegantly against a background of bright, pale green, feathery foliage. A close relative of the false acacia, but from southern Europe, is the Judas tree. It prefers the warmer climate of southern England, in mid-May producing bunches of bright rosy-pink flowers. A peculiar feature of this species is that the flowers are borne directly on the trunk as well as on the younger shoots—a phenomenon known as cauliflory.

The horse chestnut must be one of our most familiar and best-loved park trees. It is a

NORTH AMERICA

Dawn redwood
Douglas fir
False acacia
Indian bean tree
Lawson cypress
Magnolia
Noble fir
Sitka spruce
Swamp cypress
Tulip tree

native of Albania and Greece, and was introduced into Britain as long ago as 1616. Two other trees that seem to stand the rigours of city life are the Indian bean tree and the tulip tree, both large North American species. For the Indian bean tree, spring starts late, because it is not until June that its leaves begin to appear. It is planted primarily for its bun-shaped panicles of white flowers spotted with yellow and purple and its long dangling pods. During hot summers the tulip tree also produces a marvellous show of flowers. These are, as the name suggests, tulip shaped and stand upright among the curiously lobed leaves.

Ornamental conifers It is among the coniferous cedars that we find the truly majestic species which add such dignity to Britain's stately homes. There are several species, of which the most famous is the cedar of Lebanon, with its layers of flat horizontal branches.

Another conifer often associated with large country estates is the curious-looking monkey puzzle tree. Sometimes known as Chilean or Chile pine, this species became very popular in Britain during the 19th century and was much used in planting schemes.

Garden exotics The private gardener has benefited greatly from the range of species brought into Britain, especially during the past decade with its growth of garden centres. Several types of flowering cherry are now

Above: The London plane owes its success as a town and city tree to the ability of its roots to function in compacted and covered soils; in Britain this hybrid has never been known to blow down.

Below: Among our most popular street and garden trees are the ornamental cherries, most of which come from the Far East. Many cultivars have been developed, including 'Kanzan', a cultivar of the Japanese cherry.

1 Douglas fir
(*Pseudotsuga menziesii*). Native to western North America. Introduced 1827.

2 Indian bean tr
(*Catalpa bignonio* Native to the Unit States. Introducec here in 1726.

Introduced trees

Britain's 1700 different species of exotic trees include representatives from all five Continents, though the majority are from Continental Europe, North America or the Far East. Here is a sample of the most common—or unusual—introductions.

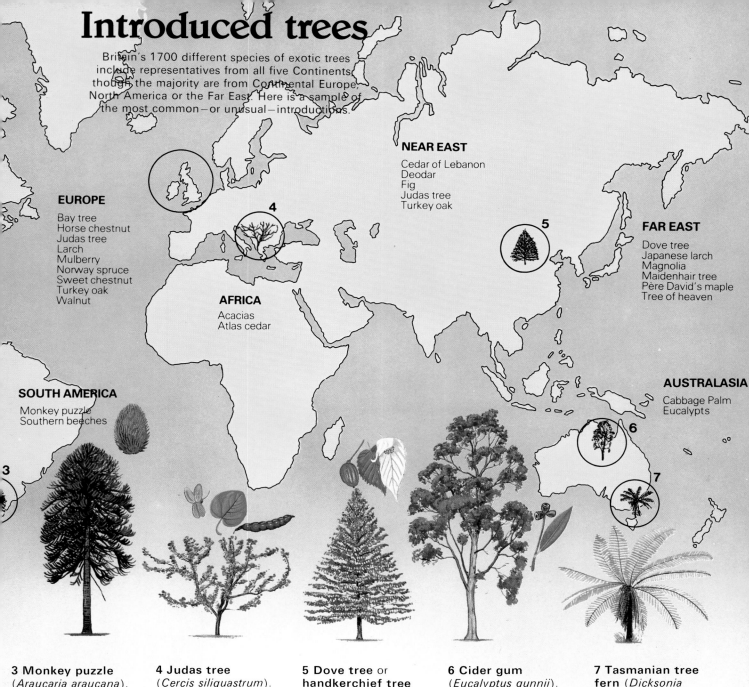

NEAR EAST

Cedar of Lebanon
Deodar
Fig
Judas tree
Turkey oak

FAR EAST

Dove tree
Japanese larch
Magnolia
Maidenhair tree
Père David's maple
Tree of heaven

EUROPE

Bay tree
Horse chestnut
Judas tree
Larch
Mulberry
Norway spruce
Sweet chestnut
Turkey oak
Walnut

AFRICA

Acacias
Atlas cedar

SOUTH AMERICA

Monkey puzzle
Southern beeches

AUSTRALASIA

Cabbage Palm
Eucalypts

3 Monkey puzzle (*Araucaria araucana*). Native to Chile and Argentina. Introduced here in 1795.

4 Judas tree (*Cercis siliquastrum*). Native to southern Europe and west Asia. Introduced pre-1600.

5 Dove tree or **handkerchief tree** (*Davidia involucrata*). Native to western China. Introduced in 1904.

6 Cider gum (*Eucalyptus gunnii*). Native to Australia and Tasmania. Introduced in 1846.

7 Tasmanian tree fern (*Dicksonia antarctica*). Native to south-eastern Australia.

available, as well as such species as magnolias, laburnums and more unusual exotics like Père David's maple with its attractive orange colour in the autumn.

Success or failure Not all the exotic species introduced to Britain succeed here. The reasons why a particular species does or does not survive in Britain are many, but the most important reason is the question of hardiness. The amount of rainfall and the type of soil, for example, both contribute to the success of a tree, but the most decisive factor is whether or not that tree is hardy enough to withstand the lowest winter temperatures.

During the hard winter of 1981-2, the hardiness of our exotic trees was put to the test. Many came through unscathed, while others did not. For example, many eucalypts and bay trees, the former from Australasia and the latter from the Mediterranean area, suffered severely from frost damage, sometimes dying.

The reason why these three species fared particularly badly is that they are all broad-leaved evergreens. In general, such trees are more vulnerable to low winter temperatures than either conifers or deciduous broad-leaved trees. They have no need to shed their leaves in readiness for winter because they come from parts of the world where the winters are mild. By retaining their broad leaves they become very susceptible to our climate.

Coniferous trees and their allies

The vast assemblage of seed-bearing plants is divided into two groups, depending upon the amount of protection given to the ovule (the ovary-containing structure) at the time of flowering. These two groups are the angiosperms, in which the ovule is enclosed in a structure termed an ovary, and the gymnosperms, in which the ovule is exposed. The gymnosperms are a large, highly heterogenous group, which have been split further into three distinct groups: the cone-bearing plants and their allies, and two smaller groups, the cycads and the Gnetales.

The most obvious feature of many of the trees in the group known as the conifers is that the clusters of 'flowers' are borne aggregated into a strobilus or cone. The cones are always all male, or all female. The young female cone of a pine tree is made up of a number of scales, arranged in a close spiral around the stem. At the base of each scale is a number of ovules. The male cone consists of a number of small stamens, arranged in a spiral cluster. These release winged pollen. The pollen is taken into the female cone, often on a small drop of exuded sap and, once inside, the cone closes up. After closing, it may even become sealed to prevent any danger of drying out. The cone then remains on the tree for several months—even years in the case of some conifers. During this time fertilisation occurs, forming a zygote, and this develops into a seed. After the seed has been formed, the cone re-opens, and the seed is liberated and dispersed.

It is important to mention two genera that occur in this book which, whilst not true conifers, are closely related, and show the typical characters such as dense wood, needle-shaped or fan-shaped leaves, a basic dichotomous venation, and bilaterally symmetrical seeds. These are the yew (*Taxus baccata*), which possesses male cones but has a single female flower which becomes surrounded by a fleshy aril; and the maidenhair tree (*Ginkgo biloba*), which has male flowers borne on catkin-like structures rather than cones, and female flowers which occur as single ovules at the end of short stems.

Conifers and their relatives are very distinctive trees. They tend to grow in a regular shape, with a straight, central trunk and branches which radiate symmetrically. Many of them have very large and well-defined cones, and nearly all have needle-like foliage. As a group, they are very old, very successful and, as far as man is concerned, very useful. By far the oldest is the maidenhair tree. Leaves identical with those of the modern maidenhair tree have been found as far back as the Triassic Period, over 200 million years ago. Our more modern conifers, by comparison, have an ancestry of 150 million years at the most. This great antiquity coupled with a basic design needing little if any change is a good recipe for success, and it is not surprising that vast areas of the earth's surface are covered by coniferous forest. It is further no surprise that in mixed forests it is very often coniferous trees that are the tallest, projecting well above the main canopy. The group contains many fine trees, such as the cypresses, *Wellingtonia*, the magnificent cedars, the firs, the pines, and the larch—one conifer that has adopted the deciduous habit. It also includes the amazing Chilean pine or monkey puzzle tree—so named because its curious branching pattern was reckoned to be able to puzzle even monkeys!

In this country, it is as a resource that conifers are most commonly encountered. Pine was once used for furniture making when it was an inexpensive form of timber. Today, stripped of years of paint and well treated, it can be found on sale at prices that would make the original manufacturers blanch! Softwood timber is still much used for every kind of construction work, of course, and the sight of vast acres of the tall, straight Norway spruce planted over what was previously a bare hillside are testament to our need for poles, paper, and even, in the season of the year, Christmas trees. Conifers become everything from the highly prized specimen tree in a large garden to a simple box of matches.

Opposite: During winter, when deciduous trees have shed their leaves, coniferous trees retain theirs, adding colour to the landscape.

Cones

Autumn is the time when most cones ripen from green to brown before releasing their seeds. But this is only the final stage in a long and complicated process of growth and development from a tiny bud first formed as much as four years ago.

Above: A larch in summer with its maturing green cones. These cones were fertilised in the spring of that year. By the autumn they will turn brown and will release their seeds the following spring by opening their cone scales. Once the seeds have dispersed, the old brown cones remain on the tree for a while before falling. In this picture, some old cones that have already released their seeds earlier in the year can still be seen on the tree.

A great many of the world's trees produce their seeds in structures known as cones, so-called because some of the most prominent cones are roughly conical in shape. This huge group of trees – known to us as the conifers – constitutes an order called the Coniferales. As well as bearing cones, all the trees in this order have narrow, needle-like leaves. A few broad-leaved trees seem to have cones, notably alders, but these are not true cones because their structure is entirely different.

Besides liberating the seeds, the cones also bear the ovules and pollen, earlier on in the cycle. In this capacity, they are equivalent to the flowers on a broad-leaved tree, yet the two structures differ in several important respects. Most flowers have petals and sepals, and stigmas to catch the pollen. Plants bearing flowers are called angiosperms (meaning 'seed in a vessel').

Cones, on the other hand, lack petals, sepals and stigmas. The ovules lie at the base of a leaf-like scale instead of being enclosed in an ovary. Hence plants with cones are called gymnosperms (meaning 'naked seed'). All conifers have separate male and female cones, unlike some flowers in which the male and female parts are found on the same structure.

First appearances The very first step in the production of a cone occurs in early spring before the current year's growth has begun. Tiny buds, called bud primordia, start to appear along the shoots. In early summer, the bud primordia begin to develop in one of three possible ways. Some form vegetative buds, which will later develop into next year's shoots, while the others form either male or female cones.

For a long time, the three different types of bud look exactly the same, but after some months they begin to develop into cones or shoots. The male cones consist of stalkless anthers arranged around a central column, each anther containing pollen grains. The female cones consist of scales, also arranged around a central stalk. On the scales sit the ovules. These can best be seen on cypress or juniper cones, where the ovules are just visible to the naked eye as minute dots. In cones of the pine family, the ovules are partially hidden between the cone scales and bracts. Male cones are usually most abundant on the middle and lower parts of a tree, whereas the female cones are most often seen higher up. This reduces the possibility of a tree pollinating itself by the pollen falling on the female cones below.

Pollination A few weeks after the cones have begun to develop, pollination takes place. The male cones, shaken by the wind, release clouds of bright yellow pollen grains, which are equipped with air sacs to help them float—for cones are pollinated by the wind, not by insects as is the case with most flowers. The pollen grains enter the female cones, which then grow to enclose the pollen inside with the ovules.

In most conifers, pollination takes place in spring or early summer, though some cypresses produce their pollen during winter, and on cedars this occurs during autumn. Once pollination has been effected, the male cones are of no further use and they die off. The female cones, however, continue to grow into mature seed-bearing structures.

Once the pollen is trapped inside the cone it sends out a tube which burrows through the ovule to the egg cell lying inside (as on angiosperms). When the tube reaches the egg cell, fertilisation takes place. On most conifers, fertilisation occurs within a few weeks,

Above: Mature cones on a cedar of Lebanon. All cedars have distinctly barrel-shaped cones borne upright on the branches. The white marks are resin secreted by the cones to seal in the pollen with the ovule after pollination.

Right: Cones of a Douglas fir after the scales have opened out to release the seeds. The three-pronged bracts on each scale once covered the ovules. This is another species that secretes white resin.

Growth of a larch cone

The very first step is the production of tiny bud primordia in early spring. On the larch, some of the buds begin to form young male and female cones the following spring (stage **1**). A week or two later pollination occurs, as yellow pollen grains are transferred from the male to the female cones (stage **2**). A short while afterwards, the pollen fertilises the egg cells, and the female cone elongates and the scales close up (stage **3**). By September, the ripening cone is green (stage **4**) and, by late autumn, brown. The following spring, the scales open to release the seeds (stage **5**).

stage 1

young female flower

vegetative bud

young male flower

stage 2

close-up of female flower at pollination

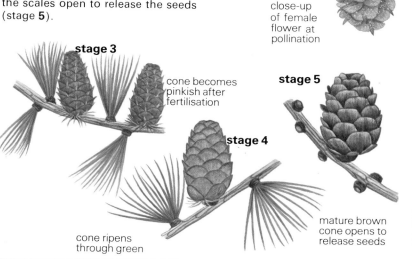

stage 3

cone becomes pinkish after fertilisation

cone ripens through green

stage 4

stage 5

mature brown cone opens to release seeds

or even days, of pollination, but on pines it takes a whole year for the pollen tube to reach the egg cell.

After fertilisation, the seeds develop. At the same time, the cone is growing and turning green, then brown at maturity. In most species, the female cones are mature by the autumn or winter after pollination. Pines, however, take one or two more years to mature; some cypresses also take two years and the monkey puzzle takes at least that long.

Distributing the seeds Once mature, the final function of the female cone is to release the seeds. Several different methods are used for this. In the most common, the cone scales contract and open out, allowing the seeds to fall. Although the seeds are equipped with small wings, the wind does not carry them further than the spread of the tree. Normally, this method of dispersal occurs in warm dry weather in spring. Spruces, larches, Douglas firs, Scots pine and hemlocks all use this method of distribution, as do members of the redwood family and all but one of the cypress family.

The next commonest method is that used by silver firs, cedars and members of the monkey puzzle family. In these species, the cone disintegrates to scatter the seeds. Silver firs and cedars have winged seeds, which are released with the cone scales, leaving just the central stalk on the tree. In the monkey puzzle, the seeds are large and unwinged; they are gathered and dispersed by animals feeding on them.

A number of pines also have large wingless seeds and rely on animals for their dispersal. Some species in this group release their cones intact. The seeds are then spread by animals foraging among the cones in the forest litter; an example of this group is the Swiss stone pine, also called the arolla pine.

The final method of dispersal is found only in pine trees growing in dry open forests that are prone to fires. In these species, the cones remain intact for years, and only open after a forest fire. The advantage to the species is that the fire removes competing vegetation and provides an excellent seed-bed. Trees with this type of cone are common in western North America and include the Monterey pine, but in Europe only the maritime pine has this characteristic.

Uses of cones As well as being a food source for birds and mammals, conifer seeds have, in some parts of the world, long been an important part of man's diet. For example, South American Indians eat the seeds of the monkey puzzle tree and the Romans used to eat the seeds of the stone pine – indeed they introduced the species to this country for that purpose.

Cones have also been used as a source of fuel and for dyeing; in the Himalayas the Himalayan fir is still used for dyeing. In Britain, however, we neglect our cones, except as Christmas decorations.

Berry-like cones

Juniper and yew are both conifers, yet they do not seem to bear cones. In fact, both do. The juniper berry is a cone in which the scales have fused together and become fleshy and edible. It takes two years to ripen – the berries shown here are a year old. Similarly, on a yew the red fleshy aril is formed out of cone scales.

Above: A maturing cypress cone. The scales on this cone are arranged around a point to form a ball, rather than the more familiar cone-shaped arrangement around a stalk. The immature male (pink) and female (blue) cones are shown below.

Seed-release mechanisms

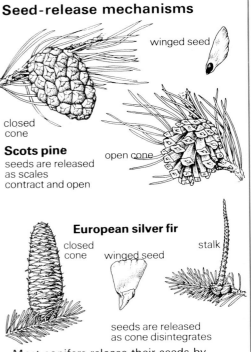

winged seed

closed cone

Scots pine
seeds are released as scales contract and open

open cone

European silver fir

closed cone   winged seed   stalk

seeds are released as cone disintegrates

Most conifers release their seeds by contracting and opening out their cone scales. A familiar example of a tree using this mechanism is the Scots pine. The only other common method of releasing seeds is one in which the whole cone distintegrates, leaving just a stalk. The European silver fir uses this method.

Maidenhair

The maidenhair tree, or ginkgo as it is often known, the sole survivor of an ancient group of plants, is found growing wild only in remote parts of China. During the past 200 years it has been planted here for its graceful shape and distinctive foliage.

The maidenhair tree, or ginkgo, is one of the most ancient surviving trees. Imprints of the characteristic fan-shaped leaves have been found in fossils dating back over 190 million years. Then the ginkgo enjoyed a world-wide distribution, but later its place was taken by more 'modern' trees – the enormously successful conifers and flowering trees that came to dominate the world's forests. Over millions of years its range contracted and now the species has become relegated to a few scattered mountain forests in China.

In some ways the ginkgo could not have been in a worse place for its 'last stand', because for centuries the pressure on China's forests has been so intense that only fragments of the natural tree cover remain. The rest of the forest has been cleared to make way for agriculture and to provide firewood and timber.

Today the ginkgo is all but extinct in the

Right: **Maidenhair** or **ginkgo** (*Ginkgo biloba*). Introduced, deciduous, grows to 30m (100ft). Planted in botanical gardens, city parks and gardens. Flowers spring, rarely fruits in the British Isles.

Overleaf: The famous ginkgo in Kew Gardens was planted there in 1754. Like most ginkgos in the British Isles, it is a male tree. Both male and female specimens grow in the Chelsea Physic Garden in London.

Below: In autumn the distinctive foliage of the ginkgo turns a beautiful golden yellow colour.

wild, but fortunately over the centuries it was widely planted in temple gardens throughout China and Japan where it was kept as a sacred tree. Those gardens supplied the first specimens to Europe in about 1730. Kew Gardens obtained their first specimen in 1754, and it still grows there.

Unique tree When botanists first studied the ginkgo they were puzzled as to how it should be classified. At first they thought it must be some sort of primitive conifer and it was put into the Yew family. Later they realised it was indeed a unique tree and deserved a class of its own – the Ginkgoales – of which *Ginkgo biloba* is the sole surviving representative.

The Japanese nick-named it the duck's foot tree, because the leaf shape is rather like a webbed foot. The French called it the '40 sovereign tree', from the price they paid for one of the first specimens to be planted in France. The common name we use – maidenhair – indicates the close resemblance between the shape of its foliage and the fronds of the delicate maidenhair fern.

Graceful appearance The ginkgo is a deciduous tree which grows to about 30m (100ft) tall, forming a crown which is generally triangular in outline. In the early stages of growth the tree can be angular and rather ungainly, especially in exposed sites. The trunk often forks quite close to the ground, sending up two or more main stems which carry the spreading side branches. These divide further into the leaf-bearing shoots that tend to droop, and with age the tree acquires a distinctly graceful appearance. In old trees the trunk is often fluted, and the brown cork-like bark develops deep fissures and rugged longitudinal ridges.

The distinctive pale green leaves are borne on slender stalks 4-9cm (1½-3½in) long. The

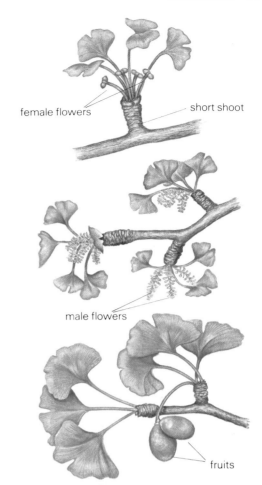

female flowers   short shoot

male flowers

fruits

...n-shaped leaf blade is marked by a central ...otch at the broad end (hence the Latin ...pecies name, *biloba*, which means two-...bed). The veins fan out from the base, ...ometimes forking before reaching the slight-...y wavy leaf margin. Before falling in autumn, ...hey turn a beautiful rich yellow – the colour ...preading slowly from the broad edge to-...ards the leaf stalk.

Like some conifers, such as pines or ...edars, the ginkgo is unusual in having two ...ifferent kinds of shoot. Some are slow-...rowing and remain short and bear leaves in ...lusters at their tips. Others are much longer, ...aster growing shoots, with leaves placed ...lternately along their length.

The ginkgo flowers in spring as the new ...eason's foliage is unfolding. The trees are ...ither male or female, and the flowering ...tructures sprout from little woody short ...hoots, each about 3cm (1¼in) long. The male ...owers are simply a bunch of greenish pollen-...earing stamens; the female flowers consist ...f a slender stalk about 4cm (1½in) long, ...ipped with two tiny green ovules. The ...vules are exposed and naked, which means ...hat they can be fertilised on direct contact ...ith wind-blown pollen.

After fertilisation a yellow-green fruit, ...esembling a little plum, is formed. The ...esh of the fruit has a horrendous rotting ...mell, but the woody stone it surrounds has ...n edible kernel prized by the Japanese.

It is rare for the trees in Europe to produce ...ruit because they are usually planted as iso-...ated ornamentals in parks and gardens and ...long city streets, too widely separated ...rom each other for the successful transfer of ...ollen. And curiously, in any case, most of ...he trees that have reached flowering age in ...he British Isles have proved to be males.

The ginkgo has a pale creamy yellow wood ...vhich has a fragrant smell and was much ...sed in China for making coffins.

Above: The gingko's young bright green leaves resemble the maidenhair fern – hence the tree's other name, maidenhair.

Below: The bole of a ginkgo forks close to the ground, making the tree easy to identify in winter when the leaves have fallen.

Yew

With their hollow gnarled trunks and huge girths, some yew trees are believed to be more than a thousand years old. Not surprisingly, they are surrounded by legend and were once a symbol of everlasting life, despite being highly poisonous.

Below: Yew trees are usually encountered as solitary specimens, either in the open, as here, or in oak woods. Of the few yew woods that have survived, most are found on the chalk downs of southern England.

The common yew is often called the English yew, but in fact it is found wild from the west of Ireland eastwards to the Himalayas. From north to south it ranges from the lowlands of Scandinavia to Greece, Sicily, Spain and North Africa.

In Britain the yew occurs naturally in many areas, but usually only as isolated specimens.

Woods wholly of yew are believed to have been plentiful at one time, particularly on the chalk hills of southern England and elsewhere on steep limestone ridges, both areas where the normally dominant oak would have failed to flourish.

Today, the best place to see wild yews on the South Downs where Sussex meet Hampshire. Here you can still find yew wood the most famous of which, Kingley Vale, four miles north-west of Chichester, is regarded as the finest yew wood in Europe. The area now a National Nature Reserve and contains both young and old trees, some having been there at least five centuries.

Short and wide Yews occasionally grow to height of 20m (70ft), but they usually reach only 12-15m (40-50ft). They are conical or rounded in outline and spread out to a great width, sometimes greater than the height of the tree. The shade beneath a large yew extremely dense, so dense in fact that no enough sunlight passes through to allow any green plants to grow there.

The trunk is reddish-brown or grey and

Wind pollinated flowers The flowers are borne on separate trees. Male flowers consist of small yellow spheres clustered together on the undersides of leaf sprays. In late February and March they release great quantities of pollen to be dispersed by the wind. The female flowers are smaller than the male flowers, and green, which means they are hardly noticeable until they develop into the fruits.

Fleshy cones When young the fruit resembles an olive-green acorn (the seed) set in a pale green cup (called the aril). In August the aril swells to envelop the seed almost completely and becomes fleshy and bright red, resembling a berry. Birds are much attracted to the fleshy arils, particularly mistle thrushes and blackbirds, and are the chief means of spreading yew seeds through the countryside.

Although the foliage of the yew resembles that of a typical conifer, its fruit is distinctly un-conelike and for many years botanists classified the yew separately from the conifers. But modern practice is to recognise the fruit of the yew as being a greatly modified cone, and the yew is now classed as a conifer.

How poisonous is yew? A notorious feature of yew is that nearly all its parts are poisonous: bark, leaves and seeds. The fleshy aril is, however, harmless and tastes sweet. Only this part of the fruit is digested by birds; the seeds pass through their bodies intact.

Its poisonous nature is due to the presence of several chemicals known as alkaloids peculiar to yew, one of which is called taxine. There are strangely differing reports about the effects of this poison on domestic animals. Some authorities are emphatic that yew foliage is highly toxic to all domestic animals, especially horses. Others state that it is only deadly poisonous when it is cut and dried. Still others report farm stock eating it without

above: In February or March male yew flowers produce great quantities of yellow pollen. Usually it is blown away on the wind to fertilise nearby yew trees, but on a calm day it settles on the ground below, colouring it yellow.

right: The fleshy red aril containing a seed. The aril is one of the few parts of the yew that is not poisonous. It is much sought after by birds, which eat it and excrete the poisonous seed intact.

below: Yews are often found growing in the deep shade of a wood, though they may not flower in such dark surroundings. Yews themselves cast such a dense shade that no green plants can grow beneath.

often deeply fluted. In older trees its girth can be as large as 10m (35ft), though the trunk rarely grows to any great height.

The foliage is rich dark green, sometimes appearing black from a distance. Each leaf is about 10-20mm long, needle-like, pale green underneath and arranged spirally round the twig.

Common yew (*Taxus baccata*). Native, evergreen tree, growing to a height of 21m (70ft). Some specimens have huge girths, up to 10m (35ft) round, though hollow, and are believed to be up to 1000 years old. Male and female flowers are borne on separate trees. Male flowers are rounded, turning yellow in Feb-March. Female flowers are smaller, greenish and inconspicuous. Fruit consists of a fleshy aril containing a single seed. The aril turns red in Aug.

Above: One of the few pests to attack yew is the yew gall-midge. It causes tufts of leaves to appear on shoots, but these galls seem to cause little or no damage to the tree.

Left: The yew, shown here with twig and fruit. The crown of the tree is often broad and conical.

Below: Many churchyards traditionally have a yew planted in them as a symbol of good fortune and everlasting life.

old trees are hollow inside where the heart wood has rotted away, so they cannot be dated by counting the annual rings. However there are yew trees that are known to be about 300 years old, and they still look youthful, so it seems reasonable to guess at an age of about a thousand years for the oldest specimens. This estimate is supported by counting the rings in the outer wood; the oldest trees can have as many as a hundred rings squeezed into an inch of wood.

Many of our most ancient yews are to be found in churchyards, and if they are much more than a thousand years old they may well have marked the sites of pagan worship before Christianity. The shelter of a wide spreading yew would have been an ideal place for the rituals of our Celtic predecessors.

With the arrival of Christianity these sites would have had churches built upon them. So began the traditional association between yews and churchyards, with the yew coming to represent the forces of good overcoming evil. The yew was also a symbol of everlasting life and sprigs of it were buried with the dead.

Yet, against that, the yew has a long tradition as a gloomy, even dangerous tree. For example, in the 17th century it was thought unwise to sleep beneath a churchyard yew because the roots sucked up death and disease from the graves and exhaled them through its leaves. Probably man has always felt uneasy about a tree that is both sacred and poisonous

any ill effects, and one account even says that on parts of the Continent it is given to animals as a winter feed. Most likely, the truth is that yew is more poisonous in some districts than in others, that animals differ widely in their resistance to its poison and that the toxicity of yew varies with the season, according to whether the sap is running or not. Whatever the truth of the matter, it seems wise to treat yew with respect and to keep its foliage, whether green or dead, away from animals and the seeds away from children.

Durable wood The wood of yew is fine-grained, heavy and hard, yet springy. Even out of doors it is extremely durable: some of the oldest wooden weapons that archaeologists have discovered are made of yew. They date from the Palaeolithic times, about 10,000 years ago.

Because of the yew's strength and elastic nature the traditional use of its wood until the 17th century was for making long bows, though most English archers preferred the more expensive foreign-made bows, which were stronger and freer from knots. Other uses for yew wood have included furniture making, veneering and tool making. These days, however, there is so little yew wood available that its use is limited mostly to carving, turning and a little furniture production.

Difficult to date The age of the oldest yew trees is still a controversial subject. All these

Juniper

Juniper—our only native member of the Cypress family—has the greatest world range of any conifer. In the British Isles it grows only in Scotland (below) and southern England, usually as a low-growing shrub.

Juniper (*Juniperus communis*). Native, evergreen, usually low-growing but may reach 10m (33ft). Grows on chalk downs, heaths, moors, limestone, mainly in S England and Scotland. Fruits Oct.

female flowers

greyish undersurface

green flowers

broad white stripe on uppersurface

uniper grows throughout the northern hemisphere in a broad belt which sweeps across North America, Europe and northern Asia. In the British Isles, it has a particularly interesting distribution. In Scotland it is found in native Scots pine forests, birchwoods and on heather moorland. On high mountains it sometimes forms low-growing scrub just above the tree line.

In southern England it grows in the chalk down grassland, especially on steeper hillsides where the soil is shallow. In the rest of the British Isles it is absent except for a few scattered localities in Ireland, north Wales and northern England. For reasons that are not fully understood the juniper is declining

in southern England; in many sites only old plants remain and there are no young bushes. Although the old specimens produce plenty of berries, their seeds are either failing to germinate or the seedlings do not get properly established in the turf.

The two main strongholds of juniper are not only widely separated, but based on completely different soil types. Junipers in Scotland thrive on acidic soils, whereas in southern England the soils overlaying the chalk are alkaline. However on chalk junipers seem to grow best on steep slopes where the soil is thin and poor in nutrients, a characteristic in common with the shallow soils weathered from hard rocks further north.

Female flowering cones, 3mm ($\frac{1}{8}$) across, consist of a three-scaled cup.

male flowers

flowers arranged in bunches

Male flowering cones are 6mm ($\frac{1}{4}$in) across and bear the pollen sacs.

The juniper is a rather rigid bush, its branches densely packed with narrow needle-like leaves arranged in whorls of three. Each leaf is about 2cm ($\frac{3}{4}$in) long; the upper surface has a waxy sheen and is blue-green in colour, whereas the underside is a much darker grey-green. The leaves taper to a stiff point which makes the foliage prickly to touch.

In some ways the juniper resembles the yew and they frequently grow together on steep-sided ridges and combes on southern downland. Indeed, in north Wales the juniper is known as the dwarf yew.

Shaped by wind and weather The shape of juniper bushes varies considerably with age and area. On young plants numerous short, rigid side branches grow upwards from the central stem to form a tight spire-shaped crown. In sheltered sites this may eventually result in a substantial bush up to 10m (33ft) high.

Where the bushes are subjected to strong winds or heavy snow they rarely exceed 3m (10ft) in height. In such exposed sites their growth tends to become rather lop-sided, shaped by the wind; sometimes the weight of snow snaps off branches, resulting in a more open, ragged bush. On bleak windswept moors and mountain sides junipers become flat-topped, creeping shrubs, rarely exceeding 20cm (8in) in height.

Small hard cones The juniper 'flowers' in May or June and is wind-pollinated. The 'flowers' are in fact cones; male and female cones are borne on separate plants towards the tips of the twigs. The yellowish male cones bear the pollen sacs. The female cones consist of a cup of three to eight scales. After pollination they expand, fuse and grow around the developing seed.

In autumn the female cone swells to form a hard green berry which encloses two to three seeds. They remain on the bush for two to three years, gradually ripening to fleshy berries. These are blue-black in colour and the outer skin is coated with a greyish bloom. The ripe berries are eaten by birds, such as thrushes, which disperse the indigestible seeds in their droppings. In Scotland grouse are thought to be largely responsible for the spread of juniper.

The stems of older bushes are covered with stringy, reddish-brown bark which peels off in strips. Junipers grow slowly, especially in the face of strong winds, and the width of the stem bears no relation to the age of the bush, as one research worker at The Monks Wood Experimental Station has discovered. A large juniper from a sheltered site had a stem width of about 26cm (10in); after its growth rings were counted, it proved to be 84 years old. Another specimen growing on a windswept site had a stem width of only 6.5cm ($2\frac{1}{2}$in), yet it proved to be 186 years old. In Russia a 544 year old tree had a stem of 8.3cm ($3\frac{1}{4}$in). However, no juniper over 200

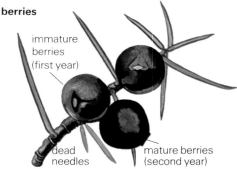

berries

immature berries (first year)

dead needles

mature berries (second year)

Above and left: Juniper berries (actually berry-like cones) have aromatic flesh. The juice is used to flavour gin. Those who assert that they drink gin 'purely for medicinal purposes' may be reassured to know that their claim does have some basis in truth: oil of juniper, which can be bought from chemists, is a powerful remedy for flatulence.

years old has been found in Britain.

Considering the stature of juniper it is perhaps surprising that it yields a useful timber. The wood is exceedingly tough and used to be much in demand for making decorative veneers. After a good polish the wood gleams a rich red colour. In the Lake District the wood was burned to charcoal which was used for gunpowder. Juniper sticks were also burnt on home fires to scent rooms with its aromatic smoke. Elsewhere in Europe this was done to keep evil spirits at bay and protect the house from sorcery.

In the past the berries were swallowed by pregnant women to induce abortion – hence one of their local names, bastard killers'.

Monkey puzzle

Few trees arouse such strong feelings in people as the monkey puzzle (below). To some it is one of our most attractive trees, whereas others are repelled by its scaly, almost reptilian foliage.

Despite its strange appearance the monkey puzzle tree is a true conifer, the only one from the southern hemisphere to grow to any great height in Britain. The tree is native to the central band of Chile (ie, neither the far north nor the far south) and to adjoining parts of Argentina. It first became known to the Western world in the 17th century, via Spanish explorers, who were looking for a local source of timber with which to repair their boats.

It took more than a century before the monkey puzzle was introduced to Britain. The botanist-explorer Archibald Menzies visited Chile in 1795 and was served with nuts from the tree as part of a banquet. For-

tunately, the nuts were raw rather than cooked, so he kept some back and succeeded in raising five plants on the voyage back to England.

At first, the strange tree was known simply as the Chile pine. The name 'monkey puzzle' was given to it in 1834 when Sir William Molesworth of Pencarrow, in Cornwall, purchased a specimen for the vast sum (in those days) of £25. Sir William assembled some friends to witness the planting and one of them, named Charles Austin, on handling the tree's spiny foliage declared that it would 'puzzle a monkey' to climb it. The name has stuck ever since.

During Victorian times there was a craze for planting monkey puzzle trees, particularly in the front gardens of the new and expanding suburban areas. It was even planted in avenues—one of the best examples is in Bicton, Devon, where an avenue of monkey puzzle trees was planted in 1844 and is still thriving.

Clothed with branches At its best the monkey puzzle is a majestic tree, growing to 15-20m (50-65ft) high and clothed with branches reaching almost down to the ground. However, in adverse conditions—dry, shaded or polluted sites—the lower, dead branches fall off, and the tree becomes much less attractive.

As with most other conifers, the branches of a monkey puzzle are arranged regularly round the central trunk in ascending whorls. In young trees the branches are well spaced out along the trunk and the crown is conical. Older trees are broader and have a rounded crown, and the branches are much denser.

The monkey puzzle retains its branches when they die. Unless they are brought down by the wind they are likely to remain on the tree for many years, gradually losing their leaves and persisting as pale grey, willow-like twigs. Old trees often present a strange contrast between the glossy green of living leaves higher up and the remains of long-dead branches further down.

Characteristic foliage The leaves are the monkey puzzle's most characteristic feature. Each leaf is egg-shaped, cupped and about 4cm (1½in) long with a spiny tip. The colour is a glossy green with a yellowish margin and the texture is leathery. Stomata (breathing pores) line both sides of the leaf and appear as pale cream or white streaks.

Male and female trees The cones are almost always borne on separate trees. The male cones are carried on shoots near the ends of side branches. They occur in clusters of up to six, arranged regularly round the shoot. By June, when they shed pollen, they are 12cm (5in) long, brown and conical.

The female cones are borne on the upper sides of branches high in the tree. They take two or three years to mature into brown globular structures up to 20cm (8in) across and covered with spiny scales. In the autumn

they break up while still on the tree and release their seeds. The seeds are large, up to 4cm (1½in) long and pointed. They are edible, though they taste better roasted than raw.

Fibrous timber The timber from a monkey puzzle is pale yellow and resinous. It is potentially useful as a source of strong wood pulp since its fibres are extremely long for a conifer (up to 11mm long as against the usual 2-4mm). As yet, however, the timber has been little used in Britain, though it is commercially important in Chile.

young female cone

cluster of male cones

Right: The leaves are spiny and egg-shaped, becoming more triangular with age. On young shoots they are bright green but soon darken and become glossy.

Monkey puzzle or **Chile pine** (*Araucaria araucana*). Introduced evergreen, native to Chile and Argentina. Height to 20m (65ft). Female cones are borne singly and ripen in autumn. Male cones are usually borne in clusters and release their pollen in June.

Left: The bark is dull grey, with age becoming wrinkled and resembling an elephant's leg.

Right: With each period of growth a whorl of new shoots is produced at the tip of each twig. Growth may occur every year or at intervals of one and a half or even two years.

Lawson and Leyland cypresses

Lawson and Leyland cypresses are two of the commonest conifers in urban and suburban areas.

Cypresses belong to the family Cupressaceae, a group of evergreen conifers found in both the northern and the southern hemispheres. The family is characterised by its opposite leaves which are usually small, adpressed (hugging the twig) and scale-like. The cones usually have a number of seeds to each scale. The buds are minute and lack protective scales.

Lawson cypress This species is native to a small area in north-west California and south-west Oregon. It was introduced to Britain by the Oregon Association, a group of Scottish landowners who were interested in procuring seeds of many of the north-western American conifers for assessment for forestry potential. The original introduction was in 1854 to the Edinburgh nursery firm of Lawson and Son – hence the name.

Lawson cypress (*Chamaecyparis lawsoniana*) forms a tall, rather columnar tree that reaches a maximum of 40m (130ft) in cultivation here, although trees over half this height are exceptional. This compares with a maximum of 60m (200ft) in the best of its native

Above: Leyland cypresses – the crown is conical but the leading shoot tends to bend to one side.

Below: The branches of a Leyland cypress, like those of a Lawson cypress, arise from near ground level.

stands.

Growth in height tends to be slow but steady. An average of 30cm (12in) a year is rarely exceeded, except over short periods. Growth in girth tends to be faster, and a short, stout, frequently forked bole is produced.

Mature trees lose the regular columnar habit and begin to develop a less formal crown. This has rather gaunt branches arching upwards and then down at the tips. Many trees, raised as cuttings from selected plants, do not naturally develop the usual open branching habit, instead remaining columnar and conical.

Bark and foliage The bark of young Lawson cypresses is a smooth purple-grey, often with a greenish tinge. It is slightly shiny. As the tree ages the bark 'fissures' into small scales on longitudinal ridges. In old trees the bark on these becomes fibrous and thick, reputedly reaching 50cm (20in) thick in old trees in their native environment.

The foliage consists of pairs of small scale-like leaves whose bases clothe the shoots. The shoots are arranged in flat sprays – a characteristic of *Chamaecyparis* species – and each pair of leaves is either in the same plane as, or at right angles to, the spray, alternate pairs having the same configuration. The sideways-facing pair are called laterals and those at right angles to the plane of the spray are called medians. The median leaves are broader and less prominent than the laterals.

The leaves are dark green above, although often yellowish or bluish green in vigorous new growth. On the underside the leaves are paler and there are white lines between the scales. The leaves breathe through the stomata in these lines. The white colour comes from secretions of glaucous wax which help to reduce water loss. On the small side shoots the white lines come together to form an X. Selected glaucous blue trees, and most seedlings from them, have a waxy covering over the foliage and over the lines between the scales on the upper surface.

. Towards the end of the first year on strong shoots, but perhaps not until the third on weak ones, the scale leaves cease to function. On the strong shoots they turn brown and form the first layer of bark; on weak shoots the whole twig is lost.

Cones The male cones of Lawson cypress are carried on the end of the weakest shoots. They open in late winter or early spring, when they are red and purple. By April they are 4-5mm long and begin to shed their yellow pollen. After the pollen is shed the cone drops off.

Female cones are blue-green and composed of eight scales. They are carried on short shoots formed near the vigorous tip of the branch. At the time of pollination the cone scales are open and the ovules or egg cells individually visible. After they have been pollinated the scales expand in an attempt, never entirely successful, to close over the seeds, the wings of which can usually be seen projecting between the scales. Each female scale carries two to five seeds.

The mature cones are globular in outline but rather lumpy in detail. Each scale is shield-like in shape and sited on a centrally placed stalk. The scales are four- to five-sided, with a ridge running across them. The cones ripen to brown in the autumn.

The seeds are flattened and narrowly winged along both sides. They are ovate in outline, with conspicuous pockets of resin. The germinating seedlings have two cotyledons—a general characteristic of the cypress family. The first true leaves produced by the seedling are linear and awl-like. Scale leaves are

produced only in the second year.

Leyland cypress Frequently seen as a hedge plant, Leyland cypress quickly forms a screen and, once established, grows 90cm (35in) a year over many years. However, left unclipped it forms a fine tall tree, usually attaining a height of about 30m (100ft). As a hedge plant it is adequate, although it does require frequent clipping.

The Leyland cypress (× *Cupressocyparis leylandii*) is a hybrid between the Nootka cypress (*Chamaecyparis nootkatensis*) and the Monterey cypress (*Cupressus macrocarpa*). Its crown is columnar and conical, and the leading shoot is inclined to one side.

The shoots are usually not set in the flat sprays characteristic of *Chamaecyparis* species, nor in the markedly three-dimensional sprays of *Cupressus* species. They occur in intermediate sprays in two or more planes. The scale leaves are dark green above and a paler, yellow green beneath.

Cones are infrequent on Leyland cypress. When female cones are produced they are 2-3cm (about 1in) across and bear about five seeds to each scale. The tree itself is sterile. Its two parents are genetically too dissimilar to allow it to produce viable seeds. It has all the characteristics of a hybrid between two distant species—and exhibits 'hetorisis' or hybrid vigour, a phenomenon in which hybrids are less susceptible to disease than their parents.

Above: The male cones of a Lawson cypress open in late winter or early spring. The foliage (below) consists of scale-like leaves whose bases clothe the shoots.

Lawson cypress

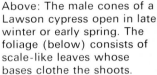

pendulous foliage

scale-like leaves are dark green on top, lighter green below

Right: Lawson cypress 'Golden King'. In cultivation this species displays great variability and over 250 different cultivars have been named.

Below: Young cones on a Lawson cypress 'Green Hedger'.

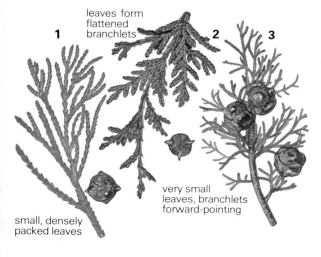

leaves form flattened branchlets

1

2   **3**

very small leaves, branchlets forward-pointing

small, densely packed leaves

Left: The Leyland cypress (**1**) is a hybrid between the Nootka cypress (*Chamaecyparis nootkatensis*), a hardy attractive tree with a conical crown of hanging branches (**2**), and the Monterey cypress (*Cupressus macrocarpa*), a true cypress (**3**). Since the parent trees belong to different genera the Leyland cypress is called a bigeneric hybrid, its scientific name being × *Cupressocyparis leylandii*. It first appeared at Leighton Hall, Welshpool in 1888.

Swamp cypress

One of only two deciduous conifers found growing in this country, the swamp cypress (below and opposite) is unique in developing strange knobbly structures called 'knees' around its base—an adaptation that helps the tree to survive in its native Florida swamps.

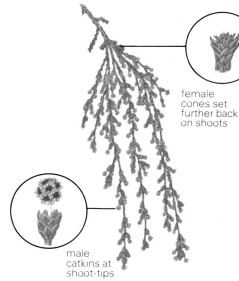

female cones set further back on shoots

male catkins at shoot-tips

The swamp cypress comes from the we swampy woodlands of the south-easter United States. One of its most famous home is the Everglades Swamp in Florida, whic contains many ancient specimens with thei branches wreathed in epiphytes such a Spanish moss, creating an eerie effect. I its native habitat the swamp cypress ca reach heights of over 45m (148ft) but, i Britain, it rarely grows to be more than 30r (100ft). The tallest specimen in this countr is 35.6m (117ft) and grows at Broadlands i Hampshire.

The first swamp cypress was introduced t Britain in 1640 by John Tradescant, a natura ist who was responsible for many other intro ductions to this country around that time It was soon recognised as being a magnificen ornamental tree, growing best in dam ground on rich alluvial soils. In the grounds o stately homes and country houses, lakes streams and rivers were planted with swam cypresses, and many have now grown int impressive specimens.

Stringy bark One of the more distinctiv features of the swamp cypress is its bark This is chestnut-brown, furrowed and fibrous so that pieces of it can be pulled away i strings. The trunk is buttressed at the bas and the crown tapers gracefully to form domed top, rather than the pointed to typical of many conifers.

The most remarkable feature of the swam cypress is the ring of aerial roots (known a 'knees' or, more properly, pneumatophores which rise out of the ground around the bas of the trunk. These develop only on tree growing in waterlogged soil for they are ar adaptation to swampy, oxygen-lackin ground, and allow the tree to breathe. Eacl knee contains a spongy wood riddled with ai spaces through which oxygen from the air car reach the submerged roots. In other words it acts rather like a snorkel by allowing the roots to breathe while under water.

In older trees, the base of the trunk is often hollow and it has been suggested that thi may act as an additional air supply for the roots, though there is no strong evidence to support this.

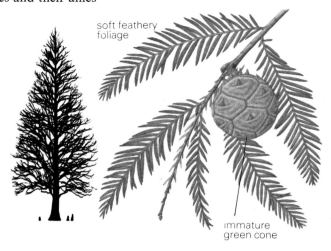

soft feathery foliage

immature green cone

Deciduous leaves Apart from the larch, the swamp cypress is the only deciduous conifer growing in Britain. Its leaves have the usual conifer shape: linear (needle-like) with pointed tips. However, unlike most conifer leaves, which are hard and waxy, swamp cypress leaves are soft and feathery. When they first emerge in April they are fresh pale green, becoming bright emerald later in the season.

The leaves are borne on two kinds of shoots: long shoots, in which the leaves are arranged spirally, and short shoots, in which the leaves are arranged in opposite pairs. The long shoots remain on the tree for many years but the short ones are shed along with the leaves in the autumn.

Autumn is, perhaps, the time of year when the tree is at its most attractive, for then its leaves turn a superb fiery-red colour before they fall off. In the winter the bare long shoots are marked with rough scars from where the short shoots were attached. Beside these are tiny round scaly buds which are destined to develop into the next year's short shoots.

Catkins and cones The male flowers are borne in catkins in groups near the tips of the long shoots. In March they lengthen to become 8-10cm (3-4in) long. The following month they ripen, turning a dull yellow, and release clouds of pollen which are snatched away by the wind.

The female flowers are set further back on

Above: **Swamp cypress** (*Taxodium distichum*). Deciduous coniferous tree, native to south-eastern USA. The fruits are rounded and about 2.5cm (1in) across. They turn brown when mature.

the long shoots. They consist of small globular cones, each constructed from a few thick scales. After being fertilised by the wind-blown pollen, the female cones enlarge, gradually change colour from green to purplish-brown and become woody.

By the autumn the cones have ripened and the scales separate to disperse the seeds, two of which lie beneath each scale. These seeds are woody and triangular with tiny flattened vanes along their edges. In the tree's usual swampy habitat, these vanes are thought to act as water-wings to keep the seed afloat until it is washed up on soft mud.

Durable timber The timber is, not surprisingly, durable when exposed to constant wetting, and for this reason it was extensively used in the United States for making barrels. Being resistant to shrinking, it is ideal for window frames, especially in greenhouses.

In Britain, the swamp cypress has not so far been planted as a timber tree. Yet it is a hardy and vigorous tree over here and will grow quite well on dry soils, so it need not be confined to swampy ground.

Above: Despite its name, the swamp cypress is not a member of the cypress family. Instead it is closely related to the sequoias and giant redwoods. The similarity can be seen clearly in the barks. All three species have a fibrous bark that peels away easily in strips.

Knees for breathing

The roots of a tree perform several functions. The most obvious one is to anchor the tree to the ground, but they also extract water and minerals from the soil. To fulfil these functions roots need a continuous supply of oxygen, just as we do. Normally, this is extracted from pockets of air lying in the soil but, in swampy land or near water, the soil is often waterlogged and contains little or no air. To overcome this, a swamp cypress growing in such conditions develops conical growths, called knees, on its roots. These rise out of the water or ground to gain access to the air and, therefore, to a supply of oxygen. These knees (a long row of which can be seen growing here), which can reach a height of 40cm (16in), have domed tops and are clad in a greyer bark than that of the parent tree.

Thuja

Commonly called cedars, although they look much more like their close relatives, the cypresses, thujas have the most delightfully fragrant foliage of any tree.

Above: A majestic stand of western red cedars. These trees grow best in moist fertile soils but they can tolerate conditions in the drier eastern half of Britain and are also capable of withstanding a degree of exposure.

Sometimes referred to in old books, though never in practice, as the 'arbor vitae', the western red cedar can be distinguished at a distance from the Lawson cypress by the fact that you can always see through the former's crown.

The cypress family (Cupressaceae) is a large family of conifers containing some 18 genera, one of which is *Thuja*. This genus consists of just five species, one having been recorded only once, in central China, and is now probably extinct.

The main difference between *Thuja* and other genera in the cypress family is in the cones. That of a *Thuja* is oval and the cone scales are attached at the base of the cone. The usual cypress cone is roughly spherical and the scale is shield-shaped with a stalk at the centre attaching it to the cone.

In Britain, the most familiar *Thuja* is the western red cedar (*Thuja plicata*), which is commonly planted in parks and gardens as an ornamental tree, and also has a minor role in forestry schemes. Despite its common name 'cedar', the western red cedar bears no relation to the true cedars, such as the cedar of Lebanon, which belong to the genus *Cedrus*. The name 'cedar' has been given to many conifers with a fine durable timber.

American native The western red cedar is native to the temperate rain forests along the Pacific Coast of North America and on moist sites inland across the Rocky Mountains. It was introduced to Britain by Thomas Lobb, who was in western North America collecting for the nursery firm of Veitch.

In its native stands the western red cedar can grow taller than 60m (200ft) and in Britain some specimens have already exceeded 40m (130ft).

The western red cedar is often confused with the Lawson cypress because of the similarity of the foliage. However, the two species are easy to distinguish. Apart from the differences in the cones, the crowns are quite different. When viewed against the sky, you can always see through the crown of a western red cedar, whereas the crown of a Lawson cypress is either completely dense or consists of dense branches with clear spaces between. The crown of an old western red cedar lacks the irregular arching branches that give an old Lawson cypress such character.

The two species also differ in their leading shoots (the shoot at the very top of the tree). On the western red cedar it is always stiff and erect, never pendulous as it is on the Lawson cypress.

Leaves and cones The foliage is carried on short sprays borne alternately on each side of the twigs. In most specimens these sprays are flat, but in older trees they may become cupped with the tips arching upwards. The foliage remains green and alive for about two years, after which the leaves on the side shoots of the spray—called the laterals—die and are shed. Those on the main shoots of the spray—the primary shoots—may die and turn brown within a further year, after which they are slowly shed.

The foliage consists of sharp-tipped scaly leaves lying flat on the stem and completely clothing it. They are arranged in the same way as the leaves of a cypress: the leaves are borne in opposite pairs, each pair being set at right-angles to the pair next to it.

The leaves are yellowish-green, or sometimes dark shiny green if the tree is growing in shade. On the underside they are a pale shiny green with a broad whitish waxy band covering the stomata.

The young cones appear in spring on the ends of the shoots. After fertilisation, the female cones mature into elliptical structures about 1cm ($\frac{1}{2}$in) long. The cones consist of five or six pairs of cone scales, with just the middle three or four pairs carrying seeds, which are pale brown and about 3mm long.

Durable timber The western red cedar produces a very light, easily worked timber. In colour, it is reddish-brown (hence the epithet 'red' in the name of the tree) and it is very durable. It is most commonly used in Britain for building 'cedar' sheds and shingle roof tiles. The trunk of a western red cedar, being straight, uniform and rarely forked, is ideal for the tall round posts used in rugby.

White cedar The only other species of *Thuja* common in Britain is the white cedar (*Thuja occidentalis*). This tree is found in eastern North America, where it has a widespread though scattered distribution around the Canadian/USA border. It was introduced to France in 1536 and to Britain at about the same time. This makes it probably the earliest North American tree to be introduced to this country.

The white cedar is a much smaller tree than the western red, rarely reaching 20m (65ft), and has a thin regular crown. The foliage is a distinctive yellow-green and looks somewhat unhealthy. In the middle of each leaf, just below the tip, is a prominent pale gland, raised above the surface of the leaf. These glands are also found on the western red cedar but are not nearly so obvious on that species. The underside of the foliage is a pale yellow-green. It lacks the white waxy coating of the western red cedar.

The male and female cones are borne on the tips of the shoots. In March the male cones open to release pollen. The females mature to become similar in colour and shape to the cones of the western red cedar, though the former are usually slightly smaller. They differ in having only four fertile cone scales to each cone. However, they compensate by being borne profusely on the tree.

Unlike the western red cedar, the white cedar has no forestry use in Britain, though it has given rise to a large number of dwarf and slow-growing varieties which are often seen in gardens.

Above: A bushy variety of the white cedar, var. *filiformis*. Most *Thuja* species have distinctively fragrant foliage. The white cedar is said to smell of apples.

Right: The foliage and cones of our two most common species of *Thuja*. **Western red cedar** (*Thuja plicata*). Evergreen tree native to western North America. Height to 40m (130ft).
White cedar (*Thuja occidentalis*). Evergreen tree native to eastern North America. A much smaller tree than the western red cedar. Height to 20m (65ft).

Left: The bark of a western red cedar develops greyish fibrous ridges that separate to leave reddish-brown fissures in between. With age the trunk of this species often becomes heavily fluted.

Bottom right: The bark of the white cedar is orange-brown with vertical ridges, here covered with algae.

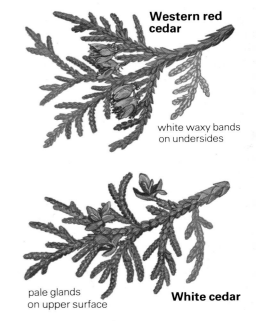

Western red cedar

white waxy bands on undersides

pale glands on upper surface

White cedar

Wellingtonia and coast redwood

Two of the tallest species of tree in the world – the wellingtonia and the coast redwood – come from the west coast of the United States, where some exceed a height of 90m (300ft). Introduced to Britain in the last century, they now provide us with some of our most spectacular trees.

The wellingtonia is one of the largest and most stately conifers to be found in Britain. Several specimens are around 45m (150ft) tall, and the largest is 47.2m (155ft), but in its native North American habitat it may reach 75-90m (250-300ft), with a huge tapering trunk 6-9m (20-30ft) wide at the base.

Spongy bark Wellingtonia is an easy species to identify. From a distance its rich dark brown or red bark is a characteristic feature. The bark can be 30-60cm (1-2ft) thick and is extremely spongy, which means that you can punch it hard without any fear of being hurt – a useful way of identifying it! The lower part of the tree tends to be bare of branches and the crown of the tree is narrow. In Britain, because it is likely to be the tallest tree for miles around, the crown is often rounded as a result of being struck by lightning.

The leaves are blue-green, hard and awl-shaped, tapering from a broad base to a fine point. They lie along the twigs, overlapping each other and pointing forwards, with their tips curling out away from the twigs. When crushed they smell strongly of aniseed.

For such a large tree, the cones are surprisingly small, growing to a length of no more than 8cm (3in). They are more or less spherical in shape and the cone scales have a characteristic groove.

American native The wellingtonia is native to California on the west coast of North America, where it is found on the western slopes of the Sierra Nevada mountains, usually growing at an altitude of 1400-2100m (4500-7000ft). It was discovered in the 19th century, when North America was being combed by botanist-explorers looking for plants to take back to Britain. The first European to see a wellingtonia was John Bidwell in the autumn of 1841. In 1853 it was introduced to Britain and was named the wellingtonia, after the first Duke of Wellington, by the great English botanist John Lindley.

The discovery of this huge tree was an important botanical event to the Victorians, who were fascinated by extremes of size and shape in the plant kingdom. The ages of some of the trees in the wild created a sensation. One tree that had been felled was estimated to be 3000 years old. Lindley wrote that 'it

must have been a little plant when Samson was slaying the Philistines.'

Growing wellingtonias soon became something of a craze. Veitch's famous nursery was selling plants by 1854 and they were soon growing fast in the extensive arboreta and gardens of the time. It was also widely planted in churchyards, where many of the best specimens are still to be seen.

Thoughtless destruction Sadly, however, the discovery of wellingtonia trees was quickly followed by their destruction as the lumber merchants and the tourists moved in. A chalet hotel was built in one of the wellingtonia groves, with a dance floor created out of the massive stump of one tree. By the 1870s, there were five saw-mills cutting up the best and biggest of the trees. One mill was said to have cut a staggering 2 million cubic feet of the timber in one year alone.

The rate of destruction shocked the Victorians, and botanists predicted that the wellingtonia would be extinct by the end of the century. As a result of the agitation, the best remaining groves had, by 1900, been protected, though by then all the tallest specimens had been cut down. The wellingtonia groves now form a part of the United States' National Parks.

The devastation at that time is similar in some ways to the present-day destruction of

Wellingtonia
(Sequoiadendron giganteum)

leaves overlap with tips curling outwards

grooved cone scales

Coast redwood
(Sequoia sempervirens)

leaves have two prominent white bands underneath

grooved cone scales

leaves arranged in two rows along twig

Below: The male cones of a wellingtonia are borne on the tips of the shoots. They turn yellow and release their pollen in the spring. You can recognise the trunk of a wellingtonia because it is so soft and spongy that you can punch it without fear of hurting your hand.

to tell apart. The bark of a coast redwood, though red and equally thick, is stringy rather than pulpy. It is also much harder and it would hurt to punch it.

The foliage is also quite different. The leaves are much thinner and they are arranged in opposite rows along the twigs–the typical conifer arrangement. Underneath, the leaves have a prominent white band on each side of the midrib. On the leading shoots, the leaves are shorter and arranged around the tip of the shoot, instead of in opposite rows. The cones are smaller than those of wellingtonia–about 2.5cm (1in) long–and bear the same groove in their scales.

Native habitat The coast redwood comes from the Pacific coast of North America, from the southern tip of Oregon south into California. It grows in a narrow belt along the coast (hence its name) which, in the summer, is frequently covered in mist from the Pacific Ocean, providing the tree with an excellent source of moisture. In its native habitat it can grow to be even taller than the wellingtonia, sometimes reaching as high as 110m (350ft). In Britain, it grows best in the damp climate of the west of England, where it can reach a height of 40m (130ft) or more.

In the open, it may bear branches from close to the base upwards but in its native forests, where it grows in deep shade, the lower branches tend to die and fall off, leaving a clear bole often as high up as 25m (80ft).

our tropical rain forests. The timber of wellingtonia is very brittle and has little economic value. It was used for mundane purposes, such as fencing and roofing, and the timber companies did not, in the end, make much profit out of their destruction. In much the same manner, the rain forests of today are being felled and burned without the timber being properly used, and so it is bringing hardly any benefit to the people of the country concerned.

Relic of the past Most wellingtonias seen growing today date from the second half of the 19th century; they are much less planted now than they used to be. With their dark, gloomy appearance, they cannot be said to fit happily into the British landscape and, moreover, the days of planting grandiose trees such as the wellingtonia in large private arboreta seem to be gone. Today, they are much more a relic of our Imperial past than trees for the future.

Coast redwood A close relative of wellingtonia is the coast redwood. Although it belongs to a different genus–wellingtonia being *Sequoiadendron giganteum* and the coast redwood *Sequoia sempervirens*–they are both members of the same family, the swamp cypress family, Taxodiaceae.

From a distance, the coast redwood looks very similar to the wellingtonia, with its huge tapering trunk, red bark and slender conical crown. Close to, however, the species are easy

Above: In its natural habitat, the base of a wellingtonia can be as much as 9m (30ft) wide. Some idea of the size of these giant trees can be gained if you go to the Natural History museum in London, where there is a massive cross-section of a wellingtonia trunk. This trunk is 4.5m (14ft) across and the tree from which it was taken was estimated to be 1300 years old when it was cut down in 1892.

Opposite page: The rich brown tapering trunk and the narrow conical crown make the wellingtonia easily recognisable from a distance, but the size of many specimens alone should indicate the species.

Right: The coast redwood is often seen with suckers growing round its base. A similar, though more unusual, form of reproduction is shown here, where a knot (called a burl) from the trunk of a coast redwood has begun to sprout after breaking off.

The pine family

To the unpractised eye, firs, spruces
and the other members of the pine family
look much like one another–until
you know what to look for.

Cedar *(Cedrus)*

Spruce *(Picea)*

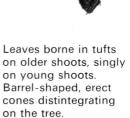

Leaves borne in tufts on older shoots, singly on young shoots. Barrel-shaped, erect cones distintegrating on the tree. Characteristic broad outline with branches in layers.

Stiff, sharp-tipped needles borne singly on the shoots and attached to them via woody pegs. Cones hang down from the shoots.

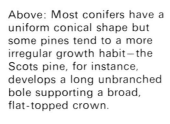

Above: Most conifers have a uniform conical shape but some pines tend to a more irregular growth habit – the Scots pine, for instance, develops a long unbranched bole supporting a broad, flat-topped crown.

Left: Like all pines, the Scots pine has stiff needle-shaped leaves borne in small bundles; in this case pairs.

Many budding naturalists find it much more difficult to identify the various species of conifer trees than the broad-leaved trees. They soon learn to tell, for instance, an oak from an ash because the leaves and fruits are all markedly different. But conifers, with their needle-like leaves and cones, can all seem to be much the same. Yet, after a little practice, telling a spruce from a pine becomes just as easy as telling an oak from an ash.

Most conifers seen in Britain belong to one large family, the pine family or Pinaceae. This is the largest of the conifer families, with about 200 species spread through the Northern Hemisphere. Members of the pine family can usually be easily distinguished from other conifers by their oblong, linear or needle-like leaves and their cones, whose woody or leathery flat scales carry pairs of

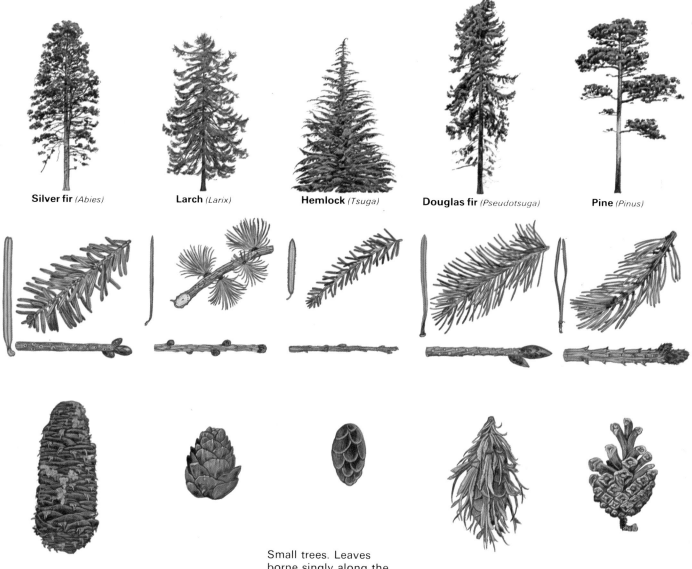

Silver fir *(Abies)*   **Larch** *(Larix)*   **Hemlock** *(Tsuga)*   **Douglas fir** *(Pseudotsuga)*   **Pine** *(Pinus)*

Regular, conical outline. Needles leave a flat pale scar on the shoot when they fall. Cones borne erect.

Pale green, deciduous needles borne in tufts on older shoots, and singly on young shoots. Cones are small and may remain on the tree for many years.

Small trees. Leaves borne singly along the shoots and less regularly set along them than on other genera. Except for one species, the mature cones are very small— smaller than larch cones.

Soft-textured needles borne on two clearly defined ranks on the shoots. Needles arise from raised angular bases. Cones have long bracts which terminate in three sharp points.

The only genus to have its needles borne in bundles of 2, 3 or 5. Some have a long unbranched bole topped by a broad spreading crown.

seeds, usually winged.

The other conifer families differ in various ways. They may have awl-shaped leaves, as do some members of the swamp cypress family; or, if the leaves are oblong and more typically pine-like, then the cones develop either into fleshy cups bearing seeds (as in the yew family) or into plum-like bodies (as in the yellow-wood and plum yew families). The maidenhair tree of the ginkgo family has distinctive fan-shaped leaves, and the Chile pine family— which is quite different from the pine family— is an unmistakable group from its only common British species, the monkey puzzle tree with its 'spiny' foliage. The remaining family of conifers is the cypress family, which is characterised by its small scale-like leaves that clasp the stem in opposite pairs.

Into the pine family Deciding whether or not a particular tree is a member of the pine family is fairly straightforward. But, having established that the tree does belong in the pine family, deciding which genus it belongs to can be more difficult at first.

There are ten genera in the pine family, of which three are very rare in Britain. The remaining seven occur in parks, gardens and forestry schemes and can almost always be distinguished by their twigs and foliage, though you must beware of species whose features place them at the boundaries of the groups.

The pines This genus (*Pinus*) is the largest in the family with almost a hundred species, although only about a dozen are at all common in this country. Members of the genus *Pinus* are uniquely characterised by their foliage—their needle-like leaves are borne in bundles of either two, three or five. The leaves that are borne in twos are semicircular in cross-section, and those borne in threes or fives are roughly triangular. The mature cones are woody and vary in length from 3cm (1¼in) to 40cm (16in), depending on the species.

The spruces There are about 40 species of spruce (*Picea*), of which some 15 are found in Britain. Their leaves differ from those of pines in being stiffer, sharp-pointed and flattened. They are borne singly on the shoots and are carried on small woody pegs, which remain attached to the twig when the leaves fall. Spruce cones are less woody when compared with those of pines and have a more cylindrical shape.

The silver firs Many species in the genus *Abies* can be recognised at a distance by their even, conical shape with regular circles of branches. Of the 50 species in existence, about half are cultivated in Britain. The leaves are firm and leathery, and more or less evenly spread on each side of the shoots. Only rarely do they have a tip as sharp as spruce leaves. The bases of the leaves are circular and, when the leaves fall, the twig remains marked with a distinct flattish pale scar. The mature cones vary in length from 5cm (2in) to 25cm (10in) and are borne erect on the tree. They are frequently encrusted with dried resin and when they shed their seeds they break up on the tree, leaving behind candle-like cores. On other conifers the cone scales open to release the seeds, but otherwise the cones stay intact.

The larches Of the ten species of larch (*Larix*) found in the wild, only three are anything but rare in this country and one of these is a hybrid. All larches have pale green, linear leaves, and they are all deciduous—the only

Above: The erect barrel-shaped cones are a unique and unmistakable feature of cedars—in this picture a cedar of Lebanon. Cedars and larches are the only two genera in the family to bear their leaves in tufts (except on the young shoots, where the leaves are borne singly). All other genera bear their leaves in bundles (pines) or singly.

Below: The leaf arrangement of cedars and larches can be seen more clearly in this picture of a larch in autumn. Note how the leaves are dying and about to fall.

members of the pine family to be so, apart from one minor genus, the golden larches, species of which are rare in Britain.

Another distinguishing feature of larches is that their leaves are borne in tufts or whorls, except on new growth where they are borne singly. The young male cones are inconspicuous and reddish; young female cones are also reddish but mature to become brown and up to 4.5cm (1¾in) long.

The cedars Of the four species of cedar (*Cedrus*), three are common in large gardens and parks in Britain. Fully grown, they are all massive trees, similar in outline to the familiar cedar of Lebanon. The leaves are flattened somewhat and needle-like, often with translucent tips. They have the same manner of growth as larches: the leaves are borne singly on the young shoots and in tufts further back. Only these two groups have this arrangement, and the cedars are easily distinguished from the larches by their evergreen leaves.

The mature female cones are large (up to 8cm/3in long) and distinctively barrel-shaped. Like those of the silver fir, the cones are borne erect on the branches.

The Douglas firs Only one species of this genus (*Pseudotsuga*), the Douglas fir itself, is at all frequent in Britain, though two or three others are cultivated here. The leaves of this group have a soft texture and lack a sharp tip. They are narrower than the leaves of spruces or silver firs and they are borne on the shoots in two more clearly defined lateral ranks. The leaves arise from raised angular bases which, after the leaves have fallen, give the bare twig a rough feel. The mature cones have long three-pointed bracts which extend beyond the cone scales. The terminal buds on the stems are also characteristic, being spindle-shaped, reddish-brown and smooth.

The hemlocks Three species (*Tsuga*) are common in Britain. They are all smaller trees than the rest of the pine family. Their leaves are densely set on the shoots, but they are less regularly arranged than on other species. The mature cones are very small—less than 3cm (1in) long—except for one species, the mountain hemlock, which has cones up to 7cm (2½in) long.

Cedars

The first cedar trees were introduced to this country from the Middle East about 300 years ago and soon came to be regarded as our most decorative conifers. Today you can find them planted in parks and gardens in most parts of Britain.

Above: A grove of stately cedars of Lebanon at Attingham, near Shrewsbury. This was the first species of cedar to be brought to this country and it is still the most widely known, partly because of the many biblical references and partly because of its unusual shape. The flat top and layered branches of a mature cedar of Lebanon are quite distinct, even when compared to other cedars, and make this tree perhaps the handsomest of all our conifers.

As well as the familiar cedar of Lebanon, there are three other species of cedar, all of which are native to the Mediterranean or the foothills of the Himalayas. Two of these, the Atlas or Atlantic cedar and the deodar, are as common in this country as the Lebanon cedar. The third species, the Cyprus cedar, is seldom found here. However, it is the cedar of Lebanon that comes to most people's minds when asked to name a cedar.

Timber for Solomon's palace The familiarity of the cedar of Lebanon is probably due in part to the number of times it is mentioned in the Bible–more times than any other tree. The timber was highly valued in Palestine in Old Testament days (it still is), and was once used for building Solomon's palace and the Temple of Jerusalem. Such was the demand for the wood that whole forests were cleared, reducing the landscape to desert.

Now the Lebanon cedar is limited in its natural distribution to south-east Turkey and Mount Lebanon in Syria. The grove of trees on the slopes of Mount Lebanon (after which the tree is named) is thought to be extremely ancient. Legend has it that Solomon's palace was built from cedars growing in this grove.

The cedar of Lebanon was introduced to Britain in 1638. In the 18th century, with the advent of landscape designers such as 'Capability' Brown, it became popular in the parklands and gardens of country houses. Its evergreen habit and large spreading branches added a new shape to the English countryside.

Deodar and Atlas cedars It was almost a hundred years before the next cedar species, the deodar, with its paler foliage and drooping branches, was introduced to Britain. The deodar is native to the western foothills of the Himalayas, where the tree is valuable both as a source of timber and for the way that its roots hold the soil firm to control erosion during the monsoon rains. The deodar was introduced to this country in 1831 and soon found its place in formal garden design.

The introduction of the deodar was fol-

Left: **Lebanon cedar** *(Cedrus lebani)*. Introduced evergreen, native to the eastern Mediterranean. Common in parks, large gardens and churchyards. Grows to a height of 40m (130ft).

Below: Male cones on a Lebanon cedar. They are about 5cm (2in) long and stand erect on the shoots. They ripen in the autumn, releasing clouds of yellow pollen to fertilise the inconspicuous green female cones.

lowed closely by that of the Atlas or Atlantic cedar, brought over here in 1841. This species is native to the Atlas mountains of Algeria and Morocco. It quickly became more popular than the deodar, and is now often seen planted next to a cedar of Lebanon, sometimes in its green-foliaged form but more usually in its blue form, known as the blue cedar. Blue cedars occur naturally in the Atlas mountains and are now particularly popular in suburban gardens.

Also from the Mediterranean, but limited to Cyprus, comes the Cyprus cedar. This species has smaller leaves than the other cedars. It was introduced in 1879 but is seldom seen in Britain, though it forms fine forests in the Troodos mountains of Cyprus.

Which is which? In Britain, cedars are easy to identify since their dark evergreen leaves occur as rosettes: bundles of leaves emanating from short shoots. Other conifers have rosettes of leaves, but only in the larch do they resemble those of the cedar. The larch and cedar are easily distinguished by their cones and the fact that the larch is deciduous.

However, it is not easy to distinguish one cedar species from another. Indeed, they are so similar that they should, perhaps, be regarded as different forms of the same species. The Atlas and Lebanon cedars are particularly easy to confuse. A useful way to tell them apart, especially with young trees, is

scales fall to leave a stem

Left and below: The cones of all three species are erect and barrel-shaped, those of the Atlas cedar being distinguished by a hollow in the top. All shed cone scales to leave a bare central stem.

Right: **Deodar** *(Cedrus deodara)*. Introduced evergreen, native to the western Himalayas. Often distinguished from other cedars by its drooping branch tips. Common in parks and gardens. Height to 35m (120ft).

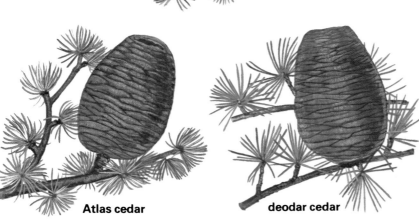

Atlas cedar

deodar cedar

...by their shape. The Atlas cedar has ascending branches; the deodar has drooping branch tips and a drooping leading shoot (the shoot at the top of the tree); the Lebanon cedar bears its foliage in horizontal layers. A good way to remember this is the mnemonic: *A*tlas *a*scending, *d*eodar *d*rooping, *L*ebanon *l*evel.

Leaves and cones The current year's growth of twigs bears single leaves, which drop off after about a year. Thereafter, the twigs develop the rosettes described earlier. These contain between 10 and 20 leaves and remain on the tree for between three and four years before falling.

The leaves of the Lebanon and Atlas cedars are about 2cm (¾in) long. On the deodar they are longer: 3-5cm (1-2in). The leaves of the deodar are also softer and a lighter colour green.

The young cones appear in the autumn. The male cones stand erect on the branches and shed their pollen to fertilise the smaller inconspicuous green cones.

The female cones mature into brown barrel-shaped cones. Unlike those of most other conifers, cedar cones remain upright on the branches as they mature. The ripening process takes two to three years, after which the cone scales are shed to disperse the seed contained inside, leaving a woody stalk standing on the branch.

Bark and growth rate The bark of all cedar species is alike: dark grey and smooth when young, breaking into flat scaly plates as the tree grows and the trunk expands.

Because cedars are planted in open parkland rather than in crowded woods the increase in their girths is about the same from year to year. This growth rate depends in part on the soil conditions and the rainfall, but 30cm (1ft) every five years is average. So a tree with a girth of 6m (20ft) would be about 100 years old.

Young cedars are fast-growing trees, but with age, they slow down and the tops spread out. In Britain they do not grow higher than 40m (130ft), which is less than many other conifers growing here.

Cedars live for a long time, given the chance, but with age they often become dangerous. This is because growing in open parkland encourages the trees to develop large heavy branches that are prone to fall off, particularly if rainwater gathers in the angle between the branch and the main trunk, encouraging rot to set in.

To prevent this from occuring, large branches are often removed from old trees, though it is better to fell the whole tree. Cedar trees much more than 150 years old are frequently dangerous and unsightly and are better replaced with young vigorous trees.

Sweet-smelling wood All cedars have a similar yellow-white durable timber that does not warp. These qualities make it ideal for high-class furniture and joinery. But its

Above and left: **Atlas or Atlantic cedar** *(Cedrus atlantica)*. Introduced evergreen, native to the south-west Mediterranean. The variety *glauca*, with its blue foliage (see above), is more common in Britain than the species which has green foliage (see left). The branches of an Atlas cedar often ascend.

Below: The bark of the Atlas cedar. All cedars have similar bark: dark grey and breaking into flat scaly plates.

greatest characteristic is its sweet aromatic smell, which in Victorian times made the wood much sought after for linen cupboards and chests of drawers.

True and false cedars Many species of trees are commonly called cedars, even though they are not true cedars. This confusion began with the early settlers in the United States, who called several evergreen aromatic trees that they discovered 'cedar'.

A similar thing happened to aromatic conifers from other parts of the world and now there are species of juniper, cypress and thuja that are incorrectly called 'cedar'. But none of these can be compared to the magnificent sight of a mature *Cedrus* species.

Common silver fir   **Caucasian fir**

Silver firs

The silver firs—so called for the two narrow bands of white on the underside of the leaves—number just four species in Europe. Although none grows wild in Britain, all four have thrived in our parks and forests since their introduction many years ago.

There are about 40 species of silver firs world wide in Europe, North Africa, temperate Asia and the Americas. Although none of the four European species grows wild in the British Isles, they are commonly grown in the valleys of western Scotland. They thrive in cool wet climate provided there are no late spring frosts.

The silver firs belong to the genus *Abies*. They can be distinguished from other conifers by the combination of erect cones, which break up on the tree, and single needle leaves which, on falling, break off from a circular disc-like base on the branchlet. The closely related spruces, of the genus *Picea*, are perhaps the most similar, but their cones are pendulous and the bases of the leaves are attached to the twigs via small hard pegs which stick out when the leaves have been shed.

Both spruces and firs are typical conifers. They are conical in shape, often narrowly so and regular. Growth is symmetrical, the tree developing a single main shoot with horizontal tiers of branches.

The common silver fir The most familiar species in Britain is the common or European silver fir. It comes from the mountains of central and southern Europe, where it is a characteristic and dominant tree forming large forests. It is especially common in the Alps, the Tatra Mountains of Czechoslovakia and the Balkan Mountains. To the west it reaches the Pyrenees and the adjacent Montseny Mountains of northern Spain. Eastwards it stretches to the Bialowieza forest in eastern Poland, the best example of a large natural forest in Europe.

In Britain the tree grows to nearly 46m (150ft), with a pyramidal crown and stout trunk. When young the trees are conical with regular whorls of branches. The side branches tend to be horizontal, curving up slightly at the tip. As the tree grows, the lower branches become shaded, so that they die back and fall off cleanly at the trunk, leaving a smooth straight bole.

The leaves tend to occur in rows on either side of the shoots, spreading around the shoot in layers, except at the top of the shoot where

Grecian fir   Spanish fir

ey leave a broad V-shaped gap. They are
eedle-like and of varying lengths, the longest
eing about 3cm (1in) long. The leaves are
ark green on top, with two narrow white
ands on the underside. This is the origin of
e name silver fir. The cones are brownish-
een when young, changing to brown as they
ature, when the spine-like bracts become
rotruding and reflexed.

Survival The common silver fir has been
ultivated in Britain since 1603 and the tallest
ee measured in Britain, in Argyllshire, was
robably planted in 1680. The species does
ot grow well in south-east England, prefer-
ng the moist but frost-free areas in the west.
survives well in shade and was much used
forestry for planting under other species.
has, however, proved susceptible to heavy
ttack by a minute aphid, and this has limited
s use in forestry. The trees develop gouty
vellings on the branches, and clusters of
oolly hair which spread to both trunk and
ranches. In England the common silver fir
usually seen in parks and arboreta, but on
e Continent it is widely planted as a forest
ee.

The endangered Sicilian fir The closest
lative of the common silver fir is the
icilian fir which, in contrast to the common
lver fir, is an endangered species. Today it
nly grows in one remote valley in northern
icily, but had earlier formed extensive forests
n the island. These were felled, and at one
me only 20 immature trees remained, but
e tree is now being planted once again. Its
eight remains unknown – it is estimated to
each over 15m (50ft), but as only a few young
ees have survived, it could reach much
igher.

The rare Spanish fir Although rare, the
panish fir is not in danger of extinction. It is
ccasionally planted in British gardens, but
the wild grows in the Ronda mountains in
uthern Spain, possibly also occurring in the
ountains of Morocco. It grows on north-
cing limestone slopes in a part of Spain that
especially noted for the richness and
xuberance of its spring flora.
The Spanish fir is sometimes known as the
edgehog fir because old trees consist of

dense masses of shoots, much of them dead,
and numerous twigs.

The Greek fir Common in the Greek mountains, the Greek fir reaches at least 36m (120ft).
Like the Spanish fir, the Greek fir will grow in
the drier eastern areas of England and is
sometimes seen in gardens. It is distinguished
from other silver firs by sharp-tipped leaves
which stand out around the shoot, its prominent spines below the cone scales and the
presence of resinous buds.

The Caucasian silver fir Originating from
eastern Europe, this species was discovered
in 1836 and introduced into Britain a few
years later. It is one of the handsomest of the
firs but, like the common silver fir and other
fir species, it can be attacked and even killed
by aphids.

Opposite: The common silver
fir is the most widespread of
the European species in
Britain; it grows particularly
well in the west of Scotland.

Above left: Four species of
silver fir, showing their
different cones, needles and
habit of growth.
Common silver fir (*Abies
alba*). Native to the
mountains of central and
southern Europe. Introduced
here in 1603. Height to 46m
(150ft).
Caucasian fir (*Abies
nordmanniana*). Native to the
Caucasus and parts of
Turkey. Introduced in 1848.
Height to 40m (130ft),
shown here with immature
cone.
Greek or **Grecian fir** (*Abies
cephalonica*). Native to
Greece. Introduced in 1824.
Height to 36m (120ft).
Spanish fir (*Abies
pinsapo*). Native to southern
Spain, Morocco. Introduced
1839. Height to 33m (110ft).

Above: Maturing cones of
the common silver fir. The
leaves on the cone-bearing
branches are pointed and
stiffer than those on other
branches, and they curve
upwards.

Left: Considered by some to
be the handsomest of the
silver firs, the Caucasian fir
(shown at the front here),
can grow to more than 60m
(200ft) high in the wild.

Douglas fir

The Douglas fir has the distinction of being the second tallest tree species in the world—only the Californian redwood grows higher. In the British Isles many of our highest trees are Douglas firs, and they produce some of our best timber.

The Douglas fir comes originally from western North America where it achieves its finest growth along coastal regions. The Latin name, *Pseudotsuga menziesii*, refers to Archibald Menzies who discovered the tree in 1791 while he was exploring the west coast of Vancouver Island. However, its common name comes from David Douglas, who worked at Glasgow's Botanic Gardens and was sent to North America in 1825 to collect seeds of new species.

The seeds of the Douglas fir arrived here in 1827. At first it was planted purely because it was a fine ornamental tree; as estate owners found it grew quickly and yielded a strong timber, it was soon increasingly grown in plantations, particularly in western regions of the British Isles.

The Douglas fir seems to grow best on gently sloping hillsides in moist, but well-drained, fertile soils. In particularly exposed places the tops may be snapped off by strong winds, and young trees and growing shoots are easily damaged by early autumn or late spring frosts. In favourable locations i south-western England and parts of Wales grows rapidly, and can reach a height c 23m (75ft) in just 25 years.

Young trees Young Douglas firs have a almost pyramidal outline, their wide spread ing lower branches tapering rapidly to th pointed tip. Older trees are characterised b a tall, gently narrowing crown. The bark c young trees is smooth but pock-marked wit numerous resin-filled blisters. At this stag the trees are easily killed by forest fires, fairly common natural occurrence in the native habitat.

Buds and needles The winter buds ar quite distinctive and a key aid in recognisin the species. They are glossy brown an pointed, looking rather like larger versior of beech buds (see page 135), and they ar borne on the tip of each twig or branchle They break open during April or May, an the young shoots are a pale yellow-gree colour.

The branchlets are arranged more or les opposite each other and are densely clothe in needles, each about 2·5cm (1in) long. Th current year's needles are a dull green colou at first, but they later assume the rick glossy green of their older counterparts. Th underside of each needle is marked by tw pale stripes along its length. The foliag has rather a soft texture because the tips c the needles are rounded, not stiff-pointe like those of many conifers whose needle consequently have a prickly feel.

Cones The male cones are grouped i clusters on the underside of the previou year's shoots. They are surrounded at th base by a collar of papery scales and are dar red in colour at first but turn yellow as th millions of pollen grains are released i April. The female cones sprout a tuft o long, pointed bracts. They are yellow t begin with, but soon turn crimson or pal pink. They form towards the tips of th branchlets; at first they are held erect, bu after fertilisation they droop round the shoot

Right: **Douglas fir** *(Pseudotsuga menziesii).* Evergreen, introduced from western North America. Planted throughout the British Isles but grows best on lowland sheltered slopes particularly in western regions. May reach 60m (200ft). Flowers March, cones mature in autumn.

Opposite: Douglas fir trees at Bolderwood in the New Forest. British trees are not yet mature enough to produce the superb timber which is imported from North America, although our timber is highly valued. Imported timber is known as Oregon pine.

Below: The new season's growth of young shoots.

and hang down as they ripen into seed-bearing cones.

The cones (see page 101) are made up of overlapping, rigid, brown scales. Their most conspicuous feature is their papery, three-pronged bracts which previously covered the ovules, one of which protrudes between each scale. The cones mature in one season, and as they dry out in autumn the scales gradually separate to release the small seeds, each attached to a thin, pale brown wing. They lie dormant in the ground through the winter months, and are ready to germinate the following spring.

The seedlings look rather weak and spindly at first, but their frail appearance belies the fact that a strong root system is developing underground. Once this is established, the seedlings grow more vigorously.

Tough timber The wood of Douglas fir is rather coarse, rich in resin, strong and durable. It is widely used for basic structural work in the building industry. It has also been used for pit props, railway sleepers, doors, floors, and for the wooden pallets used for storing and transporting goods.

In North America the Douglas fir is said to live from between 750 and 1000 years. British specimens have so far grown to about 60m (200ft), but we will probably have to wait at least 500 years before we know whether any of our trees will eventually rival native specimens in height.

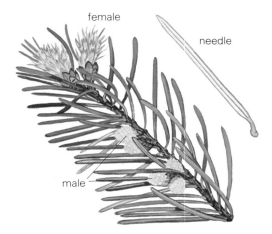

female

needle

male

Above: A shoot bearing clusters of young male and female cones. The underside of each needle is marked by two white stripes along its length.

Below: A grove of Douglas firs in the New Forest with rhododendrons growing beneath. Douglas firs are sparsely branched so they let through more light than most other conifer species.

Below: As the Douglas fir ages, a thick, reddish-brown bark develops with pronounced longitudinal ridges and furrows. This rugged bark is composed of a corky, fire-resistant material which protects the living wood inside the trunk from severe damage in forest fire

New World firs

Three handsome species of silver fir introduced to Britain from North America are among our fastest-growing trees. They are the grand, the noble (shown above) and the Colorado white firs, of which the grand fir is now Britain's tallest tree.

The first silver firs to be introduced to Britain from the New World arrived early in the 19th century, at the time when botanists were starting to explore the Pacific coast of North America. British landowners soon appreciated the value, both ornamental and commercial, of such fast-growing handsome trees, particularly in Scotland, where they seemed well suited to the climate.

Before the introduction of these trees, the most important silver fir species grown commercially in Britain was the common silver fir (*Abies alba*). This tree had been introduced to Britain from the Continent at the beginning of the 17th century and had long been widely planted for its timber. Around the end of the

Noble fir (*Abies procera*).
Introduced evergreen,
height to 47m (154ft).
Common in parks and large
gardens, and becoming
common in plantations.

Colorado white fir (*Abies
concolor*). Introduced
evergreen; height to 46m
(151ft). A variety, **Low's
fir** (*A. concolor* var.
lowiana), also introduced,
is more common. In
appearance it is intermediate
between the grand fir and
the Colorado white.
Height to 45m (148ft).

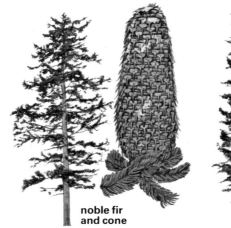

**noble fir
and cone**

**Colorado
white fir
and cone**

grand fir

Below: The male cones of a
noble fir are borne in
clusters on the undersides
of branches. As they mature
they turn purple-red and,
in May, release clouds of
yellow pollen to fertilise
the young female cones.
Notice how the leaves
of the noble fir are borne
on the shoots. The leaves
from the sides and
underside of each shoot are
swept strongly upwards, so
that the foliage is dense
above the shoot and scarcely
present below it.

Left: A cross-section of an
immature noble fir cone,
showing the developing
seeds. These are attached
to pinkish-red wings that
help their dispersal by the
wind. The seeds and their
wings are formed into pairs
clustered round a central
stalk that remains on the
tree after the seeds have
dispersed. About 250 pairs
of seeds are contained in
one cone.
Noble fir cones are
extremely large—up to
20cm (8in) long—and
covered with spiny bracts.

last century the common silver fir began to
be attacked by an accidentally introduced
species of aphid that sucked sap from the
leaves; badly infested trees usually died. Once
it was discovered that the American silver
firs were not attacked by this aphid they began
to replace the common silver fir in commercial plantations. Today the three American species are much more common.

The noble fir The first of the American
firs to be brought to Britain was the noble
fir in 1830. It is native to the far western
states of the USA, from northern California
through Oregon and into Washington. In its
native land it grows to be one of the tallest
trees in the world, with specimens higher than
80m (260ft), but in Britain none has yet
grown higher than 50m (165ft).

As its name implies, the noble is an
extremely attractive tree. When young it has
a narrow conical crown with widely spaced
spiralling whorls of branches staggered
around the central trunk. As the tree ages, its
top flattens out and the tree becomes more
cylindrical.

Young trees have a dull grey or silvery
bark. On old trees it usually becomes bright
silvery-grey, less often grey-purple, and develops a few vertical fissures. The bark is
dotted with blisters (as is the bark of the
other American silver firs). If popped, these
blisters release a small amount of clear
sticky, aromatic resin.

The foliage of all silver firs bears some
resemblance to that of spruce trees except
that on spruce the leaves are attached to the
twigs via small pegs; on silver firs they are
attached directly to the twigs.

The leaves of the noble fir are blue-green
or grey-green and about 3.5cm (1½in) long
with a rounded tip (on spruce the leaves have
sharp tips). On lower parts of the tree the
leaves are flattened, but higher up, particularly on branches bearing cones, they are
square in cross-section. They usually have a
narrow but distinct groove running down the
centre of the upper surface. Underneath, they
have two silvery bands running either side of
the centre.

Outsize cones The male cones are borne in
profusion on the undersides of twigs. They
mature and release pollen in May, by which
time they are purple-red. The female cones
are borne on the top few whorls of branches.
By the time they have matured at the end of
the year they are extremely large—about
12-20cm (5-8in) long and half as wide. They
are borne erect on the shoots. Apart from
their size, the cones are remarkable for being
covered in spiny bracts that add a greenish
tinge, though underneath these the cones are
purple, becoming olive-brown at maturity.

Each female cone contains about 250
scales, each with a pair of winged seeds.
These are released the autumn following
maturity, reducing the cone to a central stalk

Left: **Grand or giant fir** (*Abies grandis*). Introduced evergreen; height to 56m 184ft. Planted in parks and gardens as an ornamental, and becoming important commercially.

Right: The cones of a grand fir exude a white resin. When young they are yellow-green but turn brown by the time they are ripe. The mature cones of all species of silver fir – American, European and Asian – are borne erect on the branches.

left behind on the branch.

The grand fir The second New World silver fir to be brought over to Britain was the grand fir, or giant fir. It is native to the same areas as the noble fir, though it also grows further to the east and north. Its name comes from the great height to which the tree grows. In the United States specimens of grand fir reach 85m (280ft), and a grand fir is now the tallest tree in Britain. The specimen is at Leighton Park, Powys, and is more than 56m (184ft) high. Yet the grand fir was introduced to Britain only in 1831 and nearly all the trees now living were planted since 1870 – the Leighton Park tree was planted in 1888.

The young trees are narrow and conical, with whorls of branches spiralling round the central trunk. Each whorl corresponds to one year's growth – as it does on the noble fir. In fast-growing trees the whorls are spaced a metre or more apart. Smaller branches may form on the trunk between the whorls, but they last only a few years before dying. In older trees, as the rate of growth slows down, the whorls become less distinct and the shape of the tree becomes cylindrical rather than conical.

Young trees have smooth grey-brown bark, ruffled only by resin blisters. The bark of mature trees is dull grey, sometimes with a pinkish tinge, and is cracked into small plates.

Aromatic leaves The leaves of a grand fir are usually longer than those of the noble fir – up to about 5cm (2in) long. When crushed they give off a distinctively fruity aroma. They are shiny and bright green or yellow-green above with a rounded notched tip. The undersides have two silvery bands running along them.

The cones are rather less distinctive than those of the noble fir. The male cones are pale yellow and borne on the undersides of branches. They release their pollen in spring. The female cones are borne only on the topmost whorls of branches. They are pale yellow-green when immature, becoming brown when ripe, and are smaller than cones of the noble fir – about 5-10cm (2-4in) long. Like noble fir cones, grand fir cones have

Right: The bark of a mature Colorado white fir is thicker and more deeply fissured than that of other American silver firs. The bark of a noble fir remains smooth as the tree ages, apart from a few vertical fissures; the bark of a mature grand fir becomes cracked with age into small square plates.
All American silver firs have bark marked with round blisters which, when popped, release a small quantity of clear sticky aromatic resin.

bracts, but on the grand fir they are hidden by the scales containing the winged seeds.

The Colorado white fir The third most common silver fir from the New World is the Colorado white fir. It is native to the north-west of North America and to northern Mexico, and is closely related to the grand fir, though smaller. In appearance, there are few differences between these species. The Colorado white fir has a thicker, more corky bark when old, and it develops furrows. Its fertilised cones may be yellow, olive-green or violet before turning brown at maturity.

Low's fir The Colorado white fir is not widely planted in Britain. More common is a variety of the species called Low's fir. This tree is intermediate in appearance between the Colorado white fir and the grand fir.

Timber Only the grand and noble firs are grown in Britain on a commercial scale. Both are best suited to the wetter western half of the country. In its native land the noble fir is considered to have the best timber of any American silver fir, being light and straight-grained. But in Britain its timber is not of such good quality, mainly because it is susceptible to cracking during droughts, as is that of the grand fir. Nevertheless, the noble fir produces better quality timber than the common silver fir. The main uses for the timber, of both noble and grand firs, is for pulping and as general purpose sawn timber, for example, to make boxes and crates.

Record heights
Over the years several tree specimens have vied for the distinction of being the tallest in Britain. At present the title is held by a grand fir (**1**), at a little over 56m (184ft), followed closely by two other conifers, a Douglas fir and a European silver fir. Eventually, Britain's tallest tree could match some North American grand firs (**2**), which can grow to 85m (280ft). The tallest broad-leaved tree comes a long way down the list: it is a common lime (**3**) at 46m (151ft).

1   2   3

Sitka spruce

Introduced here from the New World during the last century, the Sitka spruce (below) is now our most important source of timber. Huge plantations have been established in the previously neglected uplands of Scotland, Wales and the north of England.

The Sitka spruce was discovered growing c the west coast of North America by the gre. botanist-explorer, David Douglas. He intr duced it to this country in 1831, but it wa never popular as an ornamental tree. Apa from its sharp spiky foliage, which can t painful to handle, it has the unsightly habit retaining its inner branches and twigs whe they die.

For many years the Sitka spruce remaine neglected as people failed to realise i potential as a commercial source of timbe Then, during the First World War, it becan important as a source of timber for the new emerging aircraft industry. Since then, it ha been planted by the million and is now ot

most valuable commercial conifer.

Fast growers In its native forests a Sitka spruce can grow as high as 80m (270ft). In the British Isles, however, the tallest specimens are about 50m (165ft) high, though, considering that none of these is much older than 50 years, this indicates an unusually fast rate of growth. Indeed, one specimen in Somerset grew to 42m (138ft) in its first 47 years.

The leaves of a Sitka spruce are flat, stiff and sharply pointed. Like the leaves of the Norway spruce, they grow on pegs that remain attached to the twig when the leaves fall.

The young cones are not easily seen. The male cones are small, about 2.5cm (1in) long, yellow, and occur only sporadically on the tree. The female cones are more abundant but are confined to the topmost shoots. When unfertilised, they are pale red and 2-5cm (1-2in) long. Each one contains numerous thin hard scales. When ripe, these open up to release tiny winged seeds, 3mm long.

Upland plantations Sitka spruce grows particularly well on damp, even peaty, soils, and it tolerates exposed conditions better than most other trees. This tolerance partly explains its popularity as a commercial tree. Much of the land acquired by the Forestry Commission during its existence has been in the uplands of Scotland, Wales and the north of England. On such exposed sites the Sitka spruce gives a greater yield of timber than any other tree.

Easily worked timber Another reason for the commercial importance of this tree is the quality of its timber. Although it lacks durability outdoors and is only moderately strong, Sitka wood is easy to work and takes glue and nails well. This makes it ideal for flooring, roofing and other interior construction work, for cases and boxes, chipboard, plywood and many other uses. As a source of pulp for papermaking it is unsurpassed. Its fibres mat together to form a strong yet smooth product and, because the wood is so pale, little or no bleaching is necessary.

Much maligned Despite their importance, plantations of Sitka spruce are widely disliked, mainly because of the way older plantations were laid out. Until about 15 years ago the most common method was to plant in straight lines down a hill, with little thought being given to how this would harmonise with the surrounding landscape.

Today, plantations are laid out to follow the contours of the hills, and the monotony of rows of identical Sitkas is being broken up by the occasional planting of other trees, both evergreen and deciduous.

Another improvement is that trees are now being planted further apart and thinned out properly. The resulting trees are sturdier and faster growing. As they continue to mature and be thinned out, so more and more light and air will enter the forests, making them increasingly attractive to both man and wildlife.

Above: Bright green spring growth of new leaves, still showing the brown bud scales. Older leaves are duller green above and pale blue-grey beneath.

Right: The bark of a Sitka spruce readily breaks into scales and separates from the trunk.

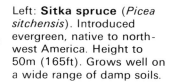

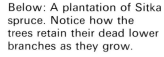

Left: **Sitka spruce** (*Picea sitchensis*). Introduced evergreen, native to north-west America. Height to 50m (165ft). Grows well on a wide range of damp soils.

Below: A plantation of Sitka spruce. Notice how the trees retain their dead lower branches as they grow.

Norway spruce

Familiar to everyone as the Christmas tree, the Norway spruce (below) is also one of our most important sources of timber, with large plantations being cultivated in the Scottish uplands.

The Norway spruce occurs naturally throughout much of northern and central Europe in both lowland and mountainous regions; in the Alps and the Pyrenees it can be found growing at altitudes of over 2000m (6000ft) above sea level. In more sheltered locations it can grow to a height of 60m (200ft).

Fossil records show that thousands of years ago the Norway spruce was native to the British Isles, but then came the great Ice Ages which forced the tree south into warmer parts of the Continent. With the retreat of the Ice Ages, the Norway spruce failed to return naturally to the British Isles, and it was not until the 16th century that it was re-introduced by man. During the next two centuries it became increasingly popular among landscape gardeners, and for the last two hundred years it has been widely grown as a commercial tree.

Nowadays, it is one of our most common forestry species. As well as being grown for their timber, hundreds of thousands of young Norway spruces are cropped each year to supply the demand for Christmas trees.

Growth and shape In the British Isles the Norway spruce does not reach quite the height of its Continental cousins. It usually grows to 40m (130ft) and is a handsome tree with a straight trunk tapering gently towards the top. The rather narrow, conical crown is formed by regular whorls of branches radiating out along the length of the trunk. Given enough space, branches develop even at ground level, but in a plantation the dark shade cast by the crowded ranks of trees causes the lower limbs to be shed as the tree grows.

Each branch, radiating out from the trunk, divides into smaller branchlets. These are arranged more or less opposite each other and tend to droop downwards to form a frill. This is especially noticeable in younger trees.

Needle-like foliage Each branchlet is densely covered with needle-shaped leaves of rich green colour.

Look at these needles closely and you will see that they have four sides and are roughly diamond-shaped in cross-section. Each needle sprouts from a tiny wooden peg on the branchlet. After the needles have been discarded—usually after six or seven years—these pegs remain behind, giving the twigs a rough feel. On the upper half of the twig, the needles point forward and overlap each other, but lower down they spread out and point away from the twig.

New leaves appear from buds each April or May. The buds are about 5mm ($\frac{1}{4}$in) long and are wrapped in smooth pale brown scales. With the start of the new season's growth they break open, sending out young shoots covered with bright yellow-green needles, in marked contrast to the darker green of older needles. As the year progresses, the new needles darken and the contrast in colour gradually disappears.

Below: A plantation of Norway spruce. They grow best in areas of high rainfall and will tolerate damp ground provided it is well drained. In drier areas they are less happy since their shallow root system means they are not always able to extract enough moisture from the soil, and they become susceptible to drought.

Left: **Norway spruce** (*Picea abies*). Evergreen, introduced from Europe in the 16th century. Grows to 40m (130ft) in moist woodland soils. Dislikes chalky soils. Male flowers mature late May, cones ripen the following spring.

Cones Both male and female cones are borne on the same tree, but they tend to be confined to separate parts. The female cones are usually found on the tips of the uppermost branches, while the male cones appear lower down.

Male cones are borne on short stalks clustered towards the tips of the side-shoots. When young they are reddish, and resemble half-ripe strawberries. As they mature they turn yellow with the production of pollen and reach a length of 2.5cm (1in). They shed their pollen in early May. Such vast quantities are formed that the ground beneath a Norway spruce becomes covered with a dusting of pollen.

The female cones consist of an erect column of overlapping crimson or white scales. After fertilisation they turn green, sometimes tinged dark purple. By the autumn they have turned over to hang from the twigs and have ripened into reddish-brown cones. The cones are covered with stiff papery scales, each of which encloses two developing seeds. Unlike many conifers, which distribute their seeds

Above: Mature and young Norway spruce cones. A single cone can yield up to 350 seeds, each seed being attached to a wing to help its dispersal by wind.

Right: The male and female cones and leaf. The male cones are borne in clusters at the ends of side-shoots. They are reddish at first, turning yellow in late May. Young female cones are crimson or less commonly white.

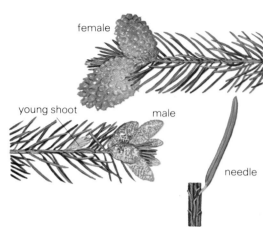

female

young shoot   male

needle

The Christmas tree legend

The tradition of decorating a Norway spruce is an essential part of Christmas for people throughout Europe and North America. How this practice began no-one really knows, but it is thought to have originated in Germany during the 17th century.

There are many legends relating to the origin of the Christmas tree. One of the most charming is a German legend that tells how an old farmer and his family were disturbed one winter's night by a loud knock on their door. The farmer found a small boy standing outside, wet through, shivering with cold and weak with hunger. The young lad was promptly dried, fed and put to bed. The next morning the family was awakened by the sound of a choir singing, and they were astonished to see that their young guest was surrounded by a shining halo—for he was the christ-child himself. The boy departed, but before doing so he snapped a branch from a nearby spruce tree and stuck it in the ground, saying that the branch would flourish as a symbol of the good fortune with which the kind family would be blessed. Since that day, the legend goes, the Christmas tree has stood as a symbol of goodwill.

One of the most famous Christmas trees in the world is the one erected each year in London's Trafalgar Square. Every December a 20m (70ft) Norway spruce is shipped to this country. The tree is a gift from the people of Oslo in Norway to the City of London in appreciation of the role played by Britain during World War II. A special lighting ceremony marks the hand-over, and at the flick of a switch the tree is lit by 650 light bulbs.

only after two or three years, the Norway spruce distributes its seeds the following spring when a combination of sunshine and wind dries out and separates the thin cone scales, thus allowing the seeds to fall out. The seeds are then dispersed by wind.

Plantations and timber Most of our Norway spruce timber is imported from Scandinavia but there are large plantations in Scotland.

Growing the Norway spruce presents a problem because it has a very shallow root system. Instead of growing deep into the soil, as do the roots of most trees, the roots of the Norway spruce spread out just below the surface to become entwined with those of its neighbours. Such shallow rooting makes the tree vulnerable to being toppled by gales, and one falling tree is likely to uproot several near by. On exposed sites, strong winds can flatten large areas of valuable timber.

The wood from a Norway spruce is light-weight and rather elastic, but tough and durable out of doors. It is widely used in the building industry for flooring and scaffold boards. The straight trunks are ideal for telegraph poles and the masts and spars of small boats. The wood is also used for making packing cases, and in parts of Europe the trees are tapped to yield a resinous pitch from which turpentine is extracted. Finally, a lot of spruce wood goes to paper mills, particularly in the vast spruce forests of Canada, the USSR and Scandinavia.

Below: The springy nature of the branches allows them to survive heavy snowfalls without snapping. They are helped in this by the shape of the leaves, which retain much less snow than would a broader leaf.

Left: Scots pine beside Loch Rannoch in Perthshire. In Germany and France it is known as the red pine because of its glowing reddish bark and pinkish buds.

Female Scots pine cones
One to five tiny female cones form at the tips of delicate new shoots. At this time the cones are pale pink, slowly deepening in colour to dark red as the year advances. By the second year the cones have grown considerably and have turned green. As the cones have grown, the twigs which support them have become tougher and woodier. In their third year the cones turn brown and can now open and release their seeds in dry weather.

first year cone

second year cone

first year cone

Scots pine

The reddish bark and windswept outline make the Scots pine immediately recognisable. Our only native pine can be found from the Scottish Highlands to Surrey.

In the Scottish Highlands the Scots pine is a native tree; elsewhere in the British Isles it has been planted extensively only in the last two centuries. In the 18th century it was a favourite tree of English landowners who wanted something new, attractive and hardy for their parks and gardens. It provided sweet-smelling shady walks on hot summer days and shelter for wild animals, particularly deer.

Sometimes you may see a clump of seven trees growing together on the top of a hill; they were thought to bring good luck, and the trees' imposing silhouette against the sky made them an attractive focal point. Indeed, wherever in the world the Scots pine grows, it is thought of in folklore as a symbol of fer-

Looking inside a pine cone

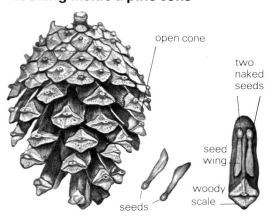

open cone

two naked seeds

seed wing

seeds

woody scale

tility, longevity (it may live for a couple of centuries or more), and good fortune—perhaps because it is a tree that stands firm amid the relentless snows of mountain winters and still keeps its leaves miraculously green.

Except when very young, Scots pines are easily recognisable by the redness of their smooth, shining branches and upper trunk, the colourful bark peeling off in thin flakes. In mature trees the lower part of the trunk is also reddish, but much darker and rougher, and the thicker bark is quite heavily cracked. In natural woodlands the pines are well spaced with wide-spreading boughs and shapely rounded crowns. In old age they lose this conical outline as their lower branches fall off and they become flat-topped and sometimes rather stricken-looking.

Needles, flowers and cones The needles, blue-green and slightly twisted, are mostly about 5cm (2in) long, shorter than those of most other pines. They stand stiffly in pairs and remain on the tree for two or three years.

Like all pines, the Scots pine is wind-pollinated. It flowers in May: the female flowers are solitary, small pinkish red globes which develop at the tip of the shoot. If they are fertilised by some of the millions of male yellow pollen grains, they produce green to light brown cones; these take two years to become fully grown and may reach 7cm (3in) in length. There are two winged seeds attached to the inside of each woody scale of the cone. When the cones open in warm sunlight the seeds are scattered by the breeze and many are avidly eaten by all kinds of birds and mammals.

Pine forests Until the end of the Middle Ages much of the Scottish Highlands were covered with forests of Scots pines. From the 17th century onwards man began to attack these forests: for example, the forest of Loch Maree in Western Ross was cut down in 1612 and the timber used in iron-smelting. Deforestation continued with ever-increasing enthusiasm and sadly today the native pine woods of Scotland survive only as pathetic remnants.

Scots pine trees grow mostly on well-drained slopes covered by gravel and coarse

sand left by glaciers. The soil is not fertile enough to be farmed but the pines, along with some birches and junipers, find it acceptable. To see Scots pines at their best you should go to places such as Glen Affric in Inverness-shire, the Ballochbuie district of Aberdeenshire or Rothiemurchus on the north-eastern slopes of the Cairngorms.

These Scottish pine forests, where pines of all ages and sizes grow amid majestic scenery of mountains and lochs, support a rich variety of wildlife. The best known mammals are the deer: roe deer live among the trees all year, red deer seek forest shelter mainly in winter. A rare carnivore of the weasel family, the pine marten, is aptly named, for the old forests are among its haunts. The forests are one of the last refuges of wild cats and red squirrels. Rare orchids and wintergreens, and birds such as crested tits, capercaillies, crossbills and even occasionally osprey also thrive there.

Pine cultivation Because it thrives in poor, rather dry soils, Scots pine is still a favourite tree to plant in sandy areas of south and east England where the ground is unsuitable for agriculture; hence the various long-established plantations in Surrey and elsewhere, such as those near Hindhead, Leith Hill and between Weybridge and the Chobham ridges. The Forestry Commission has planted this pine in places like Thetford Chase in East Anglia and Cannock Chase in Staffordshire. When the trees are regimented in plantations

Above: Scots pine (*Pinus sylvestris*), evergreen, native in Scottish Highlands, planted elsewhere. Grows to 40m (130ft). Lives up to 20 years or more. Found on poor, well-drained peat and sandy soils.

Below: So much pollen is produced by the male catkin that, over a large forest, it can hang in a dense cloud.

ey have little beauty; being so close to-
ther, they shade each other's branches and
come more rows of tall poles with all their
liage at the tops of the trunks.

Pine timber is in great demand these days
d as we do not produce enough ourselves
e import large amounts from Scandinavia
d elsewhere. Carpenters know it as red or
llow deal (white deal comes from spruces).
ots pine timber is used for telegraph poles,
affolding, railway sleepers, gates, buildings,
rniture, paper pulp and for many other
rposes. In the two world wars vast numbers
highland trees were felled, many of them to
ake ammunition boxes. By-products of pine
rests include tar, pitch, resin and turpentine.

The mature bark of the
lower trunk of the Scots
pine tree cracks as the tree
grows and expands its girth.
New bark is being formed
underneath.

ne cones usually
nical; thick woody
les each with 4-
ed blunt tip. Shown:
ots pine—hanging
ne initially red,
coming green and
own in third year.
ue-green needles in
ndles of two.

Larch cones small, soft, rounded. Shown:
European larch—young cone pink, later
brown. Deciduous needles single on
young twig, in clusters on older ones.

Fir cones usually conical with papery
scales. Shown: Douglas fir—hanging
brown cone has protruding scales.
Short, single flat needle-like leaves.

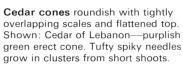

hat's that cone?

e pine family, (Pinaceae), includes pines,
dars, firs, spruces and larches. Most of
ese trees have evergreen needle-shaped
ves that remain on the tree for 2-3
ars, though the European larch is deciduous,
edding its needles each autumn. The young
nale cone looks like a bud—red, blue,
nite or green, according to the species—
nen it appears in spring. After fertilisation
the male catkins (which appear on the
me tree) it becomes brown, woody and
l of seeds.

Spruce cones long and
cylindrical. Shown:
Norway spruce—hanging
chestnut brown cone.
Short, hard, dark
green pointed needle-
like leaves.

Cedar cones roundish with tightly
overlapping scales and flattened top.
Shown: Cedar of Lebanon—purplish
green erect cone. Tufty spiky needles
grow in clusters from short shoots.

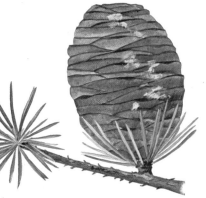

Insects you can find on pine trees

Many insects can be found
feeding on or inside a pine
tree.

**pine
hawk-moth**

Hyloicus pinastri

This large moth—8·5cm
($3\frac{1}{2}$in)—rests by day on the
trunk. The caterpillar feeds
on pine needles. Rare, but
increasing in woods in the
south.

**pine
flatbug**
*Aradus
cinnamomeus*
5mm ($\frac{1}{4}$in)

This bug lives just under the
bark. It sucks sap from the
wood.

pine weevil
*Hylobius
albietis*
12mm ($\frac{1}{2}$in)

pine beetle
*Myelophilus
piniperda*
5mm ($\frac{1}{4}$in)

Both beetles are serious
pests. They feed on young
shoots and so stunt the
growth of the tree. The pine
beetle larva lives in pine
logs; the weevil larva lives
in rotten stumps.

Lodgepole, Corsican and Monterey pines

Many pines were originally introduced for their ornamental value. Recently, however, three species, Lodgepole, Corsican and Monterey pines have been extensively planted by foresters and are highly prized for their quick growth and timber.

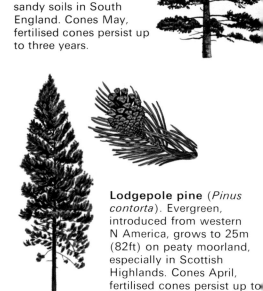

Corsican pine (*Pinus nigra* var *larcio*). Evergreen, introduced from South Europe, grows to 35m (115ft) on poor sandy soils in South England. Cones May, fertilised cones persist up to three years.

Landowners and foresters have always been on the look-out for new trees to plant for landscaping as well as for commercial timber production. During the 19th century it became fashionable to plant collections of exotic trees, and hundreds of different species were imported from all corners of the globe.

Conifers in general, and pines in particular, have excited considerable interest for a variety of reasons. For landowners the stately forms of well-grown pines are an attractive ornamental feature of parks and gardens. And, because they retain their foliage, they are effective windbreaks throughout the year.

Pines are valuable to the forester because they grow quickly and produce a timber crop that can be felled sooner than any of our native deciduous trees. Moreover, they can usually be planted successfully on poor soils that are of little use for farming.

Although our native Scots pine (see page 99) is the most widely planted species, there are three foreign introductions which are frequently planted in the British Isles. These are the lodgepole and Monterey pines from North America and the Corsican pine from southern Europe.

The lodgepole pine grows as a native tree along coastal regions of western North America, stretching from Alaska to southern California. In about 1850 it was introduced to the British Isles, initially as an ornamental pine. But in recent years it has become an important forestry tree: it thrives on poor peat moorland soils and is now increasingly planted in the Scottish Highlands.

The lodgepole pine grows up to 25m (82ft) tall, and in general profile is similar to the Scots pine, although the bark is much darker brown and more gnarled. The crown is conical in youth, becoming flat-topped with age.

The stiff light green needles, 3-5cm (1-2in) long, grow in pairs and densely cover the orange-brown twigs. The male and female cones are borne near the tips of the branches and open in late May. Having been thoroughly dusted with pollen from the yellow male cones, the fertilised female cones grow to 2-6cm (1-2½in) in length.

Opposite: Corsican pine is fairly common in parks and gardens and has been extensively planted on sandy and gravelly soils in the south of England.

Below: Lodgepole pine was so-named because its poles were used by North American Indians for the framework of their teepees. Like all conifers, it is wind pollinated. Male cones are grouped at the base of the new shoot which bears the pink female cones at its tip.

Lodgepole pine (*Pinus contorta*). Evergreen, introduced from western N America, grows to 25m (82ft) on peaty moorland, especially in Scottish Highlands. Cones April, fertilised cones persist up to three years.

The fertilised cones remain tightly closed on the tree for many years. This is an adaptation to the effects of forest fires which are frequent in the tree's native habitat. The heat generated by such a blaze as it sweeps through the stands of pines opens the cones, which shed vast numbers of seeds on the ground below. The scorched, ash-covered soil becomes a rich mineral seed bed, ideal for the germination of pine seeds. Within a few years the burnt area is covered with seedling lodgepoles sprouting beneath the charred, still-standing skeletons of their parents.

The Corsican pine, a native of Corsica, Sicily and southern Italy, is now one of the most widely planted forestry trees in southern England. It is often planted to stabilise coastal sand dunes because it is tolerant of the salty wind-borne spray. Large areas of our remaining southern heathlands have been covered by Corsican pine plantations. The trunk is clad in dark grey fissured bark and, because its lower branches are not shed as readily as those of the Scots pine, the crown appears larger at a similar age. The timber is used for the same purposes as the Scots pine.

Male and female cones, which are yellow and red respectively, open in late May. The ripe cones, 6-8cm (1½-3in) long, are light brown and the end of each scale is tipped with a short stiff prickle. The cones open on the trees in their third year, and release the seeds which fall soon afterwards.

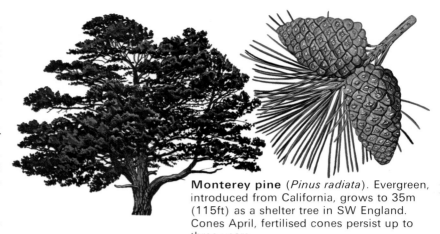

Monterey pine (*Pinus radiata*). Evergreen, introduced from California, grows to 35m (115ft) as a shelter tree in SW England. Cones April, fertilised cones persist up to three years.

Right: The male cone and maturing cones of the Monterey pine. The cones grow out from the side of the stem; because the growth hormones are richer on the cones' lower side (due to gravity), this side develops faster and the cone becomes lop-sided in shape.

Below: A stand of Corsican pine in the New Forest. This species thrives in the drier areas of England and, because of its quick growth, is largely replacing the Scots pine.

The Monterey pine has a curious history. When it was discovered in 1830 it had an extremely limited distribution, growing only in a few coastal hills near Monterey in California. Three years later it was introduced into the British Isles. It was first planted as an ornamental tree for its splendidly rugged form, but it is now being grown in experimental commercial plantations. As it is easily killed by frost, it is more or less limited to the milder climate of south-west England. Here it grows fast—up to one metre (3ft) annually on well-drained sandy soils. The timber, being soft and rather brittle, is only useful for wood-pulp.

The rugged bark is deeply fissured and the crown broadens with age as the lower branches spread upwards. The brown winter buds are coated with sticky resin which prevents attack by insect pests. The slender needles are always borne in groups of three, which easily distinguishes it from other pines. They are a striking bright green, and up to 15cm (6in) long.

The Monterey pine cones appear in early April: the yellow male cones are borne in large clusters; the less numerous females are dark red in colour. The fertilised cones are large—up to 15cm (6in) long, and grow from the side of the stem in a strangely asymmetrical way. Like the cones of the lodgepole pine, they persist on the tree for many years.

Larches

Beautifully delicate, yet amazingly resilient to bitter winters on the mountainsides, larches are our only conifers to shed needles in autumn and grow brilliant green new foliage the following spring.

Below: The European larch is oblivious to cold winters but needs plenty of rainfall during the growing season. It is small wonder then that it manages so well in the British Isles.

The larch is a lofty tree with a tall straight trunk that tapers to a sharp point, from which graceful drooping side branches radiate in all directions. Among Europe's conifers, it is unique for its habit of losing its leaves in autumn, standing bare and gaunt throughout winter.

The European larch was introduced into this country early in the 17th century. For about 150 years after its arrival it was planted just as an ornamental tree until its value as timber was realised. In the wild the larch is a mountain tree and in regions of central Europe larch forests grow as high up as 2000m (6500ft).

The larch's great advantage as commercial timber is that it is ready to be cut after only 40 years – half the time taken by our native broadleaved trees to reach maturity. Growth is amazingly rapid: starting in May, slowly at first – 2cm ($\frac{3}{4}$in) a week – but gathering apace to 10cm (4in) a week in mid-summer.

Foliage The light green foliage emerges in April, darkens during summer and then fades to golden-brown in October before falling. The leaves, or needles, sprout in bunches of 30-40 from little knobbly outgrowths on the twigs.

Flowers Separate male and female flowers appear on the twigs when the tufts of young needles begin to show themselves. The rather inconspicuous male flowers at the tips of the twigs develop into compact clusters of yellow anthers that mass-produce pollen; this is then wafted away by the wind. Just a fraction reaches and fertilises the female flowers, which are made up of a rosette of overlapping reddish-purple scales, aptly named 'larch roses'.

Cones After fertilisation the scales that were soft in flower harden to form egg-shaped cones, green at first but turning brown in autumn. As the cones ripen and dry, the woody scales slowly open to allow the seeds to slip out, though it may be several years before all the seeds inside a cone are released. Each seed is equipped with a triangular wing which acts like a sail so it may be blown some distance.

Animals are also often responsible for speeding up the process of dispersal. Squirrels spill hundreds of seeds as they gnaw the cones; and birds, such as crossbills, have beaks well-adapted for prising open all kinds of pine cones to get at the seeds inside.

Hardy tree The larch shows a number of adaptations to the harsh winters of its natural mountain habitat. Firstly, it is deciduous. If it kept its delicate foliage in winter, it would lose more water by evaporation through the leaves than its roots could possibly extract from the freezing soil. It therefore sheds them to avoid drying out and dying of thirst. (Other conifers survive because their needles are harder and tougher and covered in a thick waxy cuticle, so the rate of water loss is reduced.)

Secondly, the twigs droop downwards from the side branches. This arrangement gives the leaves plenty of exposure to light in summer but also means that the branches do not catch snow in winter. Also the cells of the wood are structurally very strong and can survive losing large amounts of water. When this happens the sugary sap freezes at a lower temperature than water.

Plantations Larches are often planted with native hardwoods to encourage the hardwoods' growth. The broadleaved saplings have to grow faster to keep up with their larch neighbours or else they would simply be shaded out of the race to the light. In this capacity larches are known as 'nurse' trees.

Foresters rarely allow plantation larches to live out their natural lifespan; but ornamental trees can reach quite an old age. There are some fine specimens growing at Dunkeld in Perthshire which are over 250 years old. In fact larches do not grow old elegantly and tend to become rather untidy trees. They lose the compact symmetry of their youth because branches are blown down in gales, leaving gaps in the conical crown, and the straggling side branches vary a lot in curvature and length. And as the trees age, the bark becomes thick and deeply furrowed.

Larch timber is tough and extremely resilient out of doors. So it is valuable for all weather purposes because it can endure constant changes from wet to dry without

Above: Larch in winter, showing the gracefully shaped branches. Like most conifers, the side branches are thin and flexible; they can bend without snapping under the weight of snow and spring back up again when the snow slips off.

Right: A fine view showing larch growing near Ulpha in the Lake District. Larch plantations are particularly attractive to wildlife as they allow in more light than other conifers.

Japanese larch (*Larix kaempferi*), introduced, deciduous, grows to 35m (115ft). A particularly hardy pioneer tree.

European larch (*Larix decidua*), introduced, deciduous, grows to 50m (165ft). May live over 100 years; commonly felled at 40 years. Both larches grow on well-drained soils. Flowers March-April, cones ripen Oct.

warping, cracking, shrinking or distorting.

Japanese larch Introduced in 1861, this larch is distinguished by its darker blue-green needles and bright orange winter twigs. It appears even better suited to our climate and grows faster than its European cousin. It is also much more resistant to larch canker—a devastating fungal disease. What has interested foresters recently, however, is the natural marriage of the two species that resulted in the Dunkeld larch, named after the place where the cross was first noticed. Like many hybrids, it probably has a bright future because it is even hardier, grows faster and is more resistant to disease than either of its parents.

Left: This beautiful larch rose has just been dusted with golden pollen grains. It will develop into a cone about 4cm (1½in) long by autumn, but will probably not release its seeds until the following year.

Window on the past

A peculiarity of conifers is that if their trunks or limbs are injured they bleed resin from the wound. Resin is a transparent sticky liquid comprising a wax or rosin dissolved in turpentine, which seeps over the damaged tissues. The turpentine evaporates, leaving a coating of rosin sealing the wound. This acts like a grease-band, gumming up potential insect pests and also shielding the tree from fungus spores. (Turpentine itself is a useful by-product from conifers such as pine and larch, and rosin is used by musicians for waxing the bows of stringed instruments.) We know that this defence strategy has been in operation for at least 70 million years, for the resin eventually becomes buried and fossilised into lumps of amber. Amber provides us with a fascinating glimpse into the past because it frequently includes perfectly preserved insects and plant remains. Much of what we know about the wildlife of primitive forests has been gleaned from the study of amber. Insects crawling over or landing on conifers run the same risk today as they did all those years ago. Should they be in the path of or touch down on the sticky drops, they soon become hopelessly stuck and eventually engulfed by the flow of resin.
Amber, highly prized for its warm shades of yellow, orange and brown, was one of the

first substances used to make jewellery. Worked amber ornaments unearthed at Stonehenge and elsewhere date back to 9000BC. The best quality amber now comes from the Baltic coastline of Russia and Poland, where it is mined and exported. But it is also dispersed by the sea, whose pounding waves and currents carry it considerable distances. Beachcombing on Britain's North Sea coast, especially around Norfolk and Suffolk, you may well find a lump of amber that has floated over 600 miles.

Ants and flies are two insects found entombed in amber. Often frozen in a macabre death pose with wings askew and legs twisted and splayed, they show all the signs of a frantic struggle to break free. If amber blocks are thinly sliced, microscopic analysis of the sections can unravel the secrets of the internal structure of ancient invertebrates as precisely as if they had just been caught.

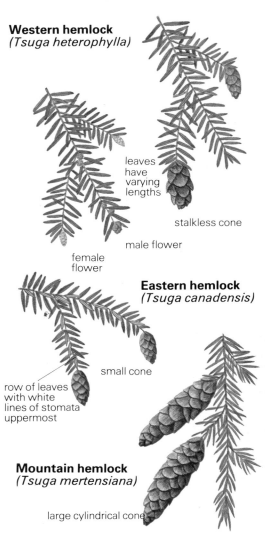

Western hemlock
(Tsuga heterophylla)

leaves have varying lengths

stalkless cone

male flower

female flower

Eastern hemlock
(Tsuga canadensis)

small cone

row of leaves with white lines of stomata uppermost

Mountain hemlock
(Tsuga mertensiana)

large cylindrical cone

Hemlocks

Most people have heard of the poisonous British herb called hemlock, but few know that the same name also applies to a group of coniferous trees from America and Asia. In Britain, only the American hemlock trees are commonly planted.

Above: The western hemlock is the most graceful of the genus and, in Britain, the most widely planted. It is common in parks and large gardens, and is also grown in plantations beneath other trees since it tolerates dense shade.

Hemlock trees are a group of conifers from North America and eastern Asia. They were given the name hemlock because the crushed leaves smell somewhat similar to the true hemlock; but there is no relation between the two. The true hemlock is a poisonous broad-leaved herb in the carrot family, whose chief claim to fame–or infamy–is that Socrates,

the Greek philosopher, committed suicide in 399 BC by drinking a draught made from it.

The botanical name for the hemlock genus is *Tsuga*, which comes from the Japanese name for one of the two species native to that country.

Although hemlocks are not native to Britain, fossil records show that they were growing here thousands of years ago. But they became extinct in the last Ice Age and never naturally returned.

Western hemlock The most common species of hemlock growing in Britain, though not the first to be introduced, is the western hemlock. It is native to western North America, from Alaska south to northern California. Specimens of this tree were first collected by the great Scottish botanist-explorer David Douglas in 1826, but seeds were not introduced to Britain until 1851.

In its native region, the western hemlock can grow to a height of 60-80m (200-250ft), but in Britain few specimens are taller than 40m (130ft), the tallest being a tree 46m (151ft) high at Benmore Arboretum in

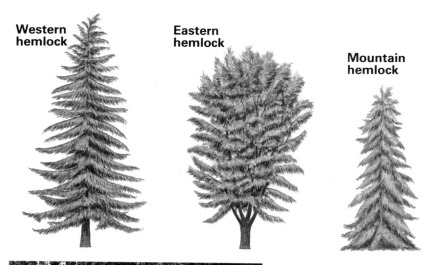

Western hemlock

Eastern hemlock

Mountain hemlock

Strathclyde.

The western hemlock has a narrow conical crown whose main characteristic is its pendulous leading shoot—in young trees the tip of the shoot may bend over so far that it grows downwards. The tips of the side branches also hang down.

The shoots are hairy and brown above, paler below. They are covered with ridges on which sit the leaves, in a similar manner to spruce trees where the leaves sit on more distinct 'pegs' attached to the shoots. The leaves are cigar-shaped and dark green above, with two broad bands of stomata beneath. Young leaves are a brighter green above.

The male cones emerge in the spring and are bright red at first, becoming pale yellow when they release their pollen. The female cones are plum-purple when young, maturing through green to become brown when ripe. Mature cones are 2-3cm (1in) long and have comparatively few scales.

Shade tolerant Ecologically, the western hemlock is remarkable for the amount of

Above: The three species of hemlock are easily distinguished at a distance. The western hemlock is the tallest, growing to about 40m (130ft) high, and has a drooping leading shoot; the eastern hemlock reaches 30m (100ft) and its trunk divides near the base; the mountain hemlock, at 20m (65ft) tall, is the shortest of the three. It has a narrow crown with pendulous branches.

Left: The bark of an old western hemlock is fissured, slightly scaly, and purple or grey-brown. On young trees, and high up on old trees, the bark is smooth and dark grey.

Below: The leaves of the western hemlock vary in length from 5-18mm ($\frac{1}{4}$-$\frac{3}{4}$in) and point forwards towards the shoot tip. Each leaf is cigar-shaped, tapering somewhat at each end. The underside has two broad white bands of stomata, through which the leaf breathes. The leaf margins are minutely toothed.

shade it can tolerate. Because of this, it is now being grown commercially in Britain, in forestry plantations underneath other tree crops. The timber is of moderate quality and is used for pulping and for general softwood purposes, such as boxes and roofing.

The only disadvantage of growing hemlocks is that they are very susceptible to root and butt rotting fungus (*Fomes annosus*, also called *Heterobasidion annosus*) which, as its common name indicates, attacks trees, causing the roots and trunk to rot. In the western hemlock, the rotting can extend 2m (6ft) or more up the trunk, destroying the most commercially valuable part of the tree.

The western hemlock grows well on a range of sites other than shady ones, and it is one of the fastest-growing trees on poor acidic sandy soil.

Less familiar hemlocks Two other hemlocks less often seen in Britain, but still not uncommon, are the eastern hemlock and the mountain hemlock. Both are native to North America, the former coming from the northeastern United States and eastern Canada, and the latter from the same region as the western hemlock, though at higher altitudes.

The eastern hemlock was the first of the genus to be introduced to Britain, in 1736. From a distance, the most striking difference between it and the western hemlock is that its trunk divides low down into several stems, giving it a shrubby appearance. Close to, the leaves have a noticeably different arrangement for, on the eastern hemlock, there is a line of leaves running along each shoot, with their white stomata uppermost. On the western hemlock all leaves have their stomata facing upwards.

The mountain hemlock is the smallest of the three species, though it has the largest cones—about 7cm (2$\frac{1}{2}$in) long. The leaves are the same colour, grey-blue or grey-green, on both sides. They are borne on small sideshoots called spurs, which look very similar to the rosettes on a cedar tree.

Neither the eastern nor the mountain hemlock is grown in Britain on a commercial scale, but both are fairly common as ornamental trees.

Deciduous trees

The cool, temperate British climate poses a very large problem for all green plants during winter months. They face difficulties in protecting themselves against cold, producing adequate food and obtaining water. Although they are not severe by Continental standards, British winters still have periods when freezing conditions can damage delicate leaves. These same conditions freeze the ground, making it very difficult for roots to obtain water from the soil. Without water, there is no possibility that the normal process of sugar synthesis from water and carbon dioxide can occur. In fact, the constant demand of a leaf for water could result in a plant dying of drought when the soil moisture is 'locked up' in the form of ice.

Plants deal with this problem in many different ways. Some wither back to a resting stage and others have developed thicker leaves that lose less water, but the vast majority of trees in Britain shed their leaves altogether. As soon as the leaves are shed, the tree shuts down its activity for the duration of the winter, for without leaves no food can be made by the plant. With the coming of spring weather, however, the leaf buds that were developed the previous season begin to unfold into new green leaves, and the cycle continues. The 'trigger' for bud break varies from species to species—with some it is increasing day length, and with others increasing temperature. New green leaves are the delight of any springtime. Their extreme greenness is because they are comparatively thin, enabling the layers containing chlorophyll (the green pigment that drives the synthesis of food-stuffs) to be exposed to as much light as possible. In this way the tree produces vast quantities of nutrients very quickly. As leaves develop, they become stronger, with more strengthening material laid down, and the initial vivid green colour fades somewhat.

Throughout the summer, the leaf continues to act as the power-house of the tree. In some species with very dense canopies, such as beech and hornbeam, sunlight is filtered out very efficiently. The slightly lighter canopies of oak and ash, together with the different shape of their leaves, mean that more light will filter through to ground level, and thus a more varied ground flora is able to flourish.

Eventually, responding to another trigger (usually the day length), photosynthesis begins to slow down, and the leaf ceases to be a food manufacturing organ, and becomes instead a site for waste disposal. All the useful molecules, such as chlorophyll and its associated compounds, are broken down and translocated away for storage in other parts of the tree. In exchange, waste products produced during the year are taken into the leaf, which is then sealed off by a waterproof layer known as the abscission layer. At this stage the leaf is very often highly coloured due to the chemicals remaining in it, sometimes producing spectacular autumn colorations. It is now that the tree parts company with the leaf, the brittle abscission layer breaking, bringing on leaf fall. The deciduous tree now returns to winter conditions, able to survive the months of cold.

Opposite: Oak and bluebell woods in the Walkham Valley, Dartmoor.

Deciduous trees of woodland and open countryside

Our countryside contains very few natural woodlands today. Even those that do remain are just the remnants of the once-vast forests that formerly covered almost the entire British Isles. Most of the forests and woodlands which we see are the result of deliberate planting and management over the years, although some natural regeneration also occurs.

The vista of the open countryside is chiefly the result of the even more intense removal of woodlands to leave just scattered and isolated trees – perhaps for aesthetic reasons, but usually as boundary markers, windbreaks and as shelter for farm animals.

For many people, oak is the typical woodland tree, with its irregular domed shape and massive appearance. Both the English oak and the sessile oak form large woodlands, often mixed with other trees such as ash. Among oaks may be found stands of hornbeam – either standing straight with long trunks or, alternatively, pollarded to encourage stick growth. Sycamore is also found growing with oak on occasions. Introduced in the 16th century, this tree has been successful ever since its arrival.

Beech must have a strong claim to be considered Britain's most elegant tree. It is at its best on the southern chalk downs, where it is the natural climax woodland. When seen from a distance, a beechwood is also revealed as not being the completely homogenous entity that it would first appear. Dotted throughout will be whitebeams and one or both of our species of native limes.

Below the deciduous woodland canopy is the under-storey vegetation – smaller trees and shrubs able to exist in comparative shade. Here can be found holly and the native box tree, for example. The edges of woods, where downland begins to creep in and scrub plants dominate, is the area where other small tree species are found: the buckthorn, with its white flowers and black berries; dogwood, with its red stems in winter; and the spindle-tree with its coral-pink berries, for instance. Also to be found are the wayfaring tree, the hawthorn, the field maple and the elder.

Wet places have their own particular trees. The best known are the many species of willow. It is hard to imagine a British riverside that does not have at least one species of willow, and often several, growing by it. Alder is another typical waterside tree, and it is in fact very useful for detecting the path of small watercourses – made visible by their attendant alder trees. Along with these, the catkin-bearing hazel is found. These two take advantage of damp areas to produce some quite impenetrable scrub.

Only a decade and a half ago, there would have been little argument as to the most commonly seen and easily recognised tree in the open countryside. Hedgerows and field margins then contained great abundance of English elm. Dutch elm disease has sadly laid most of the country's elms to rest, however, leaving spaces where once the noble trees grew.

Opposite: Trees are an integral part of the British countryside – scattered field trees and copses can still be seen on arable land.

Pussy willows

Sprouting in woods, damp hedgerows and by streams, pussy willows are most noticeable for their golden catkins, which are nectar pots for hungry bees.

Pussy willows–or sallows–belong to the willow family, many of which can only grow in waterlogged ground; but sallows grow easily in drier woodland and hedgerows. They are small, rounded-shaped trees, quietly beautiful in a way not appreciated by foresters who, when they find them growing in carefully cultivated plantations, treat them as weeds and cut them down.

Male and female Like all willows, sallows bear their male and female flowers on separate trees. The familiar grey pussy willow catkins are the emerging flowers of the male tree that turn golden yellow as their anthers mature. The female trees have less conspicuous catkins, which do not dangle like those of other

Above: Goat willow in the fens at Easter ablaze with male catkins. In the past bee-keepers used to plant sallows because their abundant nectar was taken by bees to fill honeycombs early in the season.

willows, and become woolly as they mature. Sallows tend to have broader leaves than other willows.

The female catkins are mainly insect-pollinated, with bees their chief visitors. When the fruits ripen and split open they discard hundreds of seeds, each one attached to long silver-white hairs that enable them to be blown around the countryside.

There are three species of native sallow. Finds of fossil pollen show that they have thrived in these islands for more than 100,000 years, surviving at least three glaciations.

Goat willow – or great sallow – is the commonest of the sallows; you find it growing on all types of soil, by ponds and streams, in woods and on wasteland. It gets its name because the young spring foliage was fed to goats. The soft, rounded leaves are grey, with whitish downy undersides. It is cut down so often that it rarely has a chance to grow to its full potential height of about 10m (33ft).

Grey willow – or common sallow – is a smaller, bushy tree which grows on limey, as well as acid, soils. Its leaves are narrower than those of the goat willow, harder to the touch and downy on the upper side. The male catkins tend to be more slender, with paler anthers than those of the goat willow, and the tree bears smaller fruit. The Latin name *cinerea* means ashen or cindery.

The round-eared willow – or wrinkled-leaved sallow – is so called because of the persistent kidney-shaped stipules along the shoots. Its leaves are dull grey-green and wrinkled, with grey downy undersides. It grows as a slight bushy tree or shrub in damp woods, on heaths and moors and beside streams.

Hybrids All three sallows are pussy willows. They interbreed quite easily, so these textbook examples are quite hard to find. Victorian gardeners used to plant a *salictum*, a collection of willows, but they found it difficult to keep accurate scientific records: so many hybrids were produced that their owners tended to mistake them for completely new species.

Sallow uses From Neolithic times about 5000 years ago to the present day sallows have been used to make coracles – small boats covered with skins – and coarse wattles for fending and fish-traps. Sallow stakes used to be used in fencing and sprouted into hedges; if you push a stick of willow into reasonably moist soil, it will almost certainly grow.

From medieval times taxes were receipted with tallies that were usually made of sallow wood. The tally was split with a knife into two irregular halves. The payee, particularly the Government, kept one half on receipt of payment. When the system was abolished in 1826, thousands of old tallies were fed into the boiler furnace of the House of Commons. It overheated and the building was completely destroyed. Today it has a special use as fine drawing charcoal.

Looking at the goat willow

Goat willow/Great sallow *(Salix caprea)* native, deciduous, grows to 10m (33ft). Mainly in damp woods and hedgerows, beside streams and on moors and heaths particularly in E. Anglian fens. Flowers March-April, fruits May.

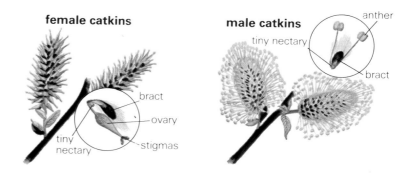

female catkins — bract, ovary, tiny nectary, stigmas

male catkins — anther, tiny nectary, bract

fruiting female catkin — fruit containing many seeds, seed

Identifying the three pussy willows

Goat willow or great sallow *(S. caprea)*   **Grey willow** or common sallow *(S. cinerea)*   **Eared willow** or wrinkle-leaved sallow *(S. aurita)*

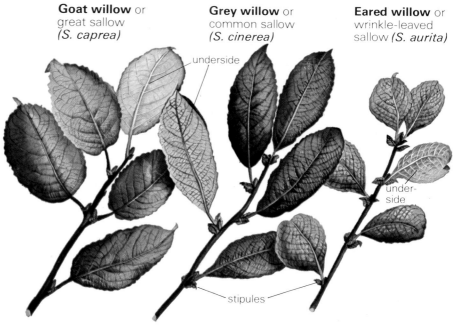

underside, stipules, underside

Weeping willows

Such an integral part of our lowland landscape is
the weeping willow that it is hard to imagine our
parks and riversides without it. Yet this tree is
not native to the British Isles, being introduced
here less than 200 years ago.

Above: The distinctively
pendulous shape of a
golden weeping willow, in
Britain the most widely
planted weeping tree of any
kind. The tree shown above
was photographed in early
spring, still in flower.

Two quite separate species of tree are commonly known as the weeping willow. Both
were introduced here from abroad – a surprising fact when you consider how naturally
suited they are to the riverbanks and parks of
lowland Britain. Yet neither species can even
be considered as naturalised here, for they
cannot propagate themselves on their own
they can spread only with man's help.

Chinese weeping willow The first species o
weeping willow to reach Britain is now by fa
the rarer of the two. This is the Chinese weep
ing willow (*Salix babylonica*), brought ove
here during the 18th century. It was name
babylonica by the Swedish botanist, Linnaeus
who thought it was the tree referred to i
Psalm 137:

'By the rivers of Babylon, there we sat
down, yea, we wept, when we re-
membered Zion. We hanged our harps
upon the willows in the midst thereof'.
However, it now seems more likely that th
tree in question is a species of poplar.

The precise origin of the Chinese weepin
willow is still uncertain. It has been in cultiva
tion in western Asia and Europe for centurie
but the plant is not native to these regions and
it is thought to have come from western China
spreading westwards via the traditional trad
routes.

The Chinese weeping willow made its firs

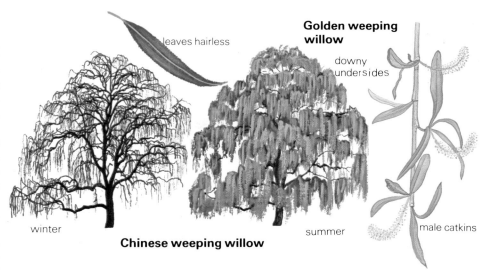

Golden weeping willow

leaves hairless

downy undersides

winter

summer

male catkins

Chinese weeping willow

appearance in Britain when it was planted in Twickenham Park in the 1730s, reputedly by a certain Mr Vernon. A more fanciful story tells that the poet, Alexander Pope, raised the first weeping willows in this country by planting the ropes used to secure a parcel sent from Spain to a friend of his.

New arrival Once introduced, the Chinese weeping willow rapidly became popular and was quite widely planted. However, it has never really thrived in this country because it is not well suited to the British climate. Today, it is rare in Britain, having been superseded by the golden weeping willow.

This species also has an obscure origin, a fact reflected in the number of different names by which it is known, such as *Salix alba* 'Chrysocoma' or 'Vitellina pendula'. Nowadays, many authorities feel that its correct name should be *Salix × sepulchralis* and it is regarded as being a hybrid. Its parents are thought to be *Salix alba* subsp. *vitellina*, a form of the white willow with yellow twigs, and the Chinese weeping willow, from where it gets its conspicuously pendulous habit. It was introduced to Britain from France in about 1800.

Similarities and differences Both the golden and the Chinese weeping willows form graceful trees with long, pendent, recurving branches reaching down almost to the ground. The former grows to a height of 15m (50ft), while the latter can reach a little higher – up to 20m (65ft). The bark of the golden weeping willow is brownish-grey and criss-crossed by shallow grooves and ridges. That of the Chinese weeping willow tends to be more brownish and deeply grooved.

Both trees have the same form of leaf: narrow and lance-shaped with a pointed tip, fine teeth and a short stalk. On the golden weeping willow the leaves can be up to 10cm (4in) long and the lower leaf surface bears very fine hairs, making it appear whitish in contrast to the shiny pale green of the upper surface. The leaves of the Chinese weeping willow tend to be shorter and lack the downy undersurface. The leaves appear very early in the year, usually in February, and remain on the tree until late in the year, sometimes not being shed until December.

Yellow catkins In common with other members of the willow family (which includes poplars and the aspen as well as willows themselves), the flowers of both species of weeping willow are borne in catkins, males and females appearing on separate trees. In both willows the catkins are yellow.

On the Chinese weeping willow the catkins are about 2cm ($\frac{3}{4}$in) long and the female flowers have a nectar-producing gland, called a nectary, to attract pollinating insects – moths and bees being particularly attracted. The pollen grains produced by this and other willows are extremely small and light, light enough, indeed, for the Chinese weeping willow to be pollinated by means of the wind.

By contrast, only male forms of the golden weeping willow are ever seen in this country. This means that the catkins are always male (though occasionally mixed catkins containing a few female flowers occur). Whether pure or mixed, the catkins are slender and about 8cm (3in) long.

Because of its almost complete lack of female flowers, the golden weeping willow has hardly any chance to set seed – though, being a hybrid, its seeds would most likely be sterile in any case. Consequently the tree can be propagated only by cuttings which, fortunately, take root very readily – as do those of many other willows.

Although the Chinese weeping willow has become a rarity in the British Isles, the golden remains one of our most popular decorative trees. Indeed, the attractiveness of many stretches along such rivers as the Thames and the Cam owe a great deal to the planting of this willow. It is difficult to imagine now that this tree has been in Britain for less than 200 years, so much is it a part of our lowland scenery.

Above: Summer and winter outlines of the Chinese weeping willow, with the catkins of the much more common golden variety. The two trees are very similar. The only major differences are that the leaves of the golden weeping willow are downy underneath and its catkins are much longer than on the Chinese species.

Chinese weeping willow (*Salix babylonica*). Deciduous tree, native to western China. Introduced around 1730, but now rare. Height to 20m (65ft).

Golden weeping willow (*Salix × sepulchralis*). Deciduous hybrid, introduced around 1800. Height to 15m (50ft).

Below: The ridged bark of a golden weeping willow.

Wickerwork willows

Three species of shrubby willows, known
colloquially as osiers, withies and dicks, are
cultivated in Britain for their stems. These are
strong yet supple – the ideal material for making
wickerwork baskets.

Most people recognise the graceful weeping
willow trailing over a stream but few are
aware of the range and diversity of this large
and distinctive genus. Willows range in size
from creeping alpine plants that cling to
rocky mountain ledges, to large trees found
in fertile lowlands. In between these extremes
a group of shrubby willows, sometimes
seen as small trees, that have long been important to us as the raw material for baskets.

The history of basket-making goes back a
very long time indeed. The earliest example
discovered in this country is fragments of
wickerwork excavated in Somerset and dating
back to 100BC. During the Middle Ages there
was a basket-maker in every English village

and the craft was considered important
enough for a Guild to be formed in 1750.
Surprisingly, however, it was not until 1800
that basket willows were grown as a crop.
Before that, people relied on harvesting wild
willows.

Willow-growing flourished in the 19th
century but has since declined, due mainly to
the increasing use of other materials for
making baskets and foreign competition from
imported basket and willows.

Basket willows Willow is the ideal material
for making into baskets. When the stems or
trunks are cut down (a process known as
coppicing) the plant sends out vigorous new
shoots that soon replace the lost wood and,

Above: Withies being
harvested at West Sedge
Moor on the Somerset
Levels. The stems, called
rods, are tied into bundles
and stacked before being
brought indoors. 'Withies'
is a local Somerset word
for the French willow, or
almond-leaved willow.

Opposite: A group of osiers
(*Salix viminalis*) in spring,
seen growing in their typical
wetland habitat.

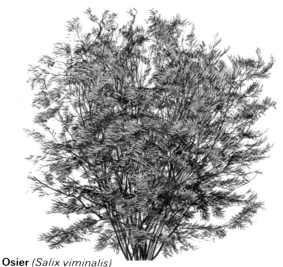

Osier *(Salix viminalis)*

long narrow leaves

osier catkins

male

female

The three species of basket willows are fairly easy to tell apart by examining the leaves, given a little practice. All are shrubby willows, though the osier can develop into a tree.

Almond-leaved willow *(Salix triandra)*

narrow toothed leaves

Bitter willow *(Salix purpurea)*

small oval leaves

in addition, the cut wood is supple yet strong–important qualities in basket-making.

Several different species of willow are used to make baskets. For example our most abundant sallows–the common sallow, the eared sallow and the goat willow–have long been used to make simple baskets. But the most important willows for basket-making are the following three species: *Salix viminalis* (commonly known as osiers), *Salix triandra* (withies) and *Salix purpurea* (dicks). Together they are known as basket willows.

Willows are often extremely difficult to identify, partly because they hybridise with each other so readily, and these three species are no exception. Yet, with a bit of practice, they become fairly easy to recognise.

Fast-growing osiers Of the three species, the osier is the easiest to identify. It can be distinguished from the other two by its leaves. These are long and narrow (at least 12cm/4in in length) with inrolled margins and a silky sheen to the lower leaf surface. The catkins flower in March and April, and sit stalkless and erect on the stems.

The osier grows faster than either of the other two species, producing thick, robust shoots that grow 2.5m (8ft) in their first year. Despite being long and thick, osier shoots are the softest of the three species to work because they contain a high proportion of pith. Various varieties and hybrids of osier, such as 'Mealy Top', are used for making rough agricultural and fishing baskets, usually with their bark still intact on the stem.

Top-quality withies The French or almond-leaved willow, known as withies in Somerset where it is mainly cultivated, is commercially the most important basket willow and yields the highest-quality rods (as cut willow shoots are called). The leaves are narrow, pointed,

smooth and glossy, having neither hairs nor waxy bloom. The margins are regularl toothed. At the base of the leaf-stalks ar small leafy appendages called stipules. Th catkins flower in May, which is late for willow, and are borne on short leafy shoot A useful way to identify this willow is t chew a small piece of the young bark. *S triandra* has a characteristic taste that re sembles the smell of roses; it is quite unlik the bitter taste of most willows.

The rods contain much less pith than thos of the osier, and are hard and pliable. The grow to about 2m (6ft) in a season. Of th many varieties that are grown, 'Black Mau is regarded as having the finest-quality rod and comprises about 80% of the crop i Somerset. Other varieties, such as 'Wissende and 'Champion Trustworthy', are inferior bu

have other characteristics in their favour, such as heavier cropping or earlier growth. The bark of *S. triandra* is usually removed after harvesting to give the white or buff rods used in commercially made baskets.

Bitter willows *S. purpurea*, also known as the purple or bitter willow (or dicks), used to be grown extensively around the Ribble Estuary in Lancashire. The leaves are small, about 5cm (2in) long, with smooth margins. The upper surface is bluish-green and glossy; the lower surface is bluish and waxy. The catkins are stalkless and have bluish-black scales.

The inner bark of the stems is yellow and has an extremely bitter taste – hence its name. The rods are tough, hard and very slender. Some varieties of *S. purpurea*, such as 'Dicky Meadows', rarely grow more than 1m (3ft) in a year, but the rods are of good quality and are ideal for making small, superior-quality basketware, such as luncheon baskets.

Cultivating basket willows Almost all the willows grown commercially in Britain are varieties of these three species and, of these,

S. triandra is by far the most important. It grows best in the moist climate of south-west England, in particular Somerset. In the Midlands and East Anglia *S. viminalis* is more common since it is better suited to the light soils and drier climate found there.

Basket willows are grown commercially in lowland river valleys with rich alluvial soils that have been built up through successive floods. Willows are ideal for such areas since they can stand flooding for months in the winter, and also – unlike other commercial crops – they can stand about a week's flooding in the summer.

To plant basket willows, cuttings about 25cm (10in) long are taken from one-year-old rods and pushed into prepared ground, usually in March and April. This used to be done by hand, but the shoots are now planted mechanically. To meet the requirements of mechanisation, the planting distances have had to be increased since the days of hand-planting. The rows are now 70cm (28in) apart, with the shoots in each row being planted 35cm (14in) apart. This allows some 40,000 plants to be grown in each hectare (16,000 per acre). The yield from mature plants varies with the type of willow, but is between 12-20 tonnes per hectare (5-8 tons per acre).

Willows are harvested each year in winter by cutting them back to ground level. Again, this is now done by machines. Only from the third year onwards does a willow bed give an economical yield of rods, though plants are still cut back for the first two years to stimulate new growth. A willow bed reaches full production by its fifth year.

The rods are tied in bundles and stacked in fields at first. Later they are taken back to the farm, where they are graded for length. At this stage they are termed 'brown', since they still retain their bark. If the rods are of poor-quality they may be marketed at this grade, but most growers prefer to peel off the bark and process the rods into one of two grades: 'whites' and 'buffs'.

Processing the rods To produce white rods, cut willows are stood in about 15cm (6in) of water during early spring. The bark is removed just at the point that the buds are beginning to burst through. To produce buff rods, the cut willows are boiled for several hours to soften the bark. During the boiling, the bark releases tannins and other products that stain the wood and give buff rods their characteristic warm reddish-brown colour.

After processing, the bark is peeled off. At one time this was carried out by hand, the bark being scraped off with a device called a brake, but it is now done by machine. The freshly peeled rods are then spread along any convenient hedge, fence or wall to dry in the sun – a familiar sight in the Somerset willow growing area. When they are dry, the rods are stored ready to be dispatched to basket-makers all over the British Isles.

Top: A bed of osiers near Welney, Norfolk, after harvesting. In the Midlands and East Anglia, the osier is the most commonly cultivated basket willow since it tolerates best the dry climate and light soils found there.

Left: Basket willows are harvested in winter before the sap begins to flow.

Above: Lower-quality rods are sold with their bark still on; top-quality ones are first processed and then peeled by machine.

Right: Finally, the rods are woven into baskets.

White and crack willows

Our two largest native willows, the white and crack willows, are often deliberately planted by man to help prevent erosion of river banks.

There are more than 130 species of willow in the world, at least 15 of which are native to the British Isles. They include sallows, osiers and many garden species, as well as white, crack and cricket bat willows, three of our most common species.

White willow In its typical form this willow has steeply ascending branches which develop into a narrow crown. The overall grey-whiteness of the tree's foliage gives it its name. The long slender leaves with sharp-pointed tips are light green on top and covered with a thick down underneath, giving the leaves a silvery sheen. The dark grey bark has a close network of deep fissures and ridges and is rich in salicin, a chemical used in the tanning

Opposite: A fine study of the bark of a riverside crack willow.

Below: White willow at Wicken Fen in Cambridgeshire. It gets its name from the grey-white colour of its foliage. In its typical form, the tree has steeply ascending branches.

White willow *(Salix alba).*
Deciduous, native, grows to 25m
(80ft). By streams, rivers, marshes,
damp woods. Flowers April-May,
fruits June.

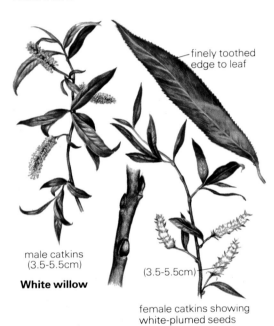

finely toothed
edge to leaf

male catkins
(3.5-5.5cm)

White willow

(3.5-5.5cm)

female catkins showing
white-plumed seeds

male
catkins
(2-5cm)

more coarsely
toothed edge
to leaf

Crack willow

female catkin
(showing seeds)

(10cm)

of leather and formerly for making asprins.
The twigs are silky when young and quite
tough, in contrast to the crack willow which
has fragile twigs.

The dangling cylindrical catkins start to
develop in spring at the same time as the
leaves. The male catkins produce large
quantities of bright yellow pollen which is
carried by the wind or insects to the green
catkins of the female tree.

Once pollinated, the female catkins develop
into small seed capsules which ripen and
eventually split, releasing large numbers of
white-plumed seeds; these in turn are dispersed by the wind. They lack a protective
layer of endosperm (or albumen, a substance
like the white of an egg) that seeds of most
other tree species possess. They must find a
suitable place to germinate within a few days
or they die. They need very moist conditions
to germinate successfully, which explains why
adult willows are so often found in watery
surroundings. Once the plants have started
to develop, their water requirement is comparatively small.

Crack willow gets its name from the fact
that its twigs are extremely fragile and snap
easily. The coarsely ridged and fissured bark
is dull grey in colour, and the twigs bluish-
green. The leaves, which are narrow with
coarsely toothed edges and tapered to an
asymmetrical point, are glossy green on top
and bluish underneath. The catkins are
drooping and cylindrical and appear in
April at the same time as the leaves and
slightly earlier than those of the white
willow; male catkins are yellow and female
catkins green.

The crack willow spreads partly by the
dispersal of its seeds in the same way as the
white willow, and also by its twigs. These
snap off easily and are carried downstream
by the river current; they lodge and readily
take root in mud banks or shingle. In common
with all willow species, the crack willow
grows very easily from cuttings and you
often see willow fence posts sprouting new
growth, or willow tree stakes outgrowing the
trees they were intended to support.

Individual willows are extremely difficult

Above: **Crack willow**
(Salix fragilis). Deciduous,
native, grows to 25m (80ft).
Common in damp places, by
streams, rivers. Flowers
April, fruits May-June.
Below: A peaceful riverside
scene—crack willows at
Bourne End in Hertfordshire.

identify and you may have problems deciding which are crack and which white, since
they hybridize freely, producing trees which
look very similar or intermediate to their
parents.

Also, willow leaves can change considerably in shape as they mature from spring
to summer, and, confusingly, two willows
of the same species may have quite different
leaf shapes. (The surest method of identification is to look at the flowers and leaves
together.) Each tree produces either male or
female flowers (catkins) and you will need to
be able to recognise both to distinguish
between the species.

Cricket bat willow is the commonest hybrid
between the white and crack willow and it
probably originated in Suffolk. It can be
distinguished from the white willow mainly
by its leaves which are grey on the underside.
It is extremely fast-growing and its wood is
tough, pliable, light and ideal for making
cricket bats. One full-sized tree makes at
least two dozen bats.

Willow hybrids between other species are

cultivated in gardens and towns for their
decorative appearance; these include the
coral bark, the silver and the golden willow
with its attractive variant the weeping willow,
probably the most familiar member of the
willow family in this country.

Willow timber is a versatile wood because
it is light and resilient. Willows were often
pollarded to produce straight branches
sprouting directly from the top of the trunk,
well out of reach of grazing animals. Pollarding was especially important in areas like the
East Anglian Fens where little or no other
timber was available. It is no longer widely
practised. You can, however, often see trees
that have been pollarded long ago now growing unchecked. They are common alongside
many river banks in the south-east of
England.

Host to wildlife Many insects depend on
willow leaves for their food. Aphids often
cause extensive leaf damage by excreting
honeydew, which encourages mould. You
also find leaf beetles, weevils, sawflies and
gall wasps on willow trees.

Above: Pollarded crack
willows near the Thames at
Wallingford. The willows in
the background have been
allowed to grow in their
natural dome shape.

White poplar

Grey poplar

White and grey poplars

For long, the decorative potential of the white and the grey poplars went largely unnoticed. Today, however, these trees are being planted on an increasingly wide scale, as planners and landscape architects come to appreciate their delicate beauty.

Above: White poplars forming a delicate arch over a country road. Both the white poplar and the grey are planted for their ornamental value, particularly in rural areas where they are beginning to replace the Lombardy poplar in providing shelter and screening.

Both the white and the grey poplars are easily distinguished from other poplars by the presence of white down on the undersides of the leaves, especially those on long shoots. The effect is very pronounced on the white poplar (hence its name) and gives the tree a white cottony appearance from a distance.

The white poplar This is the smaller of the two species, growing to no more than 25m (80ft) high. The down covers the young shoots as well as the undersides of the leaves; indeed, when they first emerge the leaves are white all over, but the loose floss on the upper surface

is soon blown off.

The leaves vary greatly in shape and siz. Those on short twigs are broad and egg shaped or rounded, with irregularly toothe margins. By contrast, the leaves on the suck shoots, and those on young trees, are lobe and resemble maple leaves. This type of lea also tends to be larger (4-10cm/1½-4in) com pared with the former type of leaf (3-5cm 1¼-2in).

Each spring, the first sign of life in a whi poplar is the emergence of its catkins. Ma and female catkins are borne on separa trees, as is the case with all other popla species. The male catkins are grey with con spicuous crimson stamens and the fema catkins are green.

The bark of a white poplar is anothe feature that serves to distinguish it from othe poplars (apart from the grey). On the lowe half of the trunk the bark is furrowed an rough. Higher up, the bark becomes covere with small smooth areas of white to pa grey, interspersed with dark diamond-shape pits.

As with so many poplars, the top of the tre tends to lean to one side. This is also often th broadest part of the tree.

Dutch import The white poplar is not nativ to Britain, nor does it grow here in the wil

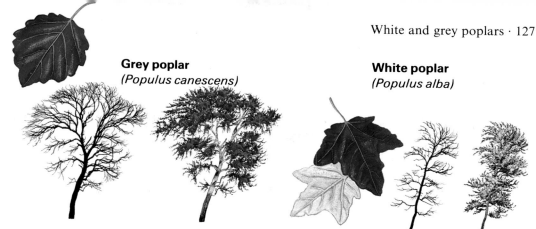

Grey poplar
(Populus canescens)

White poplar
(Populus alba)

Left: The catkins of the white and grey poplars are very similar to each other, the males being grey with crimson stamens and the females green. Catkins of different sexes are borne on separate trees and emerge in March before the leaves.

It was brought over to this country from the Netherlands, probably sometime during the 17th century, though the records are vague about this. Its wild habitat is extensive, for it is found in central, eastern and south-eastern Europe, North Africa and across the steppes and plains of Asia as far as the Himalayas.

The grey poplar Unlike the white poplar, the grey poplar is naturalised in this country. It is most common in the Midlands and southern England. It is also found in scattered localities in Wales and Ireland. It is most often seen in hedges and woods, and tends to favour damp sites near streams and rivers.

No one is quite sure whether the grey poplar is native to Britain or introduced. However, in many areas there are far more male trees than females, which suggests that it has been planted in those parts.

There is also doubt about whether or not it is a true species. Today, most botanists think that the grey poplar is a hybrid between the white poplar and the aspen (another species of poplar). Certainly, it is intermediate between the two in appearance, and poplars do hybridise readily. Another point in support of this theory is that man-made hybrids between the white poplar and the aspen are indistinguishable from grey poplars.

Similarities and differences It is not always easy to tell the grey and white poplars apart. The best way to separate them is by the leaves on the sucker shoots. Those of the grey poplar are toothed but not deeply lobed, unlike those of the white poplar. In spring the down on the grey poplar is, as the name of the tree suggests, grey rather than the brilliant white of the white poplar. Also, on the grey poplar the down is less prominent on short twigs and on the undersides of the leaves.

The only other major difference between the two trees is in their shape and size. The grey poplar is a much larger and more substantial tree than the white, reaching a height of 35m (115ft) with a trunk up to 4m (13ft) in girth. The grey poplar is also more widely and extensively branched, and it does not develop the flat top that is often characteristic of the white poplar.

The catkins of the grey poplar are similar in appearance to those of the white, though they usually emerge a little earlier in the year. The trunk is also similar, the upper part being whitish to yellow-grey and smooth, apart from a scattering of dark diamond-shaped pits; the lower part of the trunk is much darker and ridged.

Landscape plantings Both the white and the grey poplars are being planted more and more as landscape trees. The white poplar has the advantage of being resistant to sea spray and so is one of the few trees that flourishes on cold windy sites near the coast. It grows better in the countryside than in towns.

The recent popularity of these two species is due to a concern among planners and landscape architects that they should be planting more native trees – or, at least, trees that 'look right' in the countryside. This movement has developed for reasons of conservation and aesthetics. The grey and the white poplars both merge well into the British landscape, with the added bonus of providing a beautiful texture and colouring. Compare these trees with, for example, the tall narrow Lombardy poplar, which so often looks out of place in our landscape, especially when planted in rows. So the white and grey poplars have an increasingly valuable role to play in our countryside.

White poplar (*Populus alba*). Deciduous tree, introduced to Britain from the Netherlands, probably during the 17th century. A slender tree, usually seen growing with a pronounced lean to one side; it is usually broadest at the top of the crown. Height to 25m (80ft).

Grey poplar (*Populus canescens*). Deciduous tree, probably a hybrid between the white poplar and the aspen. It is a larger, more widely branching tree than the white poplar. Height to 35m (115ft).

Below: A grey poplar growing in a roadside hedge. Hedgerows and woodland are the best places to find a grey poplar, particularly in damp land. Like the white poplar, it grows better in the countryside than in towns.

Balsam poplars

The main attraction of the three species of
balsam poplar planted in this country is
the strong perfume of their buds and foliage that
fills the air on moist, warm summer evenings.

Balsam poplars are ornamental trees that
were originally introduced into the British
Isles from North America during the 17th
century. They owe their name to their buds
which are coated with an aromatic resin
called balsam. In late spring, as the buds
split open and the young leaves unfurl, they
give off their delightfully fragrant scent.

Three species have been planted in the
British Isles: the western balsam poplar
sometimes known as black cottonwood;
the balsam poplar; and the balm of Gilead.
They have a number of features in common.

Leaves The leaves, which are arranged
alternately along the smooth reddish-brown
twigs, are more or less oval shaped – rounded
at the leaf-stalk and tapering gently to a
slender point. The leaf margins are finely
toothed.

The upper surfaces of the leaves are dark
shining green, but underneath they are
conspicuously white or pale green with a
fine network of minute veins covering the
downy surface. The two-tone colouring of
the foliage gives the trees a characteristic
quivering appearance as their leaves are
shaken by the wind.

The leaves vary greatly in size from
$2.5 \times 2cm$ $(1 \times \frac{3}{4}in)$ on the side twigs to as
much as $25 \times 12cm$ $(10 \times 5in)$ on the fast
growing leading shoots. Balsam poplars
especially the balm of Gilead, tend to sprout
shoots or suckers from the base of the trunk
and here the leaves may be even bigger –
$33 \times 35cm$ $(13 \times 10in)$ has been recorded.

Unisexual trees Like willows, balsam poplars are either male or female. The catkins
that dangle like lambs' tails appear in April
some weeks before the leaves, so that the
foliage does not obstruct the free passage of
the wind-blown pollen. The male catkins are
dull reddish in colour and about 6cm $(2\frac{1}{4}in)$
long, while the greenish female catkins are
usually twice as long.

The tiny round seeds within the fertilised
female catkins ripen by mid-June. Each
seed has a plume of fine cotton-like hairs which
helps to keep it airborne as it is carried along
by the wind. The seeds are rarely released
singly, however, because their hairs tend to
tangle together, forming a fluffy mass of
seeds clinging to the catkin.

Habitat Balsam poplars grow best in rich
moist soil near running water. They need
plenty of sunlight and should not be planted
too close together or near to houses. The
timber is an extremely lightweight wood and
very pale in colour. It has limited uses because
it is soft and weak, rots quickly out of doors,
and does not burn well. However the fact that
growth is rapid, especially in river valley
floodplains, may make it important as a
future source of pulp-wood.

Left: The western balsam poplar, seen here
growing in Oxford University meadows, is the
most widely planted balsam poplar species in
the British Isles.

Identifying balsam poplars

Balsam poplar (*Populus balsamifera*). Deciduous, introduced; may grow to 25m (82ft). Sometimes planted by lakes, streams. Catkins April, fruits May.

The Balsam poplar is a native tree of N America where it grows in wet wooded areas in river valleys. In Britain it is a rare ornamental tree, planted in damp parts of parks and gardens. The branches spread upwards to form a narrow conical crown. The bark matures to a dark grey colour, its smooth surface cracked by narrow fissures. The buds at the tips of the young shoots are covered with shiny red-brown scales that smell strongly of balsam.

Balm of Gilead (*Populus gileadensis*). Deciduous, introduced; may grow to 25m (82ft). Sometimes planted beside ponds, streams. Catkins Feb-March.

This tree probably arose in N America as a natural hybrid between balsam poplar and eastern cottonwood. Introduced here in 1755, it is now the second most commonly planted species, flourishing in damp areas of parks and gardens. It is in many ways similar to the balsam poplar, but the branches are more spreading, forming a wide open crown. The leaves are broader, almost heart-shaped, and the young shoots and leaf stalks are covered with fine hairs.

Western balsam poplar (*Populus trichocarpa*). Deciduous, introduced from western N America; may grow to 35m (115ft). Catkins April, fruits May.

The young trees are rather triangular in shape and the trunk is covered with smooth, yellowish-grey bark which tends to peel off. As the tree matures the bark darkens to brownish-grey and is scored with deep vertical fissures. For a deciduous tree its growth is amazingly rapid: one specimen in Kew Gardens reached a height of 16·5m (54ft) in 13 years, a rate of growth that surpasses all other trees that thrive in the British Isles, including fast-growing conifer species.

Below and right: The catkins of the western balsam poplar are borne on separate trees. The female catkin (below) is green and when it is fertilised by pollen from the male catkins (right) it develops white fluffy seeds. Male catkins are a dull crimson colour and are often shed in early April before they have released their pollen.

Black and Lombardy poplars

In early spring before their leaves come out the black poplar
and its more familiar variety, the tall narrow Lombardy
poplar, bear masses of bright crimson-red catkins that make
these trees as attractive as any at this time of year.

The black poplar is usually regarded as being native to Britain. Certainly, it has been growing here since at least the Middle Ages, though it may have been brought over by the Romans from Italy, where it is still very common.

In Britain, the black poplar is confined mostly to central and eastern England. Its typical habitats are wet woodland and the sides of streams, since it likes moist soil, but it does not tolerate stagnant water. The reason for this is that the roots of a black poplar breathe, just as do the parts above ground, so the water in the ground must have oxygen dissolved in it. Therefore the water has to be flowing rather than stagnant.

Catkins in spring Poplars are closely related to willows: both have wind-pollinated catkins as flowers that come out early in the year before the leaves. The catkins of the black poplar mature in March. Male and female catkins are borne on separate trees. Male catkins consist of many tiny flowers, each with a pair of red or purple stamens but with no petals. The female catkins have green flowers, each consisting of a stigma to collect the pollen and an ovary in which the seed is formed.

In May, the female catkins ripen into seeds with long white silky hairs to help their dispersal by the wind. So many fluffy white seeds are released by just one female black poplar tree that the females are never planted in towns—if they were their seeds would collect along pavements and block up gutters.

Triangular leaves The leaves of a black poplar are broad and roughly triangular in shape. They are yellow-green, turning bright yellow in the autumn, and about 5–10cm (2–4in) long. The buds are reddish-brown and pointed. Like the leaves, they are arranged alternately along the twigs—this is typical of poplars and willows.

In common with most other poplars, the leaves of a black poplar have flattened stalks. This flattening causes the leaves to shimmer in the slightest breeze.

Bark and crown The bark of a mature black poplar is a much darker brown than the bark of other poplars—hence the name 'black'— and it is deeply furrowed. There are often large rounded growths near the base of the trunk.

A characteristic of fully-grown black poplars is that they lean away from the prevailing wind, which makes their crowns lop-sided. This is so typical of black poplars that they can often be identified from some distance away by their shape alone.

Easily-worked timber Black poplar has long been commercially important to man because it grows fast and can be felled easily. In the Middle Ages it used to be coppiced in Britain to provide shoots for supporting vines (which were more numerous in the days when the weather was warmer than it is now!) The timber is very pale, with a fine, soft texture. Before efficient cutting tools were developed, the softness of the timber made it a popular, though unsuitable, building material. The leaves and young twigs used to be fed to domestic animals—poplar is one of the first trees to come into leaf in spring.

Today the timber has limited but specialised uses. Its soft texture makes it easily sliced into veneers by rotating the logs against a sharp blade. The veneers are used for making matches and matchboxes, and are also turned into punnets to hold soft fruits and cress. Poplar wood is a particularly suitable material for making into matches: poplar matches do not splinter when struck, and the wood absorbs a lot of the paraffin wax in which it is soaked to help it ignite.

The trees themselves are often planted in rows to screen unsightly factories and to shelter playing fields since they grow quickly in the open. They are particularly suitable for planting in industrial areas since they are less affected by pollution than most other trees.

Black poplar (*Populus nigra*). Deciduous tree, probably native to Britain. Occurs mainly in central and eastern England where it is often planted in rows to provide shelter or screen a building. Grows to a height of about 30m (100ft).

Opposite: A black poplar in winter. The lop-sided trunk is caused by the prevailing wind and is characteristic of black poplars, allowing the tree to be easily identified from a distance.

Below: The male catkins mature in March before the leaves come out. At first they are grey but turn crimson-red as they release their pollen.

Quick to fall The black poplar's combination of large crown, fast growth and soft timber makes it unstable in a high wind. Large branches can be shed and, in a strong gale, whole trees can be blown over. Not surprisingly, black poplars do not live long and it is often wise to fell a tree before it becomes too old and dangerous.

They are also susceptible to disease, in particular bacterial canker, which attacks the bark and the wood beneath it, causing weeping wounds that slowly kill the larger branches and then the whole tree.

Hybrid poplars The black poplar hybridises easily with certain other poplars, notably the American black poplar and the western balsam poplar. These hybrids grow much more vigorously than the parent trees and quickly reach a considerable height and girth. The best of them have cylindrical stems reaching high up into the tree, with a large quantity of usable timber, and many are resistant to canker. The major poplars being planted commercially nowadays are these canker-resistant hybrids.

The most common hybrid poplar is the black Italian poplar (its cultivar name is 'Serotina'). It is often planted in parks and gardens, as well as for screening and shelter. It resembles the black poplar except that the bark is pale grey and the leaves are reddish-brown when they first emerge in late May. There are only males of this hybrid. The catkins mature in April, becoming bright red by the middle of the month. By the end of April they shed their pollen and have fallen from the tree.

The Lombardy poplar To most people the word 'poplar' refers to the tall, narrow trees often seen planted in rows. These trees are a variety of the black poplar called the Lombardy poplar; so-called because it originated

Right: **Lombardy poplar** (*Populus nigra* Italica). Introduced variety of the black poplar. Height 30m (100ft).

male catkins

Male catkins of the Lombardy poplar (above). Male catkins and mature seeds of the black poplar (below).

autumn colour

female catkins mature into fluffy seeds

male catkins

Below: The Lombardy poplar has a characteristically narrow columnar habit. Its unusual shape comes from the fact that the branches are all very small and swept strongly upwards. A tree having this shape is said to be fastigiate.

in the Lombardy region of northern Italy.

The Lombardy poplar was introduced to Britain in about 1758. Almost all trees seen here are males–like the black poplar, the female Lombardy poplar produces large numbers of fluffy white seeds that would block up drains and litter pavements.

The unusual shape of the tree is a result of the fact that the branches are all very small and grow upwards, almost parallel to the stem. Its narrow shape and lack of large branches make the Lombardy poplar a useful roadside tree and it is particularly common as such in France and Belgium.

The leaves of a Lombardy poplar are similar to those of the black poplar, but broader and more triangular. The bark is dark grey-brown with shallow ridges. The male flowers are crimson catkins and they ripen in mid-April. The female catkins are green but rarely seen since female trees are hardly ever planted in Britain.

Like the black poplar, the Lombardy poplar is planted to provide shelter and to screen buildings.

Undermining the foundations Poplars are often blamed for undermining the foundations of buildings and even causing cracks to appear in brickwork. However, the problem is much less common than is sometimes supposed and occurs only on heavy clay soils, particularly the sticky London clay. Much of the problem is due to the nature of clay itself. During rainy periods clay takes up a lot of water and swells up. When it dries out it shrinks again. The movement of the clay in wet and dry periods can cause buildings to heave and subside, and if the foundations are too shallow cracks may appear in walls.

Poplar trees tend to exacerbate the problem because they demand a lot of water. During dry periods they make a clay soil even drier than it would be naturally, and so it shrinks more. A particularly bad example occurred during the dry summer of 1976. Since then, building regulations in the areas affected (mainly London and south-east England) have been amended.

Beech

The beech is one of our most handsome trees. Its massive, smooth silver-grey trunk, the purity of its spring foliage and its vivid autumn colours give it a stature few trees can match.

Below: Early spring in the beech woods of Ashridge estate in Hertfordshire. The name beech comes from the Old English word bece.

The beech is queen of the broadleaved trees. When it grows as an isolated tree its great limbs spread out to form a gigantic crown, but in a crowded beech wood the crowns are more compact. The trunks stand like the smooth, soaring columns of a cathedral, forced to grow tall in their constant struggle to reach the light. In these more cramped conditions most of the branches sprout from the very top of the trunk.

As summer progresses, layer upon layer of leaves cast such a deep shade that few plants can survive underneath the tree. The beech wood floor, therefore, tends to be rather bare, except for the carpet of dead beech leaves—always some of the slowest to rot and form

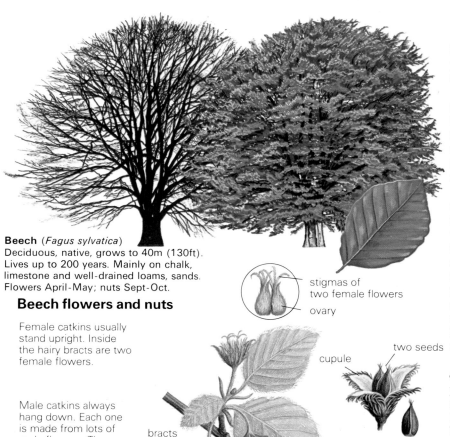

Beech (*Fagus sylvatica*)
Deciduous, native, grows to 40m (130ft).
Lives up to 200 years. Mainly on chalk,
limestone and well-drained loams, sands.
Flowers April-May; nuts Sept-Oct.

Beech flowers and nuts

Female catkins usually
stand upright. Inside
the hairy bracts are two
female flowers.

stigmas of
two female flowers

ovary

cupule

two seeds

Male catkins always
hang down. Each one
is made from lots of
male flowers. The
catkins fall off when
the stamens have shed
their pollen.

bracts

stamens

When the female
flowers have been
fertilized, the ovary
swells and the seeds
grow. The bracts now
develop into cupules.

leaf mould (humus) – and a scattering of
young saplings ready to grow up into any gap
created by the death or fall of the tree above.

A sprawling network of surface roots
anchor the tree to the ground and, because
they explore only the upper layers of the soil,
the beech is easily toppled by strong gales. In
the long drought of 1976 the beech was particularly affected because its roots could not
reach down to water deep below the surface.

Native and cultivated The beech grows as a
native tree only in southern England and
south Wales. Ancient beech forests still survive on the Chiltern Hills in Buckinghamshire, in the Cotswolds and on southern chalk
downs. Over the centuries and particularly in
the last 200 years the tree has also been widely
planted throughout Great Britain. Its value
as an ornamental and landscape tree has been
widely exploited in avenues, shelter-belts,
hedges and hilltop clumps, serving to break
up the bleak outline of rolling downland.

The beech grove at Slindon Park in Sussex
contains lofty beech trees that are at least 200
years old. A superb beech avenue flanks the
road alongside the Iron Age fort of Badbury
Rings in Dorset. In summer the interlocking
branches cast deep shade over the roadway
and form a natural tunnel; there are 365 trees
on either side of the road – one for every day
of the year. And at Meikleour near Perth in
Scotland there is a massive beech hedge a
third of a mile long and standing 28m (90ft)

Pollarding

Pollarding is the lopping of the main
branches of a tree at a height of 2-3m
(7-10ft) above ground level, out of the
reach of browsing livestock. Removal of
these growing points stimulates most
broadleaved trees to send out a mass of
small branches from buds hidden below the
bark of the main trunk. The new branches
are used in much the same way as
coppiced wood but have the added
advantage that grazing pasture can grow
underneath.

Pollarding used to be common, but as coal
replaced wood for fuel, the annual lopping
ceased and shoots were allowed to grow
into great branches. You can see overgrown
pollards in many woodlands. The tree
shown here is in Epping Forest.

branches
removed

new growth

igh – a daunting prospect for all but the most seasoned hedge-cutter.

The winter twigs of the beech are very distinctive: they are slender, smooth, and tipped with a spear-shaped bud. Additional buds are arranged alternatively along the length of the twig. Each of the long, pointed buds is wrapped in a series of overlapping protective brown scales.

Spring leaves The beech breaks into leaf in April. The oval leaves, tapering to a short point, are borne on short stalks. After they unfold from the buds, the fresh limp leaves are fringed with soft silvery hairs. The young foliage has a bright shining, almost translucent, quality; but as the season advances the leaves become stiffer and turn darker green with a glossy surface sheen.

The flowers, which are usually half hidden among the emerging foliage, are wind-pollinated. The male flowers are grouped in clusters, hanging like tassels, and pollen is blown from their bright yellow anthers. The female flowers are in pairs, bound by a collar of prickly scales forming the cupule.

Nuts After fertilisation the cupule develops into a woody husk, clad in stiff bristles, enclosing a pair of three-sided, sharp-edged nuts. In October the ripe capsule splits and the four lobes peel back to allow the nuts, known as beech-mast, to fall out. The kernels are edible and delicious.

A really heavy crop of nuts is produced about every four or five years – known as mast years; this is an important time for forest wildlife. Mammals, such as badgers and squirrels, and birds, such as nuthatches and bramblings, are particularly fond of beech nuts and a good mast year can considerably increase their chances of survival through winter when other foods become scarce. In the past it was common to turn pigs out into woodland during autumn so that they could rummage about for nuts and acorns. This practice, called pannage, is still carried out on a small scale in the New Forest.

Autumn finery In autumn the beech has few rivals. The tree positively glows with colour, displaying a brilliant mosaic of flaming orange, russet and gold. Gradually the foliage darkens to a dull copper colour, reflecting the tree's gradual accumulation of waste products that form tannin. As the leaves fall, the ground beneath becomes smothered in a thick blanket of leaves. In the past mattresses used to be stuffed with dry beech leaves and they gave a comfortable, if noisy, night's sleep. In France they were called *lits de parliament* – talking beds – because of the noise they made.

Life under beech Pure beech woods are ideal places for walks on a hot summer's day. Occasionally you see holly, yew and wild cherry growing among the trees, but on the whole few plants can tolerate the deep shade. Two interesting species are the yellow birds-nest and birdsnest orchid, both of which feed

off rotting vegetation and therefore do not need sunlight to help make their food. All kinds of fungi flourish in the autumn, including the virulent death-cap, our most poisonous toadstool, and bracket fungi are common on tree trunks.

Mixed beech woods are generally far more hospitable to wildlife. The sudden shafts of light that beam down through gaps in the canopy of oak, sycamore or perhaps hornbeam encourage all kinds of wild flowers to grow – helleborine, wood anemone, arum lily, yellow archangel and bluebell, to mention just a few. Bramble, bracken, heather and mosses often carpet the ground, providing protection for numerous insects and birds.

Timber In common with most of our native trees, beech was used for firewood, even though it does not burn particularly well. Queen Victoria was supposed to have preferred to have wood from Burnham Beeches, near Slough, burned on the fires at Windsor Castle.

Beech trees used to be pollarded every 20 years or so. Use as building timber is limited because beech decays quickly. The wood is rather soft and springy but this has always been an advantage in furniture making.

The furniture industry has long been centred at High Wycombe in the heart of the Chilterns and, until quite recently, the surrounding beechwoods were the hub of a flourishing cottage industry.

Above: the edge of the mature beech woods of Ashridge estate in autumn, where many of the leaves have already fallen. Younger trees and beech hedges keep their leaves until the following spring.

Below: A young beech seedling with the remains of the seed case still attached to the young shoot and the cupule lying on the ground.

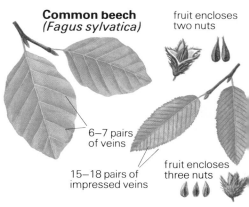

Common beech
(Fagus sylvatica)

fruit encloses
two nuts

6–7 pairs
of veins

15–18 pairs of
impressed veins

fruit encloses
three nuts

Rauli
(Nothofagus proce

Southern beeches

The southern hemisphere's equivalent to our own beech trees, southern beeches are just as beautiful and they grow much faster. Tests being carried out show that they may yet become commercially our most important group of broad-leaved trees.

Above: A stand of raulis at Benmore arboretum, Strathclyde. Some of the tallest raulis in the country are to be found here, one or two reaching as high as 25m (80ft). Raulis grow best in the damp western half of Britain. In the right conditions, it is one of our fastest-growing trees, some specimens reaching 15m (50ft) in under ten years.

The southern beeches are native exclusively to the southern hemisphere, just as our own beeches are confined to the northern. They are found in Australia, New Zealand, Papua New Guinea, New Caledonia and South America, but all of the most common species now growing in Britain come from South America, except for *Nothofagus gunnii* which comes from Tasmania.

In appearance, the southern beeches are similar to beech trees – indeed the scientific name for southern beeches, *Nothofagus,* means false beech or resembling the beech. The fruits, in particular, are very much alike, in both cases consisting of a number of nuts enclosed in a two, three or four-lobed fruit called a cupule. The number of nuts inside the fruit varies from one to as many as seven, depending on species.

Of the 37 species of southern beech that are currently recognised, only ten are deciduous, all but one of these coming from Chile. All the rest are evergreens.

This group of Chilean deciduous species includes some that are potentially of great importance to British forestry. They are all being investigated by the Forestry Commission to establish which species are commercially the most suitable in Britain, what conditions they require, and which parts of their native ranges produce the best specimens. So far, results show that two species in particular, the rauli and the roble beech, could have a great future in this country as sources of timber and could possibly become our most important commercial broad-leaved trees.

Quick-growing rauli The rauli was introduced to Britain as recently as 1910 and soon proved to be an extremely quick-growing tree here. On a suitable site it is capable of growing to a height of 15m (50ft) in less than ten years. It is best suited to the western half of Britain because it requires a fairly high degree of moisture.

In Britain, it forms a handsome tree growing to about 30m (100ft) high, with a broadly conical crown formed by the lower branches being level and the higher ones being swept upwards. The bark on young trees is grey-green and marked with lenticels; on older trees it becomes duller and develops long, broad, vertical fissures.

The leaves of a rauli are similar to hornbeam leaves. They are oval, with a downy under-surface and finely toothed margins. Their most striking feature is the pairs of impressed veins, which give the leaves the appearance of being corrugated. Rauli leaves can be between 5cm (2in) and 10cm (4in) long. They are usually yellow-green – though occasionally dark green – and turn pale or deep

Roble beech
(Nothofagus obliqua)

oblique leaf-base

coarse jagged margins

7–11 pairs of impressed veins

evergreen leaves

4–6 pairs of veins

Coigue
(Nothofagus dombeyi)

gold in the autumn.

The male flowers form inconspicuous solitary tufts of green stamens; the female flowers are even smaller and borne in the leaf axils. The fruits are deep green at first, ripening to brown by mid-summer. The mature fruits are about 1cm ($\frac{3}{8}$in) long and consist of a soft, feathery, 4-lobed cupule containing three pale brown nuts, each about 7mm ($\frac{1}{4}$in) long.

In its native areas–the central parts of Chile and Argentina–the rauli forms large forests, though these are rapidly being cut down for the valuable timber. Rauli is one of the most important sources of timber in Chile and Argentina, and is used for doors, stairs, floors and furniture. It has similar properties to beech timber, being easy to season and fairly dense.

Roble beech The word 'rauli' is Spanish for beech; 'roble', however, is Spanish for oak, since the shape of this reminded early Spanish explorers of their own oaks. The roble beech comes from central Chile, where it occurs along the coastal ranges and up into the Andes. Extensive stands are also found in western Argentina, where it is more common than the rauli.

The roble beech was introduced to Britain in 1902 and has considerable potential as a source of timber in this country. It is not quite as fast-growing as the rauli, but it is better suited to drier, poorer sites and is also somewhat hardier than the rauli. In the drier eastern half of Britain, the roble beech can be found growing as far north as Aberdeen.

The roble beech grows to a height of 25-30m (80-100ft), and has a narrow conical crown (broadening on old trees) with characteristic arching branches. The smaller branches spread out and down in slender sprays.

The leaf is oval with a blunt tip; the leaf-base is rounded or wedge-shaped and unequal where it joins the stalk–hence its Latin name, *N. obliqua*. The leaf margins are irregular with small triangular teeth or small lobes, the latter occurring particularly in the lower part of the leaf. The upper surface of the leaf is deep green with seven to eleven pairs of impressed veins that give it a slightly waved

Antarctic beech
(Nothofagus antarctica)

Above: The southern beeches are best distinguished from each other, and from the common beech, by their leaves. All bear similar fruits, except that some southern beeches contain three nuts rather than two.

Above: The leaves and shoots of the Antarctic beech form a striking herringbone pattern, a characteristic shared by only one other southern beech, the roble beech.
An unusual feature of the leaf is that the veins end not at the tips of the teeth, as is almost universally the case, but at the gaps (called sinuses) between the teeth.

Right: The bark of a roble beech is pale grey, becoming browner and cracking into small plates with age. This species has great forestry potential in this country, particularly in the drier eastern half of Britain, where it is almost as fast-growing as the rauli.

appearance, while the underside is much paler and usually hairless. The length varies from 4cm ($1\frac{1}{2}$in) to 8cm (3in), and the autumn colour is usually yellow.

An unusual feature of the roble beech, shared with another South American species, the Antarctic beech, is the way in which the leaves are arranged in a herringbone pattern down both sides of the shoot.

Less familiar species Several other species of southern beech grow in Britain, though on a much smaller scale than the rauli or roble.

The Antarctic beech was the first southern beech to be introduced to this country, in 1830. It comes from the more southerly parts of Patagonia, and is a hardy deciduous tree growing to about 15m (50ft) high. The margins of the leaves have four rounded teeth.

Another species of southern beech, the coigue, is one of the few evergreen species to grow here. Its leaves are dark glossy green above and paler matt green beneath; from a distance they appear blackish. Both leaf surfaces are studded with small black glands, best seen with a hand lens.

Hornbeam

The hornbeam grows as a native tree in oak woodlands in southern England, but it has also been widely planted as an ornamental tree in hedgerows and parks for its compact stature and autumn colours.

As our climate became warmer after the last Ice Age ended 10,000 years ago, the British Isles were colonised by forest trees which spread across from the Continent. The pollen record shows that the hornbeam was a relative latecomer, arriving about 5000 years ago, whereas the oak was already widespread 2500 years earlier.

Since the hornbeam settled here, the climate has become wetter and cooler, pushing the hornbeam southwards until today it is common only in south-eastern England. From this area its natural range extends northwards and west to the Welsh border; elsewhere it has been introduced. It is a common forest tree in central Europe and the British distribution represents the western tip of its range.

Appearance The fluted trunk, covered in smooth pale-grey bark, divides into a large number of limbs which sweep upwards to produce a densely-branched symmetrical crown. The winter buds, are 5-10cm (2-4in) long, pale-brown and set alternately along the slender twigs. The buds are closely pressed against the twig 'like a crouching mouse', in Herbert Edlin's apt description.

Flowers, fruits and leaves Flowering starts in April shortly before the leaves appear. Male and female catkins, borne on the same tree, appear towards the tips of the delicate twigs. The male catkins expand to form a

Above: A fine old hornbeam in Epping Forest. For centuries commoners held rights to firewood and until recently hornbeams were regularly pollarded, which explains their branching shapes.

Buds in winter

protective bud scales

winter buds (5-10cm 2-4in) are pale brown and set alternately along the twig

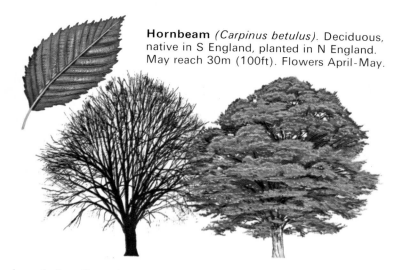

Hornbeam *(Carpinus betulus).* Deciduous, native in S England, planted in N England. May reach 30m (100ft). Flowers April-May.

Male catkins

young leaves

bracts protect clusters of orange anthers

Above: The male flowers and bracts are clustered along a central stalk.

Female catkin

toothed leaf margins

bud scales

tips of bracts curl upwards

strongly ribbed young leaves

Above: Female flowers hang down from the top of the twig and resemble leafy buds.

hanging chain of overlapping yellow-green bracts. Pollen is shed from a cluster of orange anthers that are tucked under each bract.

The female catkins consist of a loose cluster of leafy green bracts with their tips curled upwards. Under each bract is a pair of smaller bracteoles which protect the red stigmas that catch the pollen grains drifting in the air.

Shortly after the catkins have fully expanded, the bright yellow-green young leaves push their way out of a sheath of pinkish bud scales and slowly unfurl like a fan. The unfolded leaves are oval in shape with a conspicuously toothed margin. The upper surface is slightly creased along the lines of the parallel veins.

After fertilisation a pair of nutlets are formed in shallow cups, and each bracteole expands to form a papery wing with three lobes, the middle one being the longest. Later in summer this wing acts as a sail, catching the wind and steering the seed some distance from the parent tree.

The autumn foliage undergoes a vivid colour change through various shades of yellow to a rich ruddy gold before falling. On young hornbeam trees and hedges the leaves become shrivelled and rusty brown but, as in the beech, they may stay on the tree throughout winter.

The small, ribbed nutlets, each enclosing a single seed, provide a bountiful supply of food for birds and mammals. The hawfinch in particular devours hornbeam seeds, and interestingly, they both share a similar range in this country. Squirrels too eat the seeds, either climbing the trees to get them or seeking them out on the forest floor. The seeds that escape being eaten lie dormant for 18 months or so before germinating.

Beech look-alike The hornbeam is frequently confused with the beech, and they are indeed similar in general appearance. But they can easily be distinguished at any time of the year. First, the winter buds of hornbeam are shorter and fatter than those of the beech. They also hug the twig closely whereas in the beech the buds are set at an angle

and point away from the twig.

Secondly, the leaves, while similar in shape, can be seen to differ at close range. Those of hornbeam have sharply toothed edges whereas beech leaves have smooth margins. Hornbeam leaves feel rather rough to the touch, contrasting with the smooth, polished feel of beech foliage; and during summer beech foliage turns a darker shade of green.

Tough wood The name of the tree probably derives from the nature of the wood, which is hard like horn. Alternatively, some say it refers to the wooden yokes, often made of this wood, which join a team of ploughing oxen together, and are attached to the horns—hence hornbeam.

The hornbeam has the hardest wood of any tree in Europe. It is heavy, fine-grained, and creamy yellow in colour. Craftsmen have made little use of it for furniture or cabinet-making because it is too hard: their tools were blunted so quickly that much time was wasted in resharpening them. But it has been greatly used in musical instruments, particularly for the hammers of piano-keys, and for heavy-duty purposes, such as cogs and pulleys.

Although the wood is extremely tough it burns well. Before coal became the major source of energy hornbeams in woods near London, such as Epping Forest, were regularly coppiced and pollarded to provide fire wood and charcoal to fuel the city's furnaces.

Below: Hornbeam fruits appear in autumn. The bracts change into papery, green, three-pointed wings. The seeds are two tiny hard, green ridged nuts

Left: The hazel tree in early spring: the male catkins–lambs' tails–dangle from leafless twigs and release clouds of dusty golden pollen.

Looking closely at a hazel catkin

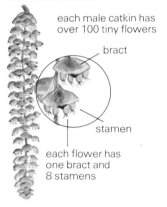

each male catkin has over 100 tiny flowers

bract

stamen

each flower has one bract and 8 stamens

The stamens will ripen when the temperature is over 0°C. The ripe stamens split open lengthways to release their yellow pollen.

Hazel

The hazel may be one of our smallest native trees, but it has had an important role to play in the history of woodland management. Apart from its value as wood, it also has–according to Celtic folklore–magical properties.

The hazel grows as a small native tree in the shade of woods and in hedgerows. In old neglected coppices it throws straggling limbs from old stools and is rarely able to form the single trunk to give it the status of a tree.

Yet it is an important tree. In the fossilized pollen records preserved in peat which are our guide to the earliest native plants after the Ice Age, hazel predominates over much of the British Isles–appearing at much the same time as the initial spread of other wind pollinated trees such as alder, willow and birch. Remains of hazel nut shells have been found at the foot of peat deposits, suggesting that the early Stone Age hunters were probably at least partly dependent on the nuts for ood, in the absence of any sort of cereal.

Since hazel is associated with man's earliest ncestors, it is perhaps not surprising that in 'eltic folkore it was known as the tree of nowledge, and was supposed to have many 1agic properties. Irish aches and pains aused by the damp climate or elfin malvolence were thought to be warded off by a azel nut carried in the pocket. A double azel nut was said to cure toothache in)evon, and defend against witches in Scotand. Hazel is one of the magic trees of May)ay, like hawthorn in England and rowan in cotland: these are the three trees of white 1agic that oppose the forces of evil which 1any people thought were present in the oods.

In 1956 there were more than 16,000 acres f hazel coppice, little of which was used. ince then the coppiced areas have dwindled s foresters have gradually turned them over o conifer production. For truly wild hazel ees you must go to the Lake District, the Vestern Highlands or the Burren in County 'lare, Ireland. You can see coppiced hazel 1 Hatfield Forest, the Sussex Weald and on 1e Wiltshire downs.

The hazel belongs to the same family as 1e hornbeam, which has more scaly catkins nd winged nutlets. The hazel leaf is a dense, eep green colour which turns to brown then ellow-gold towards the end of the year. Iazel bark is shiny, brownish grey with orizontal pores (lenticels) which enable the ee to breathe.

Catkins and flowers The brownish-yellow 1ale catkins begin to develop in autumn; arly the following spring they open to a reamy yellow colour. The female catkins re small and brown with bright crimson tyles and they generally ripen after the male atkins of the same tree, a mechanism which sually prevents self-pollination. Like all atkin-bearing trees, the hazel is windollinated.

Nuts There are between one and four, and ccasionally five, hard-shelled nuts on each talk. They are pale green in summer, but by utumn have turned to a warm, soft brown olour. Each nut is enclosed in a pair of owny husks or bracts with deep scallops. Many children's fairy stories show pixies /earing hats of a similar style.

Birds, especially pigeons and pheasants, nd small mammals such as squirrels and 1ice, take the nuts for food and bury them. 'his is one way the trees become dispersed. 'ou can grow the hazel in your garden either rom a seed or from a sapling. For your own rees to produce nuts you will need at least wo trees to ensure cross-pollination because he species is naturally self-sterile (ie the tree annot fertilise itself). A hazel tree produces uts in abundance from six years old. There re several varieties available, including *Penula* which makes a standard tree with a runk of at least 1.5m (5ft).

Selective breeding of the hazel in the 19th century produced the large Kentish cob nut which is redder and rounder than the wild nut. The more oval filbert nuts come from a different species, *Corylus maxima*. It is thought they originated in France and were named after Saint Philbert.

Today many English nuts in shops come from the Kentish nut plantations, although we import thousands of tons from the Mediterranean for use in confectionary. Richard Mabey in *Food for Free* recommends using the nuts in salads, chopped or grated, in muesli, blended into a milk drink, or as nut cutlets. Weight for weight, he says, hazel nuts have half as much protein as eggs, seven times more oil and fat and five times more carbohydrate.

Management The management of hazel woods dates back to the late Stone Age. The tough straight poles produced by coppicing the tree are still used today in fencing and as bean and pea sticks and small stakes. The rod used by a diviner to detect the source of water is often made of hazel.

In the days of open field farming, split green hazel poles were woven into hurdles to fence in pigs, cattle and sheep to stop them eating the crops on adjoining land. The tree also produced the wattles for wattle-and-daub building as well as the spurs used in thatching. The brushwood was bundled into faggots that were used for the weekly firing of bread ovens.

Hazel (*Corylus avellana*), deciduous, native, grows to 6m (20ft). May live hundreds of years if coppiced regularly. Common throughout the British Isles. Flowers Jan-April; cob-nuts Sept-Oct.

Left: At least two hazel trees growing close together are needed for fertilisation and the production of nuts. This is because the female catkin usually ripens after the male flower of the same tree.

Below: Hazel nuts are rich in oil, and the oil from a single nut rubbed over the surface of a stout hazel walking stick will give it a good polish.

Coppicing

A copse is a small wood. A coppice, however, is a special sort of woodland, and coppicing the earliest known form of woodland management. It is a method of cutting broadleaved trees down to the ground at regular intervals—anything from five to 25 years, depending on the species. A cluster of new shoots sprout up from the stump (stool) and these eventually provide new, manageable straight poles.

The word coppice comes from the French *couper* to cut, but coppices were managed long before the French came to England. Trackways across the marshy areas of Somerset were built of poles which have been identified as coppiced alder, ash, holly and hazel dating from 2500BC.

By the 15th century large areas of southern England were coppiced. In the 16th century coppice-with-standards was common: standard trees—often oak or ash—were allowed to grow to maturity above the coppiced trees to increase the national timber reserves for the construction of buildings and ships.

Strict rotation in cutting and enclosure by a deep ditch or strong fence to prevent grazing animals from eating the tender shoots have always been essential in coppicing. A hurdle maker might spend a year working two acres, so a coppice of 14 acres would keep him and his billhook perpetually employed. Old coppices often retain the name of a man who worked there, perhaps for a life time, such as Emblems Coppice and Collins Coppice in Hatfield Forest.

Today coppiced wood is once again becoming valuable as firewood in rural areas; among the other values of these woods, willow is used for hurdles (see below), sweet chestnut for fencing, ash for tool handles and hazel for hop poles.

Many old coppices have become overgrown through neglect, but coppice-with-standards is still practised in a small way, and is encouraged by conservationists.

Not only does coppiced woodland provide a number of different woods, but it is a haven for a huge variety of wildlife with its ever-changing layers: the ground of a freshly cut coppice is covered with wild flowers; the re-growing trees offer nesting places to numerous birds; and the mature coppice shelters yet more animals and carpets of bluebells.

Left: The base of a much coppiced hazel tree with dog's mercury and moss growing in the centre of the stool. Regular coppicing greatly prolongs the life of a tree.

Below: A hazel tree growing among standard oak trees. The hazel might be coppiced a dozen times before the mature oak is felled.

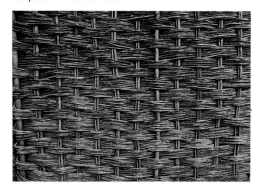

Sweet chestnut

The sweet chestnut is a large, handsome tree with fine leaves and flowers, and distinctive twisting bark. But its crowning glory is its masses of shiny dark brown autumn fruits.

We probably have the Romans to thank for introducing the sweet chestnut to the British Isles. It is a native of Asia Minor and eastern Mediterranean countries such as Greece and Yugoslavia. The Romans spread it throughout Europe because the nuts were an important source of food to them. The first evidence of the presence of sweet chestnut in Britain is as charcoal fragments excavated from sites of Roman forts and villas. It does not readily establish itself in the wild and most of the specimens you see have been planted.

The sweet chestnut is not related to the horse chestnut, and it would be difficult to confuse the two: in fact, it belongs to the same family as the oak and beech, and rivals them in grandeur. It grows up to become a massive tree reaching 30m (100ft) high, its huge trunk extending right up into the crown and sending out contorted limbs to form a broad leafy dome.

The sweet chestnut does best on deep, well-drained soils but tends to avoid chalk and limestone. It is most abundant in south-eastern England but it is widely distributed elsewhere, although it is less common in northern England, Scotland and Ireland. It can be found in woods and plantations and has also been widely planted as an ornamental tree in parks and gardens.

The winter twigs are reddish-brown and bear plump buds, about 5mm (⅕in) long, set on little ledges spaced rather irregularly along the shaft of the twig. The tree breaks into leaf towards the end of April or early in May. The fully expanded leaves are 10-25cm (4-10in) long and a rich glossy green. A short leaf stalk supports the spear-shaped leaf blade, the edges of which are cut into long teeth where the prominent veins reach the leaf margin.

Flowers Both male and female flowers are set on dangling catkins up to 15cm (6in) long, which sprout from the base of the leaf stalks on the younger shoots. The yellow male flowers, consisting of a dense tuft of stamens, are much more numerous than the females which are confined to the upper part of the catkin near where it joins the shoot. The greenish

Above: **Sweet chestnut** (*Castanea sativa*). Deciduous, introduced, grows to 30m (100ft) throughout the British Isles, lives up to 500 years, sometimes longer. Flowers July, fruits Oct.

Below: The male flowers of the sweet chestnut are more conspicuous than the female flowers which grow on the upper part of the catkin.

female flowers are in groups of three set in a small prickly collar (cupule). Although wind pollination does take place, the pleasant scent from the catkins attracts insects which collect and feed on the pollen, some of which they unwittingly transfer to the female flowers.

Glossy fruits After fertilisation the cupule grows around the ovary in which the seeds develop and forms the familiar green 'hedge-hog' case. During October, when the nuts are ripe, the spiny coat splits open, the four lobes peel back, revealing up to three glossy brown nuts packed snugly inside. The nuts are roughly triangular in shape, flattened on the side which lies next to another nut. A tuft of silvery hairs at the point indicates the remains of the stigmas.

The sweet chestnut, with its exceptionally large seeds, cannot be dispersed by the wind or by many animals. However, some animals –notably squirrels and jays–collect and bury them as an insurance against winter shortage of other fruits. Because most animal memories

Right: The most widely used chestnut timber comes from coppiced plantations; there are particularly productive areas in the Weald of Kent and Sussex. These are still cut regularly every 12-14 years to provide stacks of posts, piles and poles. Because sweet chestnut wood splits easily, the poles are cleft into sections which are wired together to make cheap, easily handled fences. In this plantation oak standards are growing in the distance. Where coppiced sweet chestnut plantations are less hospitable to other forms of wildlife because the leaves cast a deep shade.

Opposite: The bole of a sweet chestnut tree. When young the bark is smooth and brown, but with age it turns greyish and its surface cracks into deep longitudinal fissures which develop a spiral twist up the trunk. This gives the impression that the tree has been slowly twisting as it grows.

Above: Sweet chestnut seeds are well protected in spiny containers. Sadly, British sweet chestnuts rarely produce a generous crop of nuts because our climate is not warm enough. Even though they are small compared with those in the shops which are imported from Spain and Italy, they are still delicious to eat roasted.

Left: It is said that the leaves decompose to a compost unrivalled in its fertilising qualities.

are no match for their thriftiness, many caches are not relocated, and so for the sweet chestnut these creatures are important distributors and planters in the wild.

Crunchy golden leaves While the nuts are dropping from the trees the leaves acquire their autumn hues, paling first to yellow and then darkening to gold before dropping. The fallen leaves form a deep carpet beneath the tree and this rustles loudly underfoot because they remain stiff and dry – not soggy and shrivelled like those of so many other trees.

Durable wood Although mature sweet chestnuts yield a large volume of timber, the wood is not as useful as oak because cracks tend to appear during seasoning. This condition, known as 'shakes', severely limits the size of beams or length of planks that can be extracted from the bole. However, the timber is durable out of doors and even underground – it has been used for making coffins.

Long life The sweet chestnut is one of the few European trees that matches the oak for longevity. Its normal span is about 500 years but many specimens exceed this. In old age the tree becomes grotesquely misshapen with a gigantic gnarled trunk and huge twisted limbs so heavy they may touch the ground.

An enormous sweet chestnut grows in the grounds of Canford School, Dorset. The tree's bole is 13m (44ft) in circumference – the greatest girth of any living tree in Britain.

Alder

The alder, which lives on wet ground, can be recognised from afar as it tilts slightly over the water. It lines the banks of rivers and streams, invades soggy marshes and fens and colonizes wet woodland. In fact, it grows wherever its roots can bathe in water and absorb rich minerals.

Before man set about clearing forests and draining the land for farming, the alder flourished in the vast valley swamps that covered much of lowland Britain. Nowadays, although it is still a common and widespread tree throughout the British Isles, only small fragments of alder swamp forest (carr) still exist. Some of the best examples of alder carr are found in the fens of East Anglia – around the reed-fringed lakes of the Norfolk Broads for instance. Here alder forms dense, damp woods which encourage a wealth of moisture-loving mosses, ferns and flowering plants.

Appearance In suitably wet ground the alder grows to a height of 20m (66ft) or more, but in drier ground it may not get beyond a

Below: Alder trees growing beside the river Orchy in Glen Orchy, Argyll, Scotland. The presence of alder indicates an unusually rich soil.

unted, rather bushy stage. The trunk is tall
d straight and covered with rough, blackish
rk. Where there is plenty of space, the
ler's crown is fairly open and rounded, but
crowded by other trees it tends to develop a
rrow, rather conical crown. In winter this
n give the tree the appearance of a decidu-
s conifer; this impression is reinforced at
se range when you can see the small woody
nes which hang on the tree throughout
nter.

Look out for the catkins in spring. These
re formed the previous summer in pre-
ration for flowering in March and April,
out a month before the leaves appear. The
ler carries both male and female catkins on

Left: **Alder** (*Alnus
glutinosa*) Native, deciduous,
grows to 40m (130ft) in wet
places by lakes, rivers and
streams. May form pure
woods in succession to
marsh or fen. Lives up to
200 years. Flowers Feb,
fruits Oct.

Overleaf: An alder carr
brightened by marsh
marigolds at Henley Park,
Surrey. Alders may be
coppiced every 10-15 years.

Above: The alder is our only
cone-bearing broad-leaved
deciduous tree. The young
alder cones appear with the
mature foliage in late
summer. Alders retain their
leaves well into autumn, and
they turn a rather dull shade
of brown before falling.

Left: Male catkins and old
open woody cones that have
shed their winged seeds.
Some seeds are borne away
by wind and others by
water.

the same tree. Male catkins, a dull crimson
colour in winter, are made up of a column of
densely packed stamens. In spring the catkins
extend to almost 5cm (2in), almost double
their previous length. The stamens separate to
reveal masses of yellow pollen. As the flowers
dangle in the breeze the pollen is shaken out
and scattered by the wind, and some finds its
way to the female catkins.

The female catkins are club-shaped at first,
about 1cm ($\frac{1}{3}$in) long, and purple-brown in
colour. But after pollination they turn green
and enlarge to form a rounded cone which
protects the ripening seeds.

The purple-tinged leaf buds, arranged alternately along the twigs, split open in May.
The new leaves have a sticky surface coating
which acts as a death-trap for insect pests
which might otherwise chew the delicate
young foliage. When the leaves have fully
expanded they are dark green on their slightly
wrinkled upper surface, and lighter green
underneath. They are rather like a tennis
racket in shape; the rounded leaves, with
prominent veins and toothed margins, taper
at the base to join the leaf-stalks which are
5-10cm (2-4in) long.

By autumn the seed-bearing cones have
matured to barrel-shaped woody structures
whose scales split open to release the seeds.
Each seed has a hollow wing on either side
which aid wind dispersal. And, more import-
antly, since many alders overhang rivers, they
also act as floats, keeping the seed buoyant
as it drifts downstream, until it lodges in a
suitable spot and can germinate.

Many seeds that fall in the water are eagerly
eaten by wildfowl such as mallard and teal.
And the trees themselves attract flocks of
siskin and redpoll, winter visitors from
Scandinavia, which roam through the
branches pecking seeds from the cones.

The only mammal that is particularly associated with alders is the elusive otter which
inhabits undisturbed river valleys. The female
otter often makes her holt under the roots of
an overhanging riverside alder. The cubs are
protected from enemies because the entrance
to the holt is situated under the water.

Timber Alders produce a useful hard tim-

ber. It was widely used for submerged piles and supports because the wood is extremely durable under water. Indeed, it is said that most of Venice was built on alder-wood piles. Alder was reputed to make valuable charcoal and so many gunpowder mills sprung up in low-lying river plains where a good supply of alders was near at hand. The trees were usually coppiced every 10-15 years.

The timber has also been used for wood-carving and furniture, and for making the soles of clogs that were formerly worn in the north of England, especially around Lancashire. In parts of northern Europe it is used to make plywood.

The freshly cut wood is white but it soon becomes stained reddish when exposed to the air. This is due to the release of a dye from the damaged tissues. A tawny red dye can be extracted from the bark, and green and yellow dye from the female catkins and the young shoots respectively.

Alder roots

Where the river bank has been washed away you can see the alder's reddish roots straggling over the bank or streaming in the current. The smallest roots have rather a lumpy appearance. These lumps or nodules are inhabited by bacteria which form a partnership with the alder, beneficial to both (a symbiotic relationship). In return for sugars manu-factured in the leaves and pumped to the roots, the bacteria absorb large amounts of vital nitrogen from the air spaces in the soil and then pass it on to the tree.

Aspen

One of our less familiar native trees, the aspen is sometimes called the quaking aspen because its leaves tremble in the slightest breeze–a feature that has been the source of much folklore, all associating this pretty tree with evil and gossip.

Above: A stand of aspens by a lake. They are most often seen on hillsides and valleys, especially where the soil is fairly damp and light. They can be found in other habitats, however, and tolerate a wide range of soil types.

Although the aspen is not one of our well known native trees, it occurs throughout the British Isles, being more common in the north and west of the country than in the south. Valleys and hillsides are typical habitats for this tree, though it sometimes grows in hedgerows and copses, and it is quite often seen in open oakwoods.

Outside Britain the aspen is found as far north as Iceland, Norway and northern USSR, south to Sicily, Greece and North Africa, and east to Japan.

Trembling poplar The aspen is a species of poplar, its Latin name of *Populus tremula* reflecting the fact that its leaves quiver in the slightest breeze. Like other poplars, the aspen is a fast-growing tree, reaching a maximum height of about 20m (65ft). When young it has an open conical crown, which becomes broader with age.

The bole often leans to one side and suckers are freely produced around the base, so that single trees may eventually form dense thickets. The bark is grey-green and smooth, with darker oval depressions.

The shape and size of the leaves vary according to whether they come from the main part of the tree or from the suckers. Normal leaves have a blade about 3-7cm (1-3in) long and at least as broad as that, with shallow rounded teeth. The stalk is 4-6cm ($1\frac{1}{2}$-$2\frac{1}{2}$in) long and strongly flattened in such a way that the slightest breeze causes the leaf to flutter vigorously. Leaves borne on suckering shoots may be much larger–up to 15cm (6in) long– and are egg-shaped with more prominent teeth. Their stalks are also much shorter.

Both types of leaf are the same colour: copper-brown when they first emerge in the spring, gradually becoming grey-green or green on the upper surface and paler underneath. The leaf-stalks are much paler, being yellowish or almost white in colour. In late October, the leaves turn pure yellow and provide an attractive display in some years. However, aspens in other countries seem to have much better autumn colours than ours.

Spring catkins The aspen flowers in March, before the leaves appear, bearing separate male and female catkins on separate trees–as do other poplar trees. The male catkins are usually borne in great numbers and are quite thick, 4-8cm ($1\frac{1}{2}$-3in) long and greyish-brown, although they can appear yellowish when releasing pollen.

The catkins produce no scent or nectar and so are not visited by potential pollinating insects. Instead, pollination is carried out by the wind. After pollination the male catkins turn brown and soon drop off.

The female catkins are slimmer than the males and greenish with grey hairs and reddish bracts. They grow to about 4-6cm ($1\frac{1}{2}$-$2\frac{1}{2}$in) long and bear purple stigmas. After pollination they may lengthen and can be as long as 12cm (5in) by the time the seeds are fully ripe, which is in June. At this stage the female catkins appear whitish and release white woolly seeds. The seeds can often be seen carpeting the ground around female trees.

Versatile timber The timber of aspen, and indeed of other poplars, is not of particularly good quality, but it has been put to a number of different uses. The most important of these are the construction of various types of boxes

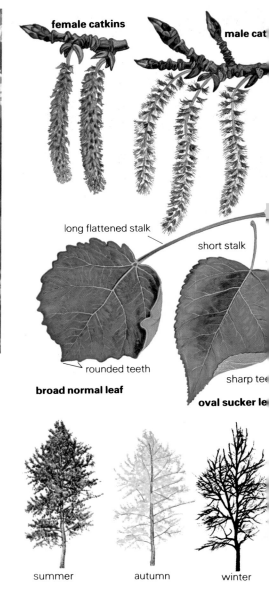

female catkins

male cat

long flattened stalk

short stalk

rounded teeth

broad normal leaf

sharp tee

oval sucker le

and the production of wood pulp. The wood is also used for making matches and, in the past, for arrows. Commercially, aspens and other poplars have the advantage over other trees of growing very rapidly in the right conditions.

Evil associations The aspen's almost constant leaf movement has been the source of much local folklore and legends throughout the range of the tree's distribution. Many have a biblical basis. In Wales it was said that the aspen was used to make the Cross and, for this reason, its leaves would never rest. In some areas of Scotland the aspen was regarded as evil because it was the only tree not to have bowed during Jesus' procession to the Crucifixion. As a result, people used to avoid using the wood. Indeed, feeling was so strong against the aspen in Scotland that some people used to throw stones at it.

There are similar legends elsewhere in Europe. In Germany, Jesus is said to have cursed the aspen because it would not acknowledge Him and, in parts of Russia, it was known as the tree of Judas.

The movement of the aspen's leaves seems to have led to associations with the sound of gossip and loose tongues, particularly (and rather chauvinistically) with the tongues of women. This association is found in parts of Scotland, where the tree is known as 'old wives' tongues'. In parts of Berkshire it was referred to as 'woman's tongue' and the Welsh name for the aspen, 'coed tafod merched', also refers to the same image, as does the Manx name of 'chengey ny mraane'.

Nowadays, it seems strange that such an attractive and pleasing tree should, in the past, have been the subject of so many evil associations and unpleasant stories. Without these, the aspen might perhaps have been more widely planted than it has been.

Above: Normal aspen leaves are short and broad with shallow rounded teeth, whereas sucker leaves are usually much larger and oval with sharper teeth. The difference can be seen clearly in a direct comparison (above right).

Aspen (*Populus tremula*). Native deciduous tree growing up to 20m (65ft) tall. More common in the north and west of Britain.

Below: Fruiting catkins dispersing their seeds.

summer

autumn

winter

Pedunculate and sessile oaks

Oak trees live longer than all other native trees and support a greater variety of wildlife than any other species in our islands.

From the top of its spreading crown to the ends of its roots, which can extend as far below the ground as its branches reach into the sky, the oak tree provides shelter and food for hundreds of different organisms. Like a crowded highrise block, the oak is inhabited at every level: birds and squirrels build nests in the crown, insects such as wasps, moths, beetles and weevils devour the leaves; ivy, mistletoe, lichens, mosses, algae and fungi invade the branches and bark; birds, insects and mammals feed on the acorns. Even the roots of the young oak are sought out by such insects as weevils and, as the oak lets in quite a lot of light through its leaves, flowering plants grow underneath it.

Below: Oak trees make up one tenth of all English woods. A fine specimen like this pedunculate oak may take up to 100 years to mature.

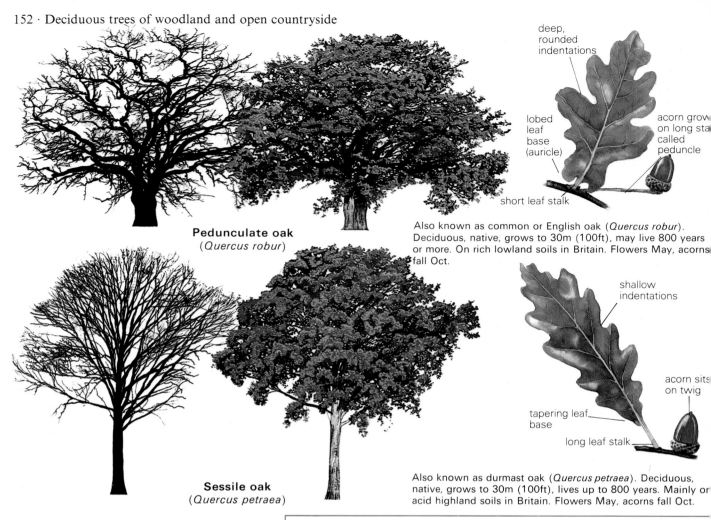

Pedunculate oak
(*Quercus robur*)

deep, rounded indentations

lobed leaf base (auricle)

acorn grows on long stalk called peduncle

short leaf stalk

Also known as common or English oak (*Quercus robur*). Deciduous, native, grows to 30m (100ft), may live 800 years or more. On rich lowland soils in Britain. Flowers May, acorns fall Oct.

shallow indentations

acorn sits on twig

tapering leaf base

long leaf stalk

Sessile oak
(*Quercus petraea*)

Also known as durmast oak (*Quercus petraea*). Deciduous, native, grows to 30m (100ft), lives up to 800 years. Mainly on acid highland soils in Britain. Flowers May, acorns fall Oct.

You may think that the oak must be quickly overpowered by this invasion of wildlife, but once a sapling becomes established the oak can live for up to 800 years, continuing to act as host to this multitude of creatures. In fact the oak has adapted itself so successfully in temperate regions that there are over 450 different species of oak in the world. Several of these oaks grow in Britain and Ireland, but only two, the pedunculate (also known as the common or English oak) and the sessile (durmast) oak are native to our islands. It is not always easy to tell the difference between them.

When it is growing in the open, the pedunculate oak is gnarled and tends to have lower, more horizontal and wider-spreading branches, so that the main trunk is hidden beneath a mass of boughs and leaves. The sessile oak has a straighter, less gnarled trunk, with branches growing from higher up.

You are likely to come across woods where both species of oak are growing, often among other trees. The huge forests of Epping and the New Forest are typical of such mixed woods. Here it is more difficult to distinguish the two species. For example, when the pedunculate oak competes for light with other trees it may lose some of its broad shape. To make it even more confusing, one species is frequently fertilized by the other and the result is a hybrid with characteristics of both species.

Close up If you get close to a true sessile or

Native or introduced?

Among the scores of different trees seen in Britain today only 35, including the sessile and pedunculate oaks, are native species (right), ie they spread into this country naturally, without the assistance of man. This was possible at the end of the last Ice Age—about 10,000 years ago—because at that time Britain still formed part of the European land mass.

To begin with only the hardiest plants, such as mosses and bilberry bushes could survive. But as the climate grew warmer trees like hazel, Scots pine, birch, elm and later oak established themselves.

Then about 7000 years ago Britain was separated from the rest of Europe. Melting glaciers caused the sea level to rise, flooding what is now the North Sea and English Channel. This watery barrier prevented further natural invasion by non-waterborne plants such as trees. So the trees that had managed to reach Britain by that time are our 35 native species.

The majority of different types now in Britain were introduced by man because they were useful or ornamental. When the Roman legionnaires settled here they brought the edible sweet chestnut. Remains of walnut trees have also been found in Roman villas. The Norway spruce, the familiar Christmas tree, arrived in the 16th century and the handsome cedar of Lebanon and the horse chestnut in the 17th century.

COMMON NATIVE TREES
Aspen (*Populus tremula*)
Bay willow (*Salix pentandra*)
Bird cherry (*Prunus padus*)
Black poplar (*Populus nigra*)
Box (*Buxux sempervirens*)
Common alder (*Alnus glutinosa*)
Common ash (*Fraxinus excelsior*)
Common beech (*Fagus sylvatica*)
Common pear (*Pyrus communis*)
Common yew (*Taxus baccata*)
Crab apple (*Malus sylvestris*)
Crack willow (*Salix fragilis*)
Downy birch (*Betula pubescens*)
Field maple (*Acer campestre*)
Goat willow (*Salix caprea*)
Grey poplar (*Populus canescens*)
Grey willow (*Salix cinerea*)
Hawthorn (*Crataegus monogyna*)
Hazel (*Corylus avellana*)
Holly (*Ilex aquifolium*)
Hornbeam (*Carpinus betulus*)
Juniper (*Juniperus communis*)
Midland hawthorn (*Crataegus laevigata*)
Pedunculate oak (*Quercus robur*)
Rowan (*Sorbus aucuparia*)
Scots pine (*Pinus sylvestris*)
Sessile oak (*Quercus petraea*)
Silver birch (*Betula pendula*)
Small-leaved lime (*Tilia cordata*)
Strawberry tree (*Arbutus unedo*)
Whitebeam (*Sorbus aria*)
White willow (*Salix alba*)
Wild cherry (*Prunus avium*)
Wild service tree (*Sorbus torminalis*)
Wych elm (*Ulmus glabra*)

pedunculate oak, however, you should be able to tell them apart quite easily.

The leaves of the pedunculate oak are pale green and virtually hairless, with two obvious 'ear-lobes' (auricles) at the base. They have deep, rounded indentations all round. In autumn, acorns grow on long stalks called peduncles—hence its name.

The leaves of the sessile oak are dark green, have no auricles and the indentations are not so deep. Leaves grow on long stalks and have a few hairs on the midrib of the underside. Unlike the pedunculate, the sessile acorns sit on the twig.

Pedunculate oak woodlands are the most common, and are usually found on heavy clay soils throughout lowland Britain. The pedunculate oaks at Bagshot Sands in Berkshire and Hovingham, North Yorkshire, are well worth a visit. Sessile woodlands are found in the highland areas of Britain and usually occur on shallow acid soils. The Birkrigg and Keskadale oaks south west of Keswick in the Lake District are excellent examples of 'pure' sessile woodlands.

Acorn bonanza Trees are flowering plants but many of their flowers are not spectacular, large or colourful and the oaks are no exception. Inconspicuous female catkins (flowers) are pollinated by the wind-carried pollen grains from male catkins (so large petals needed to attract insects for pollination are unnecessary). The oak's acorn crop varies from year to year—in a bumper year each tree can produce as many as 50,000 acorns. But few of the hundreds of thousands that fall every year grow into full-sized trees. Acorns start to form in early summer (the warmer the summer the larger the acorns), and then during a few weeks of early autumn they fall to form a dense carpet. They do not stay long on the ground for they are seized by hordes of birds and animals, either to be eaten or stored away for the winter. Jays and squirrels in particular bury them (sometimes quite a distance from the wood) and then forget about them. This is one of the ways the oak is spread across the countryside.

Valuable tree Oak woods covered much of Britain in medieval times and our ancestors quickly discovered that oak made good fuel. The sessile oak was also valued for its acorns. From the Middle Ages until the 18th century people drove their pigs into the oak woods on common land to feed on the abundant acorns. Indeed, one way of assessing and comparing the size of each manor's forest was to count the number of grazing pigs that could be supported. Such grazing rights still exist today in the New Forest in Hampshire.

Oak wood was used extensively for ship-building and many parks, such as Regents Park and Greenwich Park in London, were planted especially to supply the Royal and Merchant navies. Oak wood was used extensively for supporting beams in country cottages and is still used by builders today.

Above: Woods often contain both pedunculate and sessile oak trees, in which case it is often difficult to distinguish between the trees by shape alone. Closer inspection is necessary for identification.

Left: In May you can see these tassels of male catkins dangling on the twigs. Female flowers are hidden at the end of the new leaf shoots.

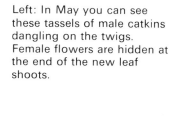

Left: Acorns fall in autumn and germinate if kept moist, not producing leaves until the spring. Seedlings grow 15cm (6in) in six months.

English and wych elms

The English elm (below)–for many people a symbol of the British countryside–is sadly now more of a memory than a reality due to the ravages of Dutch elm disease. However it is still in evidence, although the smaller wych elm, also described here, is more widely distributed.

The Elm family (Ulmaceae) comprises 200 species of tropical and temperate trees and shrubs whose best known members are the elms. There are about 20 species of elm, and all are large deciduous trees occurring mostly in the northern hemisphere.

Elm species are difficult to distinguish from one another, but the genus can be recognised easily by two obvious leaf characteristics: one half of each leaf is always longer than the other, and each leaf has double teeth round the margins. The shoots and flowers have less distinctive but equally important features. The leaf shoots are usually arranged in fives, and each is a different shape and size; the terminal bud of most species withers, and the largest leaf comes from the second bud.

The flowers, which appear before the leaves on the previous year's twigs, occur in clusters with the male and female parts together. Each flower is small with no sepals or petals, consisting of a bell-shaped, five-lobed cup of bracts containing the reproductive parts.

The six British species growing in our fields and hedgerows are difficult to recognise because they are similar to one another and most of them hybridise. (You won't find the differences easy to recognise.) In fact, some of the 11 recorded British hybrids are better known than their parent species–it is rare to see a true species in the British countryside.

Elms are best considered in four major groups–the common or English elm, the wych elm, the smooth-leaved elms and the hybrids, the best known of which is the Dutch elm.

The common elm is considered by many people to be the unique symbol of the English countryside and is found elsewhere probably only in Brittany and south-east France. It is predominantly a native of southern England and prefers well-drained valleys in areas such as the Midlands, the Home Counties and the south-west. You rarely see it in the drier parts of eastern Kent and East Anglia where other species, notably the smooth elms, are more common.

The common elm is a beautiful domed tree which has been immortalised in Constable's 1826 painting, 'The Cornfield'. The mature tree has a massive, straight bole extending well into the crown, and a few large ascending branches. The main limbs diffuse into dense, billowing profusions of curled shoots, giving a characteristic overall dark green or blackish appearance which you do not find with other elms.

The bark is dark brown and deeply fissured, forming large, squarish plates. Suckers flourish from buds hidden beneath the bark, especially at the base of the trunk, and crowd around the middle of the tree to give a distinct skirted appearance. The common elm also produces root suckers which can grow at a surprising distance

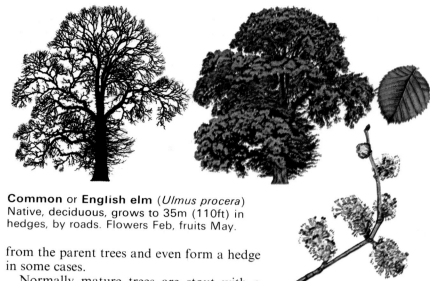

Common or **English elm** (*Ulmus procera*) Native, deciduous, grows to 35m (110ft) in hedges, by roads. Flowers Feb, fruits May.

from the parent trees and even form a hedge in some cases.

Normally mature trees are stout with a long densely leafy trunk and billowing crowns representing about a third of the height. However, many trees are cropped by hedge-cutters or foresters along the trunk, giving a naked 'lollipop' shape, rather than the characteristic egg-shape.

In all members of the elm family the flowers are clustered on the one-year-old twigs and appear before the leaves. They are dark red, profuse and regular. The fruits are small and rounded, each one appearing as a dry or fleshy notched membrane surrounding a single seed. Some botanists think the seeds are sterile and cannot germinate, and that the trees proliferate almost entirely from suckers. In reality the seeds lose their germinating capacity after a few days, and do not emerge through the seed coat unless they land on bare soil.

The leaves of the elm are distinctinctive. They are about 10cm (4in) long and 5cm (2in) wide and vary in shape according to

Above: The flowers of the common elm and (below) the fruits. The flowers appear in very early spring, before the leaves.

Below: You can distinguish the wych elm by its fruits and leaf stalks: the seeds are always in the middle of the fruits, the leaf stalk is always less than 7mm ($\frac{1}{4}$in) long, and the longer part of the leaf base never overlaps the leaf stalk.

their position on the shoot. They emerge from slender, reddish brown shoots that appear in the hedgerows in April, while those on larger trees appear in May and remain on the tree until November or December.

The wych elm can be recognised by a number of characters (see photo caption). Mature wych elms are not as tall as common elms and grow into irregular rounded shapes up to 45m (150ft) high. The lower branches start to arch from near the base of the trunk and the upper branches appear twisted, growing tortuously into the upper crown. The dull grey or blackish bark is smooth when young but becomes brownish-grey, fissured and ridged in mature specimens. The bark is another clue to the identity of mature trees: it appears twisted and parallel-ridged, but never deeply furrowed like that of its close relatives.

The flowers have brightly coloured stamens with crimson or purple anthers and white filaments. The leaves may be up to 16cm (6in) long, on very short stalks. They are bright green and rough above, and downy and rough on the underside.

The wych elm is distributed throughout the British Isles and is the only elm species in Scotland. It is sparse in the West Country and

Wych elm (*Ulmus glabra*) Native, deciduous, grows to 45m (150ft) in woods, hedgerows and beside streams. Flowers Feb, fruits May.

central Ireland, but becomes the most prevalent elm species north of the Midlands and is common in Wales.

In Scotland the wych elm is a woodland species, growing especially well beside streams. In England it is more of an isolated tree and is often removed wholesale to make way for conifer plantations. In East Anglia you often see it growing in hedgerows.

Popular cultivars Wych elm cultivars have been planted in large gardens and town parks; especially popular weeping cultivars are 'Pendula' and 'Camperdown'.

Above: The flowers of the wych elm and (below) the fruits. The green fruits hang in conspicuous bunches in spring.

Dutch elm disease

'Dutch elm disease' is a real misnomer, since it is neither restricted to Dutch elms nor did it originate in Holland. The disease, a fungus infection affecting all elms, was discovered in France in 1818, identified in Holland in 1919, and probably originated in Asia. It was first noticed in the British Isles in 1927 and surveys showed that it was then widespread. The first outbreaks declined, and although 20% of the elms were killed, many partly diseased trees recovered, so the landscape was not damaged too much. In the late 1960s a new killer version of Dutch elm disease hit the British tree population. This epidemic has been so severe that the results have been headline news throughout the 1970s. This time the effect on the landscape has been devastating and the change irreversible. Latest Forestry Commission surveys show that more than 11 million trees have been killed out of a total estimate of $22\frac{1}{2}$ million— more than half our elms have been removed from the countryside. Interestingly, the Forestry Commission surveys have enhanced our knowledge of the distribution of the different elm groups. Disease incidence is greatest in areas with dense elm populations; wych elms and the smooth elms have escaped relatively lightly because of their sporadic distribution. The highest incidence of Dutch elm disease occurs in Sussex, Essex, the Severn-Avon valley and Hampshire, where the common elm was most widespread.

Smooth and hybrid elms

Apart from the English and wych elms, you can see four smooth elms, and also many elm hybrids, cultivars and clones, growing in various localised areas of the English countryside.

There are four species of smooth-leaved elms in the British countryside–the smooth elm, the Coritanian elm, the Cornish elm and the Plot elm, and a number of elm hybrids as well.

The smooth elm is so-called because it has leaves that are smooth on both sides. It is an erect tree, with a domed open canopy, and is much broader and more spreading than the English elm (see page 154). The long branches are ascending and sinuous, and the shoots are pendulous, particularly at the edges of the tree. The flowers appear in late May, which

Wheatley elm (Ulmus sarniensis). Deciduous, native to south-east England, particularly by the coast.

is later in spring than those of other species in this group. The smooth elm is one of the most widespread elm species: it is a native of Kent and East Anglia and also of south and central Europe, south-west Asia and North Africa.

The Coritanian elm is also a spreading tree with an open crown and ascending branches. You can recognise it by the leaves which are leathery, markedly asymmetrical, bright green, shiny above and pale below, and hairless except for occasional tufts of hair in the leaf axils. Its name comes from the area around Leicestershire once occupied by the ancient Britons – the Coritanae – but it is actually known to have a sporadic distribution in East Anglia, Northamptonshire, Essex, Cambridgeshire and Nottinghamshire.

The Plot elm is named after a certain Dr Plot who wrote a 'Natural History of Oxfordshire' in 1677. He described a cultivated avenue tree with narrow leaves from Hanwell, near Banbury in Oxfordshire, which was later to become his namesake.

The Plot elm is a plume-like tree with arching, leading shoots and pendulous branches. It has very small leaves which appear to be smooth on both sides, although in fact they are lightly hairy. This species has the unique ability to produce proliferating short shoots with many small leaves that have less obvious teeth than other species. Today the Plot elm is extremely rare and is mainly found in the Trent Valley near Newark in Nottinghamshire and the Witham valley in Essex.

The Cornish elm often has a flat, wind-cut crown and in Cornwall is sculptured into a variety of shapes. The leaves are usually rather narrow, slightly leathery, somewhat concave and more or less folded. It is perhaps the most distinctive species of all the elms. Cornish elms are an important part of the west country skyline. Because many neighbouring trees have been felled, and the Cornish light is strong, many Cornish elms produce numerous shoots up and down the stems, giving the trees a clothed appearance.

Hybrid elms Although there are six important elm species in this country, most of

our trees are in fact hybrids. Elms used to be widely planted, and there are many natural crosses, cultivated crosses, crosses between natural trees and introduced trees, and even hybrids between hybrids.

Without doubt, the most important is the so-called Dutch elm, which is a group name for a number of hybrids and clones derived from crosses between the Wych elm (page 154) and the smooth elms. Dutch elms are said to have originated in Belgium and are today found in England and various parts of Europe, but are, strangely enough, absent from Holland. They have the overall appearance of the Wych elm, but are usually larger, with a more open crown. They have large leaves like the Wych elm but without the 'ear' at the base. Two cultivars, 'Hollandica' and 'Vegeta' are widely planted in southern England. 'Hollandica', which can be distinguished by the corky, flanged, stems of the suckers, is a victim of Dutch elm disease.

One of the most interesting complex hybrids is the Jersey elm, a fertile hybrid between the hybrid Dutch elm and the Cornish elm which has the characters of four different species. It has a conical crown and although it looks similar to the Cornish elm it is less prone to sculpturing by the wind. Because of its attractive shape it is highly favoured as a park and avenue tree. It has a more easterly distribution than the Cornish elm and occurs in south-east England and north-west France.

Above and opposite: **Cornish elm** *(U. angustifolia).* Deciduous, native of the West Country.

Elm wood

Because so many elm trees have been cut down as a result of Dutch elm disease, elm wood is now plentiful and has come back into fashion. It has been used for centuries: the furniture industry, based at High Wycombe, favoured elm for pieces that needed to be pinned or glued. Elm timber has been used where heavy solid wood is required. The marine trade particularly finds it useful because it does not rot below water. The keels of wooden boats, piles for wooden bridges, lock gates, and today, the centre board in the hulls of wooden narrow boats are all built of elm. Despite a glut due to Dutch elm disease, elm does not have as wide a usage as it perhaps could. The best woods are used in veneers on chipboard, kitchen fittings and coffins, and the trees that do not form perfect timber are sent to factories to be pulped for brown paper manufacture.

Smooth elm *(U. carpinifolia).* Deciduous, native in southern England.

Coritanian elm *(U. coritana).* Deciduous, native in eastern areas of England.

Plot elm *(U. plotii).* Deciduous, a rare native of Trent and Witham valleys.

Dutch elm *(U. x hollandica).* Hybrid, widely planted in southern England.

Rhododendrons

Britain's wild rhododendrons are at their most beautiful in spring when they burst into flower—indeed, the word 'rhododendron' comes from the Greek for 'rose-tree'.

Ever since the rhododendron was first introduced to Britain more than two hundred years ago it has been one of our most popular shrubs, especially for its beautiful showy flowers that open in spring. Today, more than a hundred species of rhododendron have been introduced to Britain but only two of these have become naturalised to any degree—*Rhododendron ponticum* and *Rhododendron luteum*. The first of these to appear in this country, and still the most common rhododendron in the wild, is *R. ponticum*.

Eighteenth century arrival *R. ponticum* was discovered around eastern Turkey, in the area now known as Armenia but which used to be called Pontus—hence *ponticum*. The shrub was introduced here several times during the 18th century and, by 1780, was on sale in nurseries. It was soon widely planted in woods to provide cover for game before being superseded during the following century by other more brightly coloured rhododendrons from Asia.

It was soon discovered that this species of rhododendron flourished in open woodland

Above: *Rhododendron ponticum* is naturalised in the Derbyshire Dales. The shrub can grow in the open but it prefers sheltered sites, such as woodland. This is because its flowers are easily damaged by frost and by being warmed too quickly by direct sunlight.

Rhododendron ponticum.
Evergreen shrub native to eastern Turkey. Introduced to Britain in the 18th century and now naturalised. Height to 3m (10ft).

Right: Young rhododendron leaves unfurling. The new season's leaves appear in May, before the flowers open.

and it quickly became naturalised in this country. In fact, it proved to be invasive, spreading by means of suckers and seeds. Burnt ground and fire-breaks are rapidly colonized, and rhododendron seedlings appear in profusion on soil that has just been prepared for a new conifer plantation.

To make matters worse, once *R. ponticum* is established it is almost impossible to eradicate. Weedkillers have no lasting effect because the mature bush regenerates from its stem, even though its branches and foliage have been killed. Digging the plant out is a waste of time because the smallest piece of root left in the ground grows again to form a new seedling. It is not surprising that this rhododendron is so unpopular with foresters, for it monopolises the undergrowth of a wood and prevents other saplings from growing.

Evergreen leaves Identifying *R. ponticum* is easy, especially in winter because most shrubs are bare at this time of year whereas *R. ponticum* is evergreen. It is a large shrub, reaching as high as 3m (10ft), with a multitude of greyish woody stems joined at the base. The leaves are elliptical and large—6-12cm (2½-5in) long. They are dark green above and paler green below; like so many other evergreen leaves, they have a leathery texture. They are arranged spirally around the tips of the twigs, each leaf being positioned so that it receives the maximum amount of sunlight.

The flowers open in May or June on compact racemes. Each purple flower is about 5cm (2in) in diameter. The fruit consists of capsule about 1.5cm (⅔in) long and usually divided into five sections that split to release numerous small seeds.

Hybrid rhododendrons Few specimens of *R. ponticum* originate from the pure species. Most are hybrids between *R. ponticum* and one of two other species—*R. maximum* and *R. catawbiense*. These two species are closely related to *R. ponticum*, even though they are both native to North America. The former species was introduced during the 18th century and the latter during the century after.

It is often possible to determine the parent

Acid-loving plants

Many plants grow well only on an acid soil; on a chalky, alkaline soil they fail to develop a proper root system and die. Such plants include bog myrtle and gorse, but the most familiar examples are the members of the heather family (Ericaceae), which include rhododendrons, bilberry and heather itself.

Experiments have shown that it is the alkalinity of the soil (ie its high pH level) rather than the high concentration of calcium from the chalk that kills the plants. It seems that, as the pH of the soil increases, acid-loving plants become incapable of extracting certain vital elements, such as potassium, iron and phosphorus, and die of malnutrition.

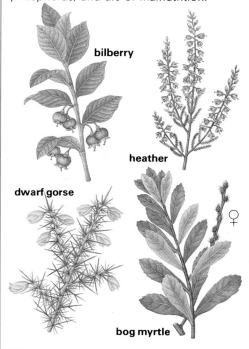

bilberry

heather

dwarf gorse

bog myrtle

entage of a particular hybrid bush from details of its floral structure. For instance, the three species have quite different ovaries, those of *R. ponticum* being hairless, those of *R. maximum* being hairy and those of *R. catawbiense* being covered in a brown felt-like material. By examining the ovaries of a hybrid bush it is often possible to tell which species were its parents.

The flowers differ in structure for, although they are all purple or pinkish-purple, they have greenish or brownish spots on *R. ponticum*, and yellow spots on *R. maximum*. There are also differences in the shape and size of the bush. *R. catawbiense* grows to the same height as *R. ponticum* (3m/10ft) but it is a much broader shrub, being especially prone to suckering to form dense thickets. *R. maximum*, on the other hand, is much taller than either of the other two species and can reach a height of 9m (30ft).

Yellow-flowering rhododendron Although the *ponticum* hybrids are by far the most common form of naturalised rhododendron, another very different species has managed to establish itself in some areas of the country. This is *Rhododendron luteum*, a deciduous shrub with stiff branches that grow to a height of 3m (10ft). The leaves are bluish, slim and pointed and about 5-13cm (2-5in) long. The flowers are bright yellow and very fragrant. They open in May before the leaves appear. The shrub is particularly attractive in autumn, when the leaves turn red, orange or purple.

This rhododendron was introduced to Britain from the Caucasus Mountains at the end of the 18th century. It is still widely cultivated and used in hybridisation since it is much hardier than many other species of rhododendron. Weak-growing azaleas are often grafted on to its rootstock. This has helped *R. luteum* to spread, since suckers growing from the rootstock are frequently stronger than the hybrid. A similar effect occurs with *R. ponticum*, since it too is used for rootstocks. More than one neglected garden, which was once a riot of colour from different rhododendron hybrids, is now swamped with yellow *R. luteum* and purple *R. ponticum*.

Above: The flowers of *R. ponticum* appear in May and June, clustered in large flowerheads known as racemes. Each flower is purple or pinkish-purple with brownish (sometimes greenish) spots inside. At its centre are ten stamens—tipped white here—and a single pistil tipped pink or orange.

Below: A rhododendron bush in its preferred habitat of open woodland. The evergreen leaves of rhododendron form an impenetrable cover year-round, blocking out the sunlight from anything that attempts to grow beneath.

maple-like leaves

spreading crown

Wild service tree

Britain's broad-leaved woods are dominated by a few familiar species, such as the oak, beech and birch. But scattered among these are some rare and little-known trees, including the oddly named wild service tree – a species once widespread in this country.

Above: In woodland, wild services usually remain small trees, though in an open glade they can reach a good height.

Wild service tree (*Sorbus torminalis*). Rare native deciduous tree. Found in woodland of south-east England. Height 27m (90ft).

The wild service tree is one of the few trees that are native to Britain. It is closely related to two other native trees, the whitebeam and the rowan, all being members of the same genus, *Sorbus*. Yet, while these two are both common and familiar trees, the service tree is now a rare tree in the wild.

Declining numbers There is good evidence to suggest that, up to the end of the Middle Ages, the wild service was abundant in many woods in southern England. Since then, however, its numbers have been steadily declining. This is partly due to forests being cleared to make way for agriculture. At the same time man has interfered increasingly with the remaining woodland so that, whenever a wood was cleared and then replanted, the wild service was unlikely to be given a place in the new plantations since it was not a particularly useful species.

You may wonder how similarly 'useless' trees like birch, holly and hawthorn have managed to survive. After all, they too are unlikely to have been planted in woods by man, yet they are still common enough there. The difference lies in the fact that, while most trees spread themselves easily by seed, the wild service tree lacks this ability. It produces large quantities of berries, yet very few of its seeds germinate to produce young trees. The reason for this failure is not known for certain but it may well be due to our climate. Perhaps, at some time in our past when our summers were warmer and our winters colder, the wild service was well adapted to the environment here. But the generally cool damp summers and mild wet winters of today seem to inhibit the production of viable wild service seed.

Where to see them The inability of the wild service tree to spread by seed means that it can now be seen only in old undisturbed woodland. Here, its main method of spreading is to send up sucker shoots from its roots a little distance from the main trunk. It therefore tends to occur in small groups.

The best places to see a wild service tree today are in the Weald of Kent, Sussex and Surrey, and also in south Essex. Elsewhere, it is thinly scattered through southern and south-west England, parts of the Midlands and south Wales. In northern England it is very rare, in Scotland almost totally absent and in Ireland entirely so.

Despite its present rarity, the wild service tree grows on a wild range of soils, which partly explains why it was so common in the days when our woodland was untouched. In south-east England it flourishes on clay soils, some of which are quite acid, as in south

Essex. Similarly, in south-west Wales it grows on acid soils in humus-rich valley bottoms. Yet in the Bristol area and the lower Wye valley it is found on rocky limestone woods, even rooting itself in crevices on limestone cliffs.

Handsome and shapely Most specimens of the wild service are small trees between 5m (16ft) and 12m (40ft) in height. But a few grow to be much taller – up to 27m (90ft) high with a girth of 3m (10ft). Such fine specimens are rare today but were presumably commonplace in our woodlands long ago.

When it has room to spread fully, as it does in a glade, the service develops a wide crown and long lower branches, making a handsome and shapely tree.

Its bark is a dark grey-brown, sometimes reddish-brown, and flaky with shallow vertical and horizontal fissures.

Leaves, flowers and fruits Like all other members of the genus *Sorbus*, the wild service is a deciduous tree. The leaves are borne alternately on the twigs and are about 10cm (4in) long. They can be distinguished from the leaves of other *Sorbus* species by their deeply lobed, maple-like shape. Their upper surfaces are glossy dark green and their lower surfaces are a paler shining green; the young leaves are slightly downy underneath. In common with the leaves of other *Sorbus* trees, the margins are finely toothed.

In late May or early June, the wild service bears clusters of white flowers, resembling a loose-headed spray of hawthorn, except that the flowers on the wild service are fewer and larger.

In autumn, the flowers are followed by clusters of round or pear-shaped brown berries covered with pale spots called lenticels. At this time of year, the leaves turn bright yellow, red or orange.

Uses for wood and berries The wild service tree is so rare today that its wood is seldom used. However, being a slow-growing, long-lived tree, its timber is very hard and close-grained, and was once employed for making cog wheels.

The berries of wild service were once a popular food source. In the days when sweeter, foreign fruits were not readily available, the berries were sold in markets throughout southern England. Their main uses were for making into jams and marmalades, and possibly also into alcoholic drinks. They have a bitter taste, however, and before being eaten raw they need to be 'bletted', that is, allowed to become half-rotten.

Why 'service'? The word 'service' is a corruption of the Latin word 'sorbus'. In south-east England it is more commonly known as the chequer tree. The reason for this name is obscure, but it may be a reference to the spots on the berries or to the bark splitting into squares. Being a native tree there are many other local names for it, including 'serves', 'lizzory' and 'lessory'.

Above: In the autumn, wild service trees are bedecked with clusters of brown spotted berries. In the days before sweeter, foreign fruits were readily available, wild service berries were sold in the markets of southern England to be made into jams or eaten raw.

Right: Wild service trees flower in late May or early June, small white five-petalled flowers appearing in loose flowerheads at the ends of twigs.

Below: In parts of south-east England, the wild service is known as the chequer tree, a name that may derive from the fact that the bark in older trees often splits into small squares.

Whitebeam

Anyone who walks the steeply wooded slopes of the South Downs in high summer will recognise the distinctive foliage of the whitebeam (below). This compact tree shimmers from green to silver as the leaves turn with the wind.

In the wild the whitebeam is found chiefly on the chalk of central, south and south eastern England. One of its main strongholds is the Chilterns where it grows amid scrub thickets, in open woods and clearings and along hedgerows. The tree is also scattered in limestone districts elsewhere and is often planted in parks and gardens and along city streets because it is tolerant of shade and pollution.

Appearance The smooth brown twigs bear large, oval, greenish buds which break into leaf in late April. A striking feature of this tree is that when the young leaves emerge they grow vertically from the bud irrespective of the angle of the twig, and are held stiffly up before unfolding. This

is in marked contrast to most native trees in which the young leaves at first hang limply from the open buds.

The expanded leaves, 5-12cm (2-5in) long, are oval in shape and borne on short stalks. The upper surface is darkish green and the underside is densely felted with white hairs that give the foliage its silvery appearance.

The blossom follows in May or June. The white, five-petalled flowers, each about 1.5cm ($\frac{3}{4}$in) across, are clustered in loose bunches on green stalks which, like the leaves, are clothed in fine white hairs. Insect visitors, and especially flies, are responsible for pollination. The fruits which are up to 1.5cm ($\frac{3}{4}$in) long, ripen by October to a rich shiny scarlet and hang heavily from the twigs. Each fruit contains two hard seeds which are widely dispersed in the droppings of birds that feed on the bright red berries. The berries are also eaten by squirrels, hedgehogs and voles.

In Lancashire and Cumbria the berries are called chess-apples. The flesh is yellow and the young berries have a rough, sharp taste, but the flavour is said to improve slightly with age. Although not poisonous to man, the berries are not recommended eating.

The wood is hard and pale yellow, but the tree seldom provides a useful volume of timber so has only been used for items turned on lathes; it also makes useful firewood.

Hybrids The whitebeam is tremendously variable. The name *Sorbus aria* is one that encompasses a large group of microspecies which differ slightly in flower form and in the size and shape of the leaves and berries. Some of these come about as a result of hybridisation with other native *Sorbus* species.

Commonly planted hybrids of *Sorbus* species include the bastard service tree which is a cross between rowan and the service tree of Fontainebleau. The service tree of Fontainebleau is itself a hybrid of whitebeam and and the wild service tree. The bastard service tree is a fairly common tree of city streets and parks.

Above: **Whitebeam** *(Sorbus aria)*, native, deciduous, grows to 20m (65ft), mainly on chalk and limestone soils in southern England. Flowers May-June, fruits Sept.

Above: Whitebeam gets its name from the white underside of the leaves. It can be distinguished from other species of *Sorbus* such as rowan because the leaves are undivided.

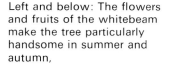

Left and below: The flowers and fruits of the whitebeam make the tree particularly handsome in summer and autumn,

Hawthorn

Of all our native trees, the common hawthorn has contributed most to the patchwork appearance of the British rural landscape. It forms dense thorny hedges and thickets, teeming with wildlife, and its glorious bloom in May proclaims the oncoming summer.

There are two species of hawthorn in the British Isles, the common hawthorn and the Midland hawthorn. The common hawthorn is abundant throughout the country, except in the far north of Scotland. It thrives on most soils, in open habitats such as hillsides, neglected pastures, on commons and in woodland and most hedgerows. Left to itself it grows in dense thickets and forms a distinct habitat during the natural transformation of grassland into woodland. In open, exposed places, especially around the coast, its growth becomes stunted and shaped by the strong prevailing winds.

The Midland hawthorn is not nearly so widespread and is more or less confined to the east Midlands and south-east England, where you often find it in the shrub layer of oak woods. You can distinguish between the two species by looking at the leaves and flowers.

The leaves of the common hawthorn have distinct lobes and indentations that may reach as far as the midrib. The tips of the lobes tend to be serrated, and the whole leaf is longer than it is broad. The leaves of the Midland hawthorn are more rounded in outline, with small lobes and shallow indentations, and are broader than they are long. The leaves of both hawthorns have a nutty flavour; they used to be eaten by children and were often called 'bread and cheese'. The foliage is devoured by huge numbers of insects, especially the caterpillars of various moths such as the winter and the burnished brass. In autumn the leaves turn in colour to rich tints of red, orange and yellow before the wind and frost strip the branches bare.

Blossom Hawthorn blossoms in May— hence the familiar name, May—shortly after the leaves have unfurled. The trees soon become smothered in clusters of white, and occasionally pale pink, flowers. (Some of the crimson and double-flowered varieties that are common in city streets have been introduced.) Common hawthorn flowers have only one style (female part) and seed which develops later inside the red berry. Midland hawthorn flowers have two or occasionally three styles and seeds. Often the two species hybridise and then both types of flower

Opposite: Hawthorn in bloom in May. An old country rhyme recommends the tree as protection for man and beast in thunderstorms:
Beware the oak—
it courts the stroke.
Beware the ash—
it courts the flash.
Creep under the thorn—
it will save you from harm.

Right: The pink anthers of hawthorn shrivel and turn brown after shedding their pollen.

Common hawthorn (*Crataegus monogyna*). Deciduous, native, grows as a hedge or a shrub; may reach 10m (40ft) as a tree. Found in woodland and scrub. Fruits Sept.

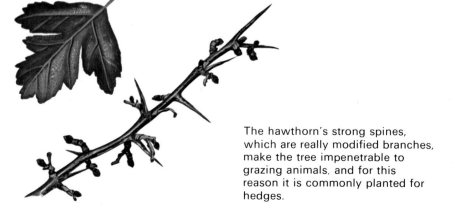

The hawthorn's strong spines, which are really modified branches, make the tree impenetrable to grazing animals, and for this reason it is commonly planted for hedges.

appear on the same tree. The hybrids are fertile.

The berries, known as haws, start to turn red in late August and provide a rich splash of colour along wayside hedgerows well into autumn. However it is not unusual to find bunches of berries which appear not to have ripened at all; these remain yellow-green.

Haws last well into winter and are a vital source of food for birds, especially during cold spells. Blackbirds, thrushes and large flocks of redwings and fieldfares–winter visitors from northern Europe–are just a few of the species that can be seen along hedgerows, settling to pluck the berries from their stalks.

Right: A dormouse tucking in to ripe haws. The carbohydrate in the flesh of the berries helps the animal to fatten up for winter hibernation.

Below: Hawthorn bearing typical red berries in autumn in Yorkshire. This species is one of the first colonizers of scrubland and uncultivated areas.

Birds are essential to the spread of hawthorns. The seeds, embodied in the berries' flesh, have a tough coat which prevents the pip being digested by the birds which eventually drop them some distance from the parent tree.

Living fences Common hawthorn has been used for about 2000 years as natural barbed fencing. Its tangle of thorny branches is an ideal barrier for enclosing livestock. Indeed, the Anglo-Saxon word is *haegthorn*, which means hedge-tree. Signs of defensive hawthorn hedges have been found round the edge of excavated Roman forts. Evidently their function was to keep out marauding native warriors bent on driving the occupying army from their homeland.

During the last 300 years hundreds of miles of hawthorn hedge were planted as an alternative to stone walls, ditches or hurdles. In this century they have increasingly been grubbed out or replaced by fencing that requires less maintenance.

Trees Unmolested by hedge-cutters, hawthorns grow into medium-sized trees with dense, rounded crowns. They live for a surprisingly long time: their natural span is usually around 100 years but specimens that have reached the ripe old age of 300 are not uncommon. In old age the trunks become gnarled, twisted and furrowed. Constant rubbing by cattle tends to polish the bark leaving it with rather a glossy sheen. The trees' slow growth produces very hard wood. Hawthorn logs burn well, but curiously this tough timber is otherwise little used, except occasionally for tool-handles and walking sticks.

May Day During the celebrations of the arrival of summer, maypoles were erected on village greens and in town squares and decorated with garlands of May blossom. However it is traditionally thought to be unlucky to bring sprigs of flowering hawthorn indoors. Superstition holds that it may result in a death in the family.

Quite recently it was discovered that one of the chemicals that make up the flowers' sweet scent is also produced during the decay of corpses. Small wonder, then, that people were reluctant to bring the 'smell of death' into their homes. It seems likely that the superstition dates back to outbreaks of the Great Plague when so many dead lay unburied.

Legendary thorn The most famous hawthorn in England is the Glastonbury thorn. One legend surrounding this unusual tree goes back to the time when that part of Somerset called Avalon was surrounded by sea. Joseph of Arimathea was supposed to have landed there during his pilgrimage from the Holy Lands of Palestine. Resting after climbing a particularly steep hill, Joseph thrust his thorn staff into the ground where it miraculously took root and flowered immediately.

Rowan

The rowan (below) has something to offer for most of the year. Its graceful foliage emerges in spring, splashes of white blossom appear in summer, and in autumn and early winter the tree is decorated with dense hanging bunches of bright red berries.

The rowan is a native tree most usually associated with high country. Indeed, it is also known as mountain ash, but is totally unrelated to the common ash (see page 206) and differs in all respects apart from its compound leaves.

In the British Isles rowan grows at altitudes up to 950m (3115ft) which is higher than any other native broadleaved tree. It also occurs throughout the lowlands, favouring sandy or gravelly soils which tend to be rather acid. On bleak mountainsides it forms a stunted, windswept tree only a few metres tall, but on the more sheltered lowlands it can reach 20m (65ft) in height. Because its berries are devoured by birds and the seeds widely

dispersed in their droppings, the rowan appears in a variety of habitats including woodland, scrubby hillsides, heaths and hedgerows.

Multi-purpose species The rowan's versatile form has, not surprisingly, made it a firm favourite with landscape gardeners. It is widely planted in parks and gardens, on motorway embankments and golf courses, for it stands up well to the stresses of urban life. Foresters have also used it as a nurse tree in plantations of hard woods when the light shade of its foliage promotes the growth of the hard wood saplings – until they eventually outgrow it and form a close canopy which is often too dark underneath for the rowan to survive for long.

Handsome appearance The slim trunk is covered with smooth slate-grey bark which is marked with shallow horizontal scars. The limbs tend to grow upwards to form a rather loosely branched crown which allows plenty of light through and so does not appreciably suppress plant growth beneath. The twigs are pale brown, sometimes tinged with violet. The alternate buds, 10-15cm (4-6in) long, and the brownish-purple bud scales are fringed with fine silky white hairs.

The foliage unfurls towards the end of April. The leaf stalks, 10-25cm (4-10in) long, bear from five to eight opposite pairs of leaflets and are tipped with a single terminal leaflet. Each leaflet has serrated edges and is

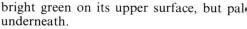

Above: Rowan berries are rich in Vitamin C and can be made into delicious jelly that goes well with game.

Below: Rowan flowers have a sweet, musty smell, rather like hawthorn blossom.

bright green on its upper surface, but pale underneath.

Rowan leaves fall relatively early in the autumn, but not before they have acquired colourful autumn tones of yellow and orange.

The rowan blossoms in May or June, producing dense, flat-topped inflorescences made up of many tiny flowers, each with five creamy white petals. Although the individual flowers are very small, because they are tightly packed together they are conspicuous and attract a variety of prospective pollinators, including flies, beetles and bees.

After fertilisation the flowers are succeeded by green berries. They ripen by September and provide a glorious display of bright, shiny fruits varying in colour from orange to scarlet. Generally this attractive sight is short-lived, because birds find the fruit irresistible and soon strip the trees bare.

Blackbirds, thrushes, fieldfares and red wings all take their share. The handsome waxwing, a winter visitor from northern Europe, which in some years migrates here in large numbers, is particularly fond of rowan berries. It has been reported that bird sown rowan seeds germinate the following spring, whereas normally they remain dormant in the soil for 18 months. This may be due to the abrasive action of the bird's gut which acts upon the seed-coat, allowing moisture to enter, so germination occurs sooner than usual when the berries fall to the ground.

The rowan's Latin name, *Sorbus aucuparia*, means 'fowler's service tree', which refers to the past use of the berries as bait by bird trappers. In some districts the berries are known as 'hen-drunks', because chickens apparently became intoxicated after gorging themselves on the fallen fruits. In Wales the berries were fermented in ale to produce an alcoholic drink with similar effects.

To the human palate the fruits have a
ther harsh, sour taste, but they are still
ed to make jelly that goes well with game
shes such as hare and venison.

Magical tree The rowan has a special place
our folklore, especially in northern regions.
any of the superstitions connected with it
iginated from ancient Nordic visitors from
andinavia. The word rowan is probably
rived from the Norse *runa*, which means a
arm, and relates to the tree's reputation
r warding off evil.

In Scotland and Ireland the rowan's
agical powers were greatly revered. A
anch was always nailed to cattle sheds to
otect the animals from witchcraft and
rcery. Similarly Highland crofters planted
rowan tree outside their homes to keep
tches at bay. Indeed, another local name
r the tree is witch-wood, and an old rhyme
gs its praises:

Rowan tree and red thread,
Hold the witches all in dread.

In Wales, Ireland and some northern
counties of England, the rowan was often
planted in churchyards. This was to keep the
dead in their graves and prevent any ghosts
appearing in the neighbourhood.

The wood is dense and strong and was
valued by crofters living in the sparsely
wooded glens of Scotland and Ireland.

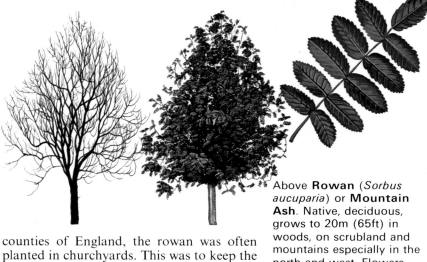

Above **Rowan** (*Sorbus
aucuparia*) or **Mountain
Ash**. Native, deciduous,
grows to 20m (65ft) in
woods, on scrubland and
mountains especially in the
north and west. Flowers
May, fruits September
onwards.

Below: The rowan in full
fruit growing on Dartmoor.

Field and Norway maples

The field maple is our only native maple species and it is rather a small tree; but what it lacks in size it more than makes up for by the brilliance of its fine autumn foliage which turns to vivid shades of golden yellow.

The field maple usually grows in hedgerow either as a small tree with a neat rounde crown, or chopped right back to a bush form ing part of the hedge itself. It is also four among hillside scrub, at the edges of wood and in the shrub layer of oakwoods where the past it was usually coppiced. It grov best on chalk and limestone soils and is th widespread in southern and eastern Englan but less common in western and northe districts. In Scotland and Ireland it has bee introduced and has a rather scanty distrib tion.

Britain's native maple The trunk is cover with pale greyish-brown bark which, older trees, is cracked by a network

ssures. The winter twigs are light brown and cored along their length by shallow furrows. Older twigs tend to develop prominent longitudinal ridges of corky bark. The small brown buds are carried in opposite pairs along the length of the twig, and they break open in early May to release the young leaves.

The fresh young leaves hang limp and are pale yellow-green with a coating of fine hairs. Their upper surface has a noticeably glossy sheen. Later, as the leaves expand, they stiffen and turn a darker shade of green. The leaf-blade is divided into three or five distinct lobes which are separated by deep indentations. Each lobe has bluntly toothed edges and a rounded tip.

Leaf size can vary enormously: the leaves on a regularly trimmed hedge are generally about half the size of those on free-growing trees. The leaves are borne on leaf-stalks 4-8cm (1½-3in) long which are light green or streaked with red. If you cut the leaf stalk it bleeds a white milky sap.

The field maple flowers shortly after the foliage has unfurled. A loose cluster of 10-20 greenish-yellow flowers is supported on a stalk that grows upwards between the terminal pair of leaves on each twig. Each flower has five green petals surrounding eight stamens, which are tipped with yellow pollen-bearing anthers.

Insects, and particularly bees, feed on the pollen and nectar and as they do so they transfer pollen from the male anthers to the central female style. The style is situated at the top of the ovary which is made up of two green flattened lobes. After fertilisation the ovary develops rapidly into a pair of broad-winged keys (samaras). They hang in bunches throughout summer, slowly changing colour from a crimson-tinged green to

Field maple *(Acer campestre).* Deciduous, native, grows to 26m (85ft) in woodland, hedgerows and scrubland mainly in southern England, rare elsewhere. Flowers May-June.

Below: The fruits of the field maple are set in a straight line: those of the sycamore, our most common maple species, are set at an angle.

Opposite: A hedgerow of brilliant field maples on a sunny autumn day.

Below: The leaves of the field maple turn red and gold in autumn.

brown by autumn. When the seeds fall from the tree the wing gives them a spinning motion.

Timber Field maple wood burns well but because of the meagre size of the tree it has never been widely used. The pale brown timber has a well marked grain which is still valued by craftsmen. The wood from the roots, with its beautiful swirling pattern of veins, shows up well when polished.

Sycamore look-alike Field maple can be confused with the sycamore (page 175) but there are several differences: the sycamore's winter twigs are smooth, with yellow-green buds; sycamore leaves, although similar in shape, are larger than those of the field maple, and the lobes more pointed and not so widely separated; also the samaras of the field maple have broader wings set in a straight line, whereas sycamore samaras are joined at an angle of about 55 degrees.

Sugary sap The sap of all maple species is especially rich in sugars. When growth surges ahead in spring there is a great flow of sugars from the winter storage organs to fuel the development of shoots and leaves. In northern Europe the sap was collected in cups set under hollow tubes driven into the trunk. The liquid was boiled over a fire to concentrate it into a thick sweet syrup. Nowadays the main source of maple syrup comes from the sugar maple (*A. saccharum*) which is widespread in much of the deciduous woodland of north America.

Spectacular introductions Norway maple is our most widespread introduced maple and it is widely grown for ornament in parks and gardens. In a few places it has escaped and become naturalised in the wild, although not nearly so vigorously as the sycamore. Its decorative value is largely due to the beauty of its foliage: when its leaves unfurl in spring their delicate green is shot with shades of pink, crimson and russet, changing in autumn to tones of bright yellow and shining gold.

There are many species of maple in North America – indeed, Canada has adopted the maple leaf for its national emblem. Maples are renowned for their spectacular displays of autumn colours. The 'fall' in New England is justly famous for the blaze of colour – reds, oranges and yellows – in great expanses of maple woodland.

Two North American species are frequently planted in the British Isles. They are the red maple (*Acer rubrum*) which has striking autumn foliage, and the silver maple (*A. saccharinum*) which has sharply toothed

leaves that flash a silvery sheen from their undersides as they are rustled by the wind. From further afield the Japanese maple (*A. palmatum*) is planted for its graceful form and deeply lobed leaves, each shaped like an outstretched hand. It thrives in the warmer areas of the British Isles.

Norway maple *(Acer platanoides)*. Deciduous, introduced but often naturalised in woodland, hedges on most soils. Often found with sycamore. Flowers May-June.

Autumn leaves

The colourful autumn finery of maples reflects a period of intense activity by the trees. Most of our broad-leaved trees are deciduous, shedding their leaves as the days get shorter and the weather colder. Leaves continually lose water by evaporation; in summer it is replaced by water pumped up from the roots, but in winter roots cannot absorb enough water to supply the needs of the foliage. This may be surprising, considering our high rainfall, but as the soil temperature drops, so the roots work less efficiently, and ice cannot be absorbed at all. To avoid water loss, many trees shed their leaves.

Evergreens can retain their foliage because the leaves are coated with a waxy surface layer that reduces water loss.

Before leaves are shed, their colour changes and the resulting tones are due to a change of pigment concentration, and the accumulation of waste products from the rest of the tree.

As the foliage assumes its autumnal tints the tree drains most of the nutrients from the leaves to store in the roots and trunk to tide it over winter. In spring they rise in the sap to fuel the intensive growth activity before the new leaves produce enough new food by the process of photosynthesis.

Once the foliage is redundant a waterproof cork layer forms at the base of each leaf stalk, cutting the leaf off from the tree. The joint is weak, and the leaves are either blown off or fall after a frost which ruptures the join. The cork seals the wound left by the fallen leaf, and so protects the leaf scar and other parts of the tree from invasion by harmful fungi and various different kinds of bacteria.

Sycamore

Sycamores, more than any other introduced species, are widely naturalised in the British Isles.
They grow in open fields (below) and parks, presenting a towering and shapely mass of luxuriant foliage, and rapidly colonize city streets and gardens.

The sycamore, a native tree of central and southern Europe, especially in upland districts, was unknown in the British Isles until it was introduced in the late 15th century to ornament the estates of landowners. Since then it has been widely planted and has also spread itself vigorously. In fact no other alien tree has naturalised itself so widely in this country.

In spacious surroundings the sycamore grows into a majestic spreading tree, quite often broader than it is tall, and carrying a huge mass of foliage which by midsummer is dark green and dense. In woods it grows as tall as oaks and beeches and is quite commonly 25-30m (80-100ft) high.

Above: Sycamore blooms in profusion in early summer, its greenish flowers hanging in clusters (racemes) along the young leaves. Both sexes are present in each raceme, and you can distinguish the males by their prominent stamens.

Below: A leaf bud which is just opening in early April.

What's in a name Its name has a curious history. Originally 'sycamore' referred to a fig species, now called the sycamore-fig or mulberry fig (*Ficus sycomorus*), which grows in Palestine. When the maple-like sycamore was first brought to the British Isles from Europe it was evidently mistaken for the Holy Land 'sycamore', a well-known tree because it is mentioned in the New Testament. However, there is little resemblance between the maple-like sycamore and the mulberry-fig of Palestine, except for some similarity in leaf shape. The 'great maple', the name used in Gerard's *Herball* of 1597, is far more appropriate. The Latin name, *Acer pseudoplatanus* is also apt: it means the maple similar to the plane—in its leaf shape and shedding bark.

Spreading tree The lowest boughs may be long, slender and held out horizontally, curving slightly down about half-way along their length, but rising gracefully again near the tips. When there are no browsing animals the lower branches sweep almost to the ground, encircling the tree with a ring of foliage 30m (100ft) or more in diameter.

Above the bottom ranks of leaves are many similar layers, spaced well apart right to the top of the tree. The opposite leaves are red-stalked, toothed, up to 20cm (8in) across, and palmate with five (occasionally only three) pointed lobes. They are bright green or a deep purple-brown when they open in April.

In high summer they often become coated with honeydew.

Sycamore fruits form quickly and you can often find them already well developed at the base of the flower clusters, while new flowers are still fresh at the tip. When all of the fruits have formed, they hang as a bunch of keys which turn hard and brown in autumn.

The keys grow in pairs, each consisting of a seed inside a shell with a long wing attached; the two wings are almost at right angles to each other and slow down the fall of the seeds; most fall directly below the parent tree but others become caught in the wind and dispersed further afield.

Like all trees of spreading habit, sycamore look especially beautiful in parks and large gardens. Unfortunately because it is extremely resistant to air pollution, it often springs up in small town gardens where it quickly becomes a nuisance, casting too much shade and shedding vast numbers of autumn leaves which smother lawns and stop up drains. While some maple relatives from North America give us wonderful scarlets and yellow in autumn, the sycamore's leaves achieve only a sober brown colour.

Wood The bark varies in colour from the grey, common on younger trees, to the reddish-brown of older specimens. In damp western woods mature sycamores may be almost entirely covered by mosses, lichens and polypody ferns. On old trees the bark often cracks into small plates which peel back at the edges.

The wood of sycamore is yellowish-white when it is in good condition. It is tough and loosely textured and is suitable for many indoor purposes such as furniture and turned items. Cut into thin sheets it makes a good veneer, especially where there is an attractive ripple mark in the grain. The wood is not durable enough however to make constructional timber. Out-of-doors it rots quickly and is thus useless for fencing and similar purposes.

Shelter tree Sycamore has long been valued as a quick growing, hardy shelter tree in cold windy places and it has been planted on the windward side of many a moorland farmhouse. Even the salty coastal gales, fatal to most trees, do not kill it. In exposed sites it may be stunted, but still stands remarkably upright. Because of its hardiness it is an especially popular tree in Scotland, where it is often misleadingly called the plane.

Resilient opportunist How has the sycamore invaded our countryside with such success? It is literally a species that grows pretty well anywhere, on all but the most waterlogged ground. Although the best specimens occur on deep, loamy soils, it grows readily on poor, thin soils. It is also particularly well adapted to our cool, wet, windy climate.

Its fertility is remarkable: while oak and beech have their good and bad years, the sycamore produces a good crop of seeds

Sycamore (*Acer pseudoplatanus*), introduced, deciduous, grows to 30m (100ft). May live up to 200 years or more. Common throughout the British Isles in open fields, woods, hedges, parks, gardens and city streets. Very tolerant of exposure and salt spray and often planted as a shelter tree. Regenerates itself easily in most soils. Flowers and fruits, April-June or July.

practically every year of its long life of up to 200 years, (and some authorities say many more,) and the seeds are dispersed efficiently.

In spring the seedlings germinate readily, eventually forming small thickets in open ground such as the site of a felled wood. Because sycamore is an aggressive pioneering species, pure oakwood can eventually become replaced by pure sycamore wood. After World War II crowds of young sycamores quickly invaded bomb sites in many cities.

In the British Isles, perhaps because it is so far from its natural place in the world, it suffers from comparatively few insect pests. Neighbouring oaks can be severely attacked by caterpillars while sycamores are hardly touched. Only in real plague years do caterpillars spill over from oaks to sycamore leaves.

Very few moths prefer to eat sycamores: there is one species called the sycamore moth, but it is not a pest species. The best-known fungus on sycamore is the tar-spot which produces innumerable black blotches on the leaves, yet it is not a threat to the tree's health. It is rare in industrial areas because it is kept at bay by the sulphur dioxide in the air.

Nature conservationists have ambivalent feelings about the sycamore. They dislike the way its deep shade suppresses the plants and hence much of the animal life below it. They are not happy to see it occupying ground which would otherwise be occupied by oak, birch or other trees more attractive to caterpillars and birds.

On the other hand there are points in favour of the sycamore. Its reliable seed production is welcomed by wildlife in years when acorns and beech mast fail. Its flaking bark harbours many small creatures which are sought by winter birds. Bees and other insects swarm to the flowers in spring, and its heavy leaf fall contributes greatly to woodland litter. And it provides a reliable shelter for wildlife in exposed areas.

Above: Sycamore fruits hang in paired keys (samaras), each of which contains a single seed. When the samara reaches the ground the fruit case does not split open, but slowly decays, allowing the seed to germinate the following spring.

Right: Sycamore seedlings grow easily and fast—up to 50cm (20in) a year in the early stages.

Holly

The holly (below) is familiar to everybody as a popular Christmas decoration, with its brilliant berries and glossy, prickly leaves. In winter, these same features make the holly one of the most distinctive of our native trees.

The holly is found throughout the British Isles and is fairly common in most regions apart from the far north of Scotland and its outlying islands. It grows on a wide range of soils, provided they are not too wet, and is very tolerant of shade. This makes it ideal for woodland, its natural habitat, where it grows freely in the shade cast by taller trees. The holly is particularly common in oak-woods, where it may come to dominate other shrubs and small trees. It also springs up in thickets of scrub on commons and in hedge-rows.

Given enough time holly will grow to about 15m (50ft) tall, though it is usually encountered as a shrub 3–5m (10–15ft) in

height. In Britain, the tallest holly on record is a specimen 21·5m (71ft) high growing at Theydon Grove in Essex.

Hats and holms The New Forest in Hampshire is noted for its abundance of hollies and you can see many fine specimens growing there. On more open ground in the forest it forms pure clumps or groves. These are often circular in shape and are known locally as hats or holms. The word holm is an old name for holly and it still survives in place names such as Holmwood and Holmsdale, indicating that the tree is or was common in the neighbourhood.

Knobbly bark The trunk is covered with a pale grey bark which is smooth apart from scattered warts and blisters. On old trees the trunk becomes rather knobbly. This is caused by the bark growing over the scars left by the lower branches falling off as the tree grows. This pattern of growth gives older trees a dense pyramidal or rounded crown. Young trees, on the other hand, retain their branches close to the ground and their foliage forms a more conical crown.

In the days when there was a market for song-birds, holly bark was widely used to help trap them. A sticky paste known as 'bird lime' was made from the bark and other materials, and spread on to the twigs of a bush where a caged bird was hung as a decoy. The calls of this bird attracted others of its species and, as they alighted in the bush, their feet became glued to the spot, ready for the trapper to pick them off.

Glossy leaves It is impossible to confuse holly leaves with those of any other tree. They are rich dark green above and pale green underneath, basically oval in outline but with wavy margins extending at intervals into long sharp spines. The leaves have a leathery feel and their upper surface has a shiny varnished appearance due to the presence of a waxy waterproof coating called a cuticle.

Because the cuticle is waterproof it reduces greatly the amount of water lost through the leaves by evaporation. This helps the tree retain its foliage through the winter. At this time of year the roots of all trees have great difficulty in drawing enough water from the cold soil to replace that lost through the leaves. Deciduous trees overcome this simply by shedding their leaves in autumn, whereas evergreens such as the holly solve the problem by having a cuticle layer, so their leaves do not need to be discarded. However, even holly has been known to shed its leaves during an exceptionally severe winter.

The individual leaves persist on the tree for about two years, turning bright yellow and falling with the emergence of new foliage in May. The fresh young leaves unfurl from small round 2–3mm buds, alternately spaced along the green twigs. At first the young leaves are soft to the touch and pale bright green, sometimes flushed with a tinge of

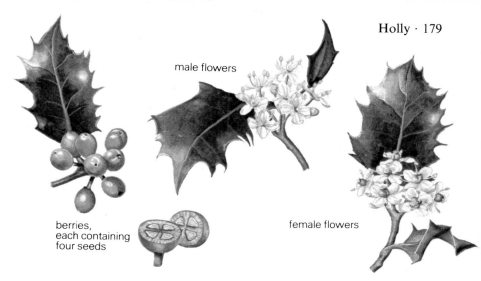

male flowers

berries, each containing four seeds

female flowers

Above: **Holly** (*Ilex aquifolium*). Evergreen, native, grows to 20m (65ft). Flowers May-July; Fruits November onwards.

Right: Holly seedling. Even the earliest tree leaves are spiny to discourage browsing animals.

Below: The trunk of an old holly tree is often knobbly where lower branches have been discarded.

purple. As they expand to their full size—about 7cm (3in) long—they turn dark glossy green and become spiny and stiff.

Prickles for defence The prickliness of the foliage discourages most, though not all, animals, from browsing off it. Horses, for example, are much less discouraged than deer from eating the leaves. Ponies in the New Forest seem to browse on holly with impunity, and older trees there have a distinct browse line marking the height to which the ponies can reach.

A curious feature of the holly is that when it reaches a height of about 3m (10ft), the upper branches—well out of the reach of browsing animals—produce leaves that are not spiny, except at the leaf-tip.

The toughness of the leaves makes them a formidable target for leaf-eating insects. One of the few successful ones is the caterpillar of a species of moth (*Stigmella aurella*). This mines tunnels and chambers inside the leaf, eating away at the soft inner tissue.

Flowers and fruits The holly has a long flowering season: about three months starting in May. Male and female flowers are borne on separate bushes, so a female bush without a male nearby will not produce any fruit.

After fertilisation the female flowers develop into small green fruits which ripen into the familiar bright red berries by late November. Each berry contains four seeds embedded in its pulpy flesh. These are dispersed in the droppings of birds, especially thrushes, fieldfares and redwings. In a severe winter birds can rapidly strip a holly bush bare, though in normal conditions the berries are likely to be left until more palatable fruits have been eaten.

Wood for burning Freshly cut holly is an excellent firewood since it burns fiercely

Above: Both flowers and berries are found clustered around twigs near the base of the leaf-stalks.

Right: Male and female flowers are very similar. Each is about 5mm across and consists of four rounded, white or slightly pink petals and four yellow-green stamens or stigmas, depending on whether the flower is male or female, respectively. The flowers shown here are male.

Below: Male and female flowers are borne on separate trees. From a distance, trees of different sex look much the same, unless the female is bearing fruit. Here, the female tree is on the left, with a male on the right.

without the need for seasoning. However, this also means that it suffers badly in bush and heath fires, especially as the foliage bursts into flames so easily; this is due to the oils that make up the cuticle and which produce an inflammable vapour when heated.

Holly timber is almost white, fine-grained and hard. It has been employed for turning small decorative pieces, for inlaid work and carving. It was also dyed black and used as a substitute for ebony.

Numerous decorative varieties of holly have been bred for the garden. Some have white or yellow berries, others variegated leaves, and there is even one variety, called Hedgehog, which grows spines on the leaf surface as well as round the edges!

Folklore There is an old superstition concerning holly and Christmas that was commonly held to be true in many parts of the country. The belief was that if you wrapped nine holly leaves in a handkerchief tied with nine knots and placed this under your pillow on Christmas night, then you would dream of the person you were destined to marry.

Common and small-leaved limes

A long avenue of lime trees provides a cool, sweet-smelling walk in summer. The only drawback is the continual rain of honeydew, a substance secreted by greenfly feeding on the sugary leaf juices.

Most of what we know of the vegetation that covered Britain following the last Ice Age, which ended some 10,000 years ago, has come from the study of pollen grains. These remain perfectly preserved in peat bogs where the process of decay is extremely slow. Pollen grains, when viewed under a microscope, have characteristic shapes, sizes and surface patterns which vary according to genus.

Peat deposits accumulate at a fairly fixed rate and so the date that the pollen was blown on to the bog can be more or less determined from the depth at which it is found. By counting the number of pollen grains of each plant species at a given layer it is possible to get an idea of the type of vegetation around the bog at that particular time.

The pollen record shows that between 3000 and 5000 years ago our native small-leaved lime was abundant in the oak forest that dominated the landscape then. The large-leaved lime, whose pollen is rarely found in peat deposits, either had a restricted ditribution or arrived much later. Limes increased in frequency as the climate gradually improved after the Ice Age. Their heyday was in the so-called Atlantic Period (3000–5000 years ago) when the climate in which they grew was warm and wet.

Wild limes are uncommon in this country today. Their decline is probably due not so much to a slight cooling of the climate since the Atlantic Period as to the fact that their foliage is so palatable to grazing animals. It is

Below: A long avenue of stately limes near Micheldever in Hampshire. The flowers can be dried and made into refreshing lime tea.

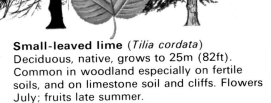

Common lime (*Tilia europaea*)
Deciduous, introduced or doubtfully native, grows to 25m (82ft). Common throughout the British Isles, especially in gardens, parks, avenues. Flowers July; fruits late summer.

Small-leaved lime (*Tilia cordata*)
Deciduous, native, grows to 25m (82ft). Common in woodland especially on fertile soils, and on limestone soil and cliffs. Flowers July; fruits late summer.

possible that when man turned his domestic animals out into the forests, lime seedlings were eaten; when older trees died there were no up-and-coming young limes to replace them.

This may not necessarily have been a sudden disappearance (because man has been changing the nature of our forests for over 1000 years); it is just that the lime was particularly hard hit. It is perhaps not surprising that today our native limes grow wild mainly on limestone cliffs or steep hillsides which have always been less accessible to grazing animals.

The common lime is an introduced hybrid derived from two species, the small-leaved lime and the rarer large leaved-lime, both of which are common elsewhere in Europe and in fact native to this country. It has long been a favourite ornamental tree since it forms a towering bright green crown, grows on a wide variety of soils, and is easy to manage.

These tall and stately common limes are widespread in parks, gardens, town squares, churchyards and avenues. There is a famous double lime avenue at Clumber Park in Nottinghamshire. At three miles long, it is the longest avenue in England.

The leaves open in April. Much of the graceful appearance of the lime is due to its foliage. The leaves are heart-shaped with a toothed margin and are borne on stalks up to 3cm (1in) long. They are a delicate pale green and have a soft texture, rather like paper tissue. In autumn the lime is one of the first trees to shed its leaves, which turn pale yellow before falling.

Flowers The common lime blossoms in July. The flowers dangle in bunches of five to eight on long stalks, surrounded for half of their length by a yellowish, oblong, papery bract attached to the stalk – a unique characteristic of limes. Each separate bloom, held on an individual stalk, has five green sepals and five yellowish-white or cream coloured petals.

Right: Common lime flowers and fruits. A sure way to distinguish lime trees is by the yellowish, oblong papery bract attached to part of the stalk. When the fruits ripen in late summer the bracts act like a sail and carry the seeds on the wind.
The fruits of the common lime are woody and slightly ribbed. The leaves are 6-10cm (2½-4in) long. The fruits of the small-leaved lime are thin-shelled, brittle and faintly ribbed, and the leaves are 3-6cm (1-2½in) long.

Pollination is carried out by insects, especi-ly bees, which are attracted by the flowers' rong sweet fragrance and swarm to the opious supply of nectar. Limes are a firm avourite of hive owners because their bees onvert the nectar into first-rate honey. The owers also attract night-flying moths, and e green caterpillar of the lime hawk moth — ne of our most spectacular moths—is among e many insects that feed on the leaves in ummer.

Fruits After fertilisation each flower forms round fruit which ripens by October to a ard grey nut with a surface texture rather ke felt. Each nut encloses a single seed. The apery bract that supported the flowers now cts like a sail to catch the wind and carry s cargo of seeds some distance from the arent tree. After dispersal lime seeds lie ormant in the soil for 18 months. When they ventually germinate they first send up a pair f finger-shaped seed-leaves which look like e fingers of a hand, and then the normal em foliage.

Tall sticky trees Limes are tall-growing ees. When mature they can achieve a height f 30m (100ft). Indeed the tallest broad-leaved ee in Britain is a common lime 47m (154ft) igh in Great Limes Wood, Duncombe Park, lelmsley, Yorkshire. The common lime has een widely planted along residential streets, ainly because it can withstand regular and orough pruning.

There is one drawback to lime trees: motor-ists who park beneath them in summer find their cars coated with a sticky sweet liquid called honeydew which is secreted by aphids (greenfly) feeding on the leaf juices. Lime sap is rich in sugars but contains only minute amounts of proteins and other substances vital for the aphids' survival. Consequently they have to suck up enormous quantities of sap to obtain the necessary food materials, and the sugary surplus is excreted.

Lime wood is pale creamy yellow in colour with no obvious grain or surface features. Its main quality is that it is light and stable and does not shrink or warp, and so it is ideal for precision work. During World War II large numbers of native limes were felled along the limestone gorges of the Wye valley. The timber was used in the manufacture of the Mosquito fighter-bomber, the frame of which was constructed of wood. Lime wood is also used for the frames of honeycombs. The lack of movement in the seasoned timber makes it especially useful in keyboard instru-ments such as pianos where accuracy is vital. It can also be worked to a smooth finish and has been used for decorative carving and sculpture.

The name lime, which has nothing to do with the familiar citrus fruit, is an altered form of linden, a name still used in some country districts. Linden is derived from the German word *linde*, meaning rope.

Above: A rare stand of mature lime trees in late summer. Limes have a habit of sprouting numerous twigs from the base of the trunk. Older trees tend to develop massive gnarled knobs (bosses) on the trunk and limbs.

Lime twig

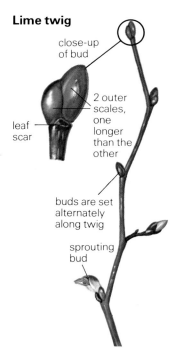

close-up of bud

2 outer scales, one longer than the other

leaf scar

buds are set alternately along twig

sprouting bud

Box

Although native to Britain, box is today as rare in the wild as it is popular for garden hedges. For years it was harvested for its valuable wood and now its distribution is limited to isolated specimens and a few scattered copses.

Above: Box growing wild on the Dorset downs. In Britain it is found in the wild only on the chalk and limestone hills of southern England. Occasionally it is seen as small dense woods but more often as isolated specimens.
Notice how the specimen shown here has several stems rather than one. This is typical of box.

Hundreds of years ago, box used to be common over the chalk and limestone hills of southern England but, over the years, large numbers of the plants have been felled for their timber, particularly during the last century. Sadly, the stock was not replenished by planting young trees, and since then box has never been as prolific.

Isolated specimens of box can still be seen in the wild, but there are only a few sites left where you can see large numbers of them. These are in the Chilterns, the Cotswolds and

on some downlands, the most notable site being at Box Hill on the North Downs in Surrey and certain dry valleys in the Chilterns. Here you can see natural box woods, growing as small dense stands of trees that block out the light and exclude almost all other vegetation.

Apart from England, box is found in southern Europe and north Africa, where it is more common than it is here.

Tree or shrub? Box can be classified variously as a tree or a shrub, depending on the particular specimen being considered. Most boxes growing in gardens are small and shrubby, but wild specimens are usually taller with a more pronounced stem, and are therefore tree-like. Some of the specimens on Box Hill grow as high as 10m (33ft).

Whether considered as a tree or shrub, the stem is never large – no more than about 20cm (8in) across – though many trees have several stems joining at the ground. There are records indicating that box trees used to have larger stems than they do now, but, not surprisingly, these were the main target for the woodman's axe. The trees we see today are probably the descendants of smaller trees that were considered to be not worth felling.

Box is very slow growing and lives to a great age, sometimes as much as 300 years. It thrives under heavy shade and can sometimes be seen growing as a low shrub beneath a dense canopy of beech – another species that grows well on chalk soils.

The stems and branches of a young box tree have an attractive yellow bark, which turns grey as the tree ages. The bark, though smooth to the touch, is broken up into fine ridges and squares, which become more pronounced as the wood beneath expands.

Distinctive leaves The leaves of box are easy to identify. They are small, about 1cm (½in) long, rounded or oval with a notch at the tip. The upper surface is shiny and dark green, and the edges roll down toward the underside, which is much paler. The leaves are arranged in opposite pairs on the twigs, each pair being at right-angles to the pair above and below them. They have a distinctively unpleasant, musty smell.

Although box is evergreen, it still produces new leaves every spring. As these emerge some of the old leaves fall off.

Flowers without petals Box flowers appear in April. Each flower head consists of one green female flower surrounded by several yellow male flowers. None of these flowers has any petals, and the whole head is only about 5mm across.

The seeds develop inside a hard protective capsule with three 'horns' on it. When the seeds ripen in September the capsule opens and releases them.

Wood denser than water When first cut, box wood is bright yellow or cream and is so dense that is sinks in water – our only native

Box · 185

timber to do this. After seasoning, the wood becomes white and less dense.

As well as being dense, box wood is also very hard – in fact, the hardest wood native to Britain. Because of its slow growth, it is also very close-grained. Indeed, the grain is hardly noticeable, showing only as faint lines of darker wood.

The closeness of its grain allows the wood to be cut into small pieces – such as for inlay work – without breaking. But its main use nowadays depends on the fact that it hardly shrinks during seasoning. All wood shrinks to some extent while it is being dried from its natural green state, but box shrinks less than most. It follows that box wood scarcely twists or warps at all during drying, and subsequently it responds less than most other woods to variations in humidity. The wood is, therefore, particularly suitable for high-class drawing and mathematical instruments. It is also used for making chess pieces and high-quality flutes.

During the last century box wood was in great demand by the printing industry for making woodcuts. An illustration was carved on to the endgrain of a block of box wood, which was then inked and used for printing. Huge numbers of box trees were cut down for this purpose, especially round London. Fortunately, the sizes of wood blocks needed meant that the smaller specimens were of no use and were spared; otherwise box trees would be even rarer in the wild than today.

Hedges and topiary Most people, if they are familiar at all with box, know it as a garden hedge rather than as a naturally-growing tree.

Box is well suited as a hedge: it is resistant to pollution and so thrives in towns; it is evergreen, providing colour throughout the year; and, because it is slow growing, it does not need frequent trimming. A dwarf form of box, known as edging box, used to be popular for planting round the edges of flower borders and graves, but it required constant care and is no longer planted.

In formal gardens, box is much used for topiary, the close and regular clipping of hedges and bushes into intricate shapes – usually those of animals.

Above: Being both slow-growing and evergreen, box is ideal for topiary work.

Right: **Box** (*Buxus sempervirens*). Native evergreen tree or shrub, growing to a height of 10m (33ft). The flowers are small and greenish-yellow, appearing in April. The brown seed capsules ripen in September.

horned capsule containing seeds

notched leaf tips

female flowers

male flower

Below: A box tree on Box Hill, Surrey, the best-known site for box trees in the country.

Spindle

For most of the year the spindle tree grows inconspicuously in hedgerows and woodland. But in autumn it produces a vivid show of coral-coloured fruits containing seeds coated in bright orange flesh – an irresistible attraction to hungry birds.

The spindle is a shrub or small tree which grows in scrub thickets, open woods and hedgerows. It is most commonly found in chalk and limestone districts in the southern half of England and occasionally extends into northern England. But it is absent from most of Scotland and confined to a few localities in Ireland.

The younger twigs are green and have a rather square cross-section because the corners often develop a layer of corky bark which extends along the length of the twig. The stem and older branches are covered with pale brown bark. Each twig is tipped with a single greenish bud, and opposite pairs of buds grow along the length. The

Right: **Spindle tree** (*Euonymus europaeus*). Deciduous, native, grows to 5m (16ft) on chalk scrub, in woodland in S England, less common elsewhere. Flowers May, fruits Oct.

buds break into leaf towards the end of April and the leaves, each about 5cm (2in) long and spear-shaped with finely toothed margins, are supported on short stalks.

White flowers The spindle blooms during May and June, but it is easy to overlook the flowers because they blend so well with the foliage. They are usually grouped in threes and borne on short stalks near the tips of the twigs. The flowers are sometimes unisexual (either male or female), but usually bisexual (with male and female parts on the same flower). Four greenish-yellow petals and pollen-tipped stamens surround the central ovary, where the seeds develop after fertilisation.

The blossom is pollinated by insects— chiefly flies—which are rewarded with nectar. The stamens of bisexual flowers release their pollen some days before the female stigmas are mature enough to be receptive to it. Visiting insects are quite likely to transport pollen grains to flowers with mature stigmas, and cross-pollination then takes place. Self-pollination can also occur later when both the male and female sexual parts of the same flower are mature.

Coral splendour During winter and throughout spring and summer the spindle remains rather a drab, insignificant bush or tree. But in autumn it becomes vividly conspicuous because of its fruits. They are a striking deep coral pink and composed of four lobes, which are fused together. In October, as the foliage turns a variety of colours from deep crimson to purplish-brown, the berries split open to reveal the seeds embedded in a bright orange fleshy jacket (aril).

This gaudy display attracts birds to the bushes to feed on the arils, and the hard white seeds are dispersed in the birds' droppings. All parts of the tree are poisonous to man and livestock, but birds come to no harm.

The wood of the spindle tree is little used nowadays, but in the past its toughness made it valuable for making small durable articles such as clothes pegs, meat skewers and knitting needles, as well as spindles.

Spindle sticks Long before the spinning-wheel was invented, woollen thread for weaving was wound on to spindles made from twigs cut from the spindle tree. Women fed wool fibres from a fleece bundle through their fingers, so forming a thread which was then wound on to the spindle stick. One end of the shaft was wedged into a hole drilled through a stone, the weight of which, when twirled, gave the necessary momentum to keep the stick spinning. Twigs from spindle trees were ideal for this purpose because they are smooth, hard and not liable to splinter.

Opposite: The spindle tree in late autumn is easily recognisable for its coral-coloured fruits which contain bright orange fleshy seeds.

Right: Autumn fruits. The spindle tree's colourful fruits and autumn tints have been exploited in cultivated varieties, which are grown for decoration in many parks and gardens.
In some districts the fruits used to be collected, dried and ground into a powder which was rubbed into childrens' scalps to rid their hair of lice. The fruits earned the name of louseberries.

Below: The small white flowers of the spindle tree grow on short stems out of the leaf axils.

Alder buckthorn

The only British buckthorn to lack thorns, the alder buckthorn is, for much of the year, one of our least conspicuous shrubs. The best time to find it is in the autumn when its black berries contrast with the red and yellow of its dying leaves.

Above: The alder buckthorn is most commonly a plant of open scrub, though it is sometimes found growing in deciduous woodland in the southern half of England. Until recently, alder buckthorn was an important source of high-quality gunpowder used in time fuses; in the gunpowder trade it used to be called black dogwood.

Alder buckthorn (*Frangula alnus*). Native deciduous shrub or small tree, growing to 4.5m (15ft) high.

The alder buckthorn is widespread throughout Europe and parts of Asia, yet in Britain it is only common in the south of the country—and even here its distribution is very patchy. In northern England and most of Wales apart from the far south, it is a much scarcer shrub; in Ireland it is rare and in Scotland it is almost entirely absent.

Despite its name, the alder buckthorn is entirely lacking in thorns. The 'buckthorn' part alludes to its close relative, the common buckthorn; together they are the only British members of the Rhamnaceae, the buckthorn family. The 'alder' part of the name was given to it by the early herbalists, who were persuaded by the shrub's straight, parallel leaf-veins into thinking that it was related to the alder tree. They were wrong but the name has stuck.

Fragile twigs The alder buckthorn is a deciduous shrub or small tree whose dainty appearance is due to its slender widespreading branches and twigs, and the sparseness of its foliage. The twigs are fragile and prone to snapping, hence the plant's generic name *Frangula*, which comes from the Latin 'frangere', meaning 'to break'. This quality is reflected in one of its English names, the breaking buckthorn, and also in its Welsh name 'breuwydd', meaning the brittle tree.

The bark can vary in colour from blackish to pale grey, but it is usually fairly dark. It is smooth, except near the ground where, with age, it roughens into slight vertical ridges. The twigs are dark purple and flecked with pale narrow lines of lenticels.

The leaves appear in April and are a shining green if the plant is growing in good light. They have a pointed oval shape with untoothed, often undulating, margins. Their most distinctive feature is their large number of straight parallel veins, quite different to the inward-curving veins on the leaves of the common buckthorn. In the autumn, the leaves turn red or yellow and hang downwards from the twigs before falling in October.

Flowers and fruits The tiny greenish-yellow flowers are borne singly or in clusters in the angle between the leaf-stalks and the stems. They open in late May and continue to appear throughout the summer, until the arrival of the first chills of September. Each flower has five, occasionally four or six, tiny petals ringed by an equal number of larger green sepals. Both male and female parts are borne in the same flower, unlike those on the common buckthorn, where the sexes are carried on separate plants.

Despite being so inconspicuous, the flowers attract bees, wasps and flies by their well-exposed nectar. Pollination occurs when these insects brush the five short dark purple stamens that are closely bent in towards the stigma.

The flowers are followed by berries. At first, these are green but by July the earliest ones have turned red and, by the end of August, violet-black. The berries are slightly larger than elderberries and contain two, sometimes three, seeds. They ripen and fall from September to November, depending on when during the summer the flowers appeared.

The berries are a useful source of food for both birds and mammals. Wood-mice carry them short distances and store them in little heaps. Pheasants also transport the berries but it is migratory thrushes that disperse the seeds over the greatest distances by shedding them in their droppings–these are often purple from the juice of the berries.

Patchy distribution A tree like the alder

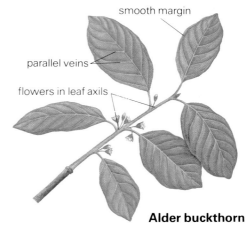

Alder buckthorn

smooth margin

parallel veins

flowers in leaf axils

Alder

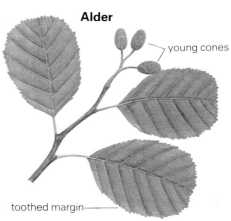

young cones

toothed margin

buckthorn has a patchy distribution because it has special ecological requirements not found in many areas. It occurs in a wide variety of habitats but they all seem to have in common a perennially damp soil, well-supplied with humus. For example, it grows particularly well in peat, except where it is perpetually waterlogged, and on the alkaline fen peats of the Norfolk Broads and un-drained areas like Wicken Fen in Cambridge-shire the alder buckthorn is more prolific than anywhere else in the country.

The alder buckthorn also grows on heath-land that has developed on lime-free clays or sands – a habitat that is characteristic of some commons in south-east England – and on limestone scrub areas, particularly in the Lake District and on the Burren Hills in the west of Ireland. On limestone extremely healthy specimens of alder buckthorn may be found growing in the wide deep fissures known as grikes.

In all these habitats, alder buckthorn is a constituent of scrub where it usually enjoys a fair share of light overhead, despite its short size. But there are districts in the Midlands and the south of England where it grows in woodland undergrowth, usually scattered rather than forming thickets. In this habitat, alder buckthorn is most likely to be found growing along the banks of a stream. How-ever, it often grows poorly in woodland. In heavy shade, particularly, it looks bowed, the leaves lack their usual gloss and the produc-tion of fruits is poor. Really deep shade may kill this shrub altogether.

Future decline In the days when both forests and wetlands were widespread, the alder buckthorn was much more common than it is now, and it seems to be declining still, as woodland management and drainage become more and more efficient. It will certainly survive in nature reserves but it deserves also to be planted in wild corners on suitably damp soils because it is such an interesting and ancient member of our native flora. Moreover, in areas away from chalk or limestone, it is the only plant that one of our most attractive butterflies, the brimstone, will feed on.

Above: Alder buckthorn bears tiny greenish-white flowers in its leaf axils from May through to September.

Right: The leaves bear some resemblance to alder leaves but they lack the toothed margins.

Below: The berries ripen from green and red to violet-black. Since the flowering period lasts for so long it is possible to find berries at quite different stages of development on one plant.

Dogwood

Inconspicuous for much of the summer, dogwood bursts into colour in the autumn as its leaves turn reddish-purple and then fall to reveal the red stems that make this plant one of our most attractive native shrubs in the winter.

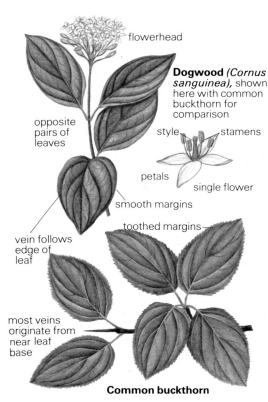

Dogwood (*Cornus sanguinea*), shown here with common buckthorn for comparison

flowerhead

opposite pairs of leaves

style

stamens

petals

single flower

smooth margins

toothed margins

vein follows edge of leaf

most veins originate from near leaf base

Common buckthorn

Below: Dogwood is a shrub both of open sites and woodland. In the open, it bears clusters of tiny creamy-white flowers around mid-summer. However, in the shade it flowers poorly if at all, though in both sites it spreads by suckers.

Dogwood is a deciduous shrub found primarily in the southern half of Britain, particularly in south-east England on the North and South Downs. On these downs it is often seen growing with its associated shrubs, the wayfaring tree and the wild privet, and when you find these three shrubs together you can be sure that you are on highly chalky ground.

Away from the chalk downs, dogwood flourishes in limestone areas such as those on the Mendips, in the Avon gorge at Bristol, in the lower Wye valley and south and north-east Wales. It is also widespread in the Midlands and East Anglia wherever there are lime-rich soils, and can be found in a few limestone areas in northern England, though it thins out rapidly north of Yorkshire. It is absent from Scotland and occurs only very locally in Ireland.

Dogwood is best known as a common, sometimes dominant, constituent of downland scrub, but it also grows in woodlands, especially where oak or ash are present, and in hedgerows.

Winter brilliance Dogwood is a shrub with grey main stems and bright red twigs. In the winter, when it is leafless, these twigs are especially eye-catching and sometimes make the whole bush glow a deep rich red. However, to achieve such brilliant colours dogwood needs to grow in the open; in shady situations its twigs are often just a dull purple-brown.

In spring, the leaves appear in opposite pairs on the twigs. They are most notable for their pattern of veining: instead of reaching straight out to the leaf margin, as happens with the leaves of most British trees and shrubs, the veins of dogwood leaves curve inwards to become roughly parallel with the margins. The leaves of the common or purging buckthorn have a similar pattern of veining, but they can be distinguished by their toothed margins, the margins of a dogwood leaf being smooth.

Flowers and fruits In June, the ends of many dogwood shoots become covered with dense flat-topped clusters of small creamy-white flowers. These flowers are particularly beautiful when seen under a hand lens: each consists of four (occasionally five) petals with a club-shaped style in the centre surrounded by four (or five) conspicuous stamens occupying the spaces between the petals. The flowers in the centre of the cluster usually open first.

Most people find the smell of dogwood flowers disagreeable but it attracts large numbers of pollinating insects. Besides these useful visitors there are also harmful ones: the larvae of the holly blue butterfly occasionally eat the flowers as an alternative to holly petals, and the leaves are sometimes attacked by green hairstreak caterpillars. But neither of these species is common enough to do serious damage.

The flowering period lasts into July and is followed by tiny round green berries. By September they have swollen to the size of small garden peas and are a glossy purple-black. Each berry is topped by the withered remains of the calyx and contains a single stone. To us the berries taste extremely bitter, but birds eat them readily. As the berries ripen the leaves turn a spectacular red-purple just before they fall in late autumn.

Why 'dogwood'? The name dogwood has been suggested to be a distortion of 'dag-wood', a reference to the fact that the wood was once used to make meat skewers. The old name for a meat skewer is 'dag', hence the modern word 'dagger'. But the real origin of the name comes from one of the old meanings of the word 'dog'–worthless. For example, people spoke of dog daisies because they were held to be inferior to garden daisies. So 'dog-wood' expressed the contempt that people held for the berries because they were so unpalatable. Thus the 17th century botanist, John Parkinson, wrote, 'We for the most part call it the dogge berry tree because the berries are not fit to be eaten or to be given to a dogge.'

The botanical name for dogwood is *Cornus sanguinea*. The name *Cornus* probably refers to the hardness of the wood, 'cornus' being Latin for 'horn'. The name *sanguinea* was given to the plant by the great 18th century botanist Linnaeus. It comes from the Latin for blood-red and possibly refers to the colour of the twigs in winter, but more likely to the lavish redness of the autumn leaves.

Long-time native Dogwood has been growing in the wild in Britain for many thousands of years. Among the remains of other plants, it has been found in the Cromer forest-bed of East Anglia, a buried fossilised forest that pre-dates the last Ice Age which started about 70,000 years ago. Presumably, dogwood retreated south during the Ice Age and returned to Britain afterwards as the temperate forest vegetation spread northwards.

As with so many of our native plants, dog-wood once had a great many uses, which are now largely unfashionable. The wood is particularly hard, which made it ideal for tools needing a sharp, durable point, such as meat skewers and toothpicks. It was also made into cogwheels, arrows and pestles. The 17th century diarist, John Evelyn, wrote about the wood in his book *Sylva*. It was, he claimed, 'of so hard a substance as to make wedges to cleave other woods with, instead of iron.'

Dogwood produces almost pure charcoal when heated in the right conditions and so was used for making high quality gunpowder, which is a mixture of saltpetre, sulphur and charcoal.

The berries also had their uses, despite their bitter taste. They contain a fair proportion of oil and, in the days before paraffin was widely available, they were boiled down to produce lamp oil. Their oily quality accounts for the Welsh name for dogwood, 'cwyros', which means 'wax bush'.

Among their other former uses, dogwood berries were an ingredient in soap and, medicinally, they were used as a natural form of laxative.

Above: In late autumn, dogwood leaves turn reddish-purple just before falling, becoming one of our most distinctive shrubs at that time of year.

Common dogwood (*Cornus sanguinea*). Native deciduous shrub found mainly in southern and central England, especially on downlands. Height to 4m (12ft).

Below: The fruits mature into glossy black berries just before the leaves turn colour (here they are just on the verge of doing so). To us, the berries taste extremely bitter though birds readily eat them, shedding the seeds in their droppings.

Strawberry tree

Named after its fruits, which resemble strawberries in all but taste, the strawberry tree is one of those rare plants that remain decorative throughout the year, helped by its evergreen leaves and its distinctive reddish-brown bark.

Above: A strawberry tree growing beside one of the lakes of Killarney in south-west Ireland. Though native to both Britain and Ireland, the strawberry tree grows wild only in a few isolated parts of Eire, and only around Killarney is it at all common.

Of the 40 or so species of trees that are native to Britain and Ireland, the strawberry tree is one of the rarest in the wild. In Britain it no longer exists in its native state, though it is commonly planted in parks and gardens as an ornamental tree. Only in a few isolated areas in southern Ireland can the strawberry tree still be seen growing wild.

Evergreen tree or shrub The strawberry tree is a small evergreen tree, usually not more than 10m (33ft) high. It is more often seen as a large shrub since, typically, the stems branch from a central bole near the ground. A distinctive feature of the strawberry tree is its fibrous reddish-brown bark, which makes an attractive contrast to the dark green leaves. These have that hard leathery texture common to evergreen broad-leaved trees and are a dark shining green. They are borne alternately on the twigs and are elliptical with serrated margins.

In Britain and Ireland, the strawberry tree grows new foliage during the spring and summer, as would be expected in our climate, but in the Mediterranean region, where it is much more common, growth takes place during winter. At that time of year there is frequent rain but still plenty of sun, with temperatures often above 15°C (59°C), whereas the summers are hot and dry, and unfavourable to plant growth.

Urn-shaped flowers The strawberry tree is unusual in that its flowering period extends from October to December. The flowers are borne in drooping panicles and are variable in colour, being white, pinkish or even yellow on some specimens. Each flower is less than 1cm ($\frac{1}{2}$in) long and shaped like a pitcher–swollen in the middle and contracted at the mouth with small reflexed lobes. Their shape is sometimes said to be urceolate, which means urn-shaped.

A particularly fine variety of the strawberry tree (var. *rubra*) has flowers deeply flushed with red and borne in even greater abundance than on the wild tree. This variety seems to have originated in gardens.

Slow-ripening fruits As the flowers die away, the previous year's fruits are finally reaching maturity. These are more or less spherical, about 2cm ($\frac{3}{4}$in) across and orange-red when ripe; when young they are yellow. Their surface is rough with small swellings, which helps them resemble strawberries. The fruits take nearly a full year to ripen and so, at one stage or other of maturity, are almost a permanent feature of the tree.

The fruits are edible, though they taste watery and insipid. The Ancient Romans found them equally unappetising, a fact referred to in the plant's Latin name, *Arbutus unedo*. The word 'unedo' is a contraction of 'unum edo', which is Latin for 'I eat one'; as the Roman naturalist Pliny explained in the first century AD, 'The fruit is held in no esteem, the reason for its name being that a person will eat only one.' In some European countries around the Mediterranean the fruits are made into a delicious liqueur.

The fruits are better fare for birds than they are for man and they are readily taken during the cold winter months. Sadly however, the climate in Britain is too cold for many of the flowers to ripen into fruits. One botanist has speculated that this may be due o the lack of insects in the autumn and winter o pollinate the flowers. This seems a likely xplanation–certainly, strawberry trees at Kew Gardens rarely show as much fruit as do hose growing in milder south-western areas.

Scattered distribution The strawberry tree as an unusual distribution. Most grow round the Mediterranean–Spain, Portugal nd Italy, and North Africa. In France it ccurs on the south coast and near the south-west coast; then there is a considerable gap efore it is found again in Brittany in north-est France. Further north, it is now found in he wild only in the west of Ireland.

Here, there is a small colony near Lough Gill in County Sligo, but the great majority re to be seen in the south-west corner of the ountry. Even there, the tree is becoming very are. Two hundred years ago the strawberry ree was much more plentiful, but large-scale elling for charcoal to smelt local ores of ilver, copper and lead has taken a heavy toll.

Today the best place to see wild strawberry rees is around the lakes of Killarney–the nly area where they are still frequent.

Clifftop and woodland sites Around Killarney, strawberry trees can be seen growing n a variety of habitats, from clifftops to oodlands.

They are best developed on cliffs and open ocky slopes, where they grow mainly with ivy nd holly, which are also evergreen. Here, nany of the trees reach a considerable age and re often deeply gnarled and bent over, ometimes with only their twigs pointing up-ards. Such trees often look dead, even hough they are still living. One reason why hese old strawberry trees survive so well is hat they can send out shoots from near the ottom of the stem, where there is a pro-

minent swelling. When the older branches die back or break, young shoots emerge from this swollen base.

The strawberry trees of Killarney can also be seen in oak woods where, with holly, they form a lower layer of the woodland canopy. Here they reach a height of 10m (33ft) or, occasionally, even 12m (40ft). However, as the oaks slowly grow the strawberry trees become shaded out. The presence of straw-berry trees in these woods is, therefore, only short-lived; perhaps the wood had been cut down for charcoal, and strawberry trees were able to grow with the young oaks.

In Ireland the strawberry tree's only long-lasting habitat seems to be small cliffs and rocky shores where oaks cannot grow to any great height. That such a habitat is rare in Britain may, together with Ireland's milder climate, explain this tree's distribution.

serrated leaves

pitted strawberry-like fruits

bell-shaped flower

Above: The shiny dark green leaves of the strawberry tree are borne alternately on the twigs. Its white, urn-shaped flowers appear in panicles or singly in October and are followed by round pitted fruits that are yellow when young but ripen to a bright red.

Left: The fruits take almost a year to ripen, by which time the following season's flowers have emerged.

Strawberry tree (*Arbutus unedo*). Native evergreen tree, commonly planted for its ornamental qualities in parks and gardens, but no longer found growing wild in Britain.

Above: A hedgerow elder in flower. The unpleasant smell of a sprig of elder leaves in the hair keeps flies at bay. In the past the leaves were dried and used as an insecticide.

Elder

Elder flowers and berries have long been used by man in wine making. Birds, too, feast on the berries, but both man and animals avoid the ill-smelling leaves.

The elder is one of our most common wood plants. It is more frequently seen as a shrub but it can grow to a tree as high as 10m (33ft) It grows almost everywhere, from heavily polluted roadsides to wind-lashed cliff-top where it is crusted with salt from the sea spray It thrives on waste ground, in hedgerows, on heathland, chalk downs, woodland and scrub and especially where the soil is rich in nitro gen from the manure of animals such as rab bits and badgers. You often see it near drain and sewers–it can be a sign to archaeologist of the site of former dwellings.

Leaves, appearing on the elder in spring are dark green, toothed and lance-shaped They have a particularly unpleasant smell

ather like that of a neglected mouse cage, and
t is rare to find birds nesting among elder—
perhaps because of the smell.

Flowers The elder is an impressive sight
when its stout branches are laden with flat-
topped clusters (corymbs) of creamy yellow
flowers. They can be up to 20cm (8in) in
diameter, and they emit a heady fragrance
which was once thought to be poisonous. The
flowers are mainly pollinated by small flies,
but occasionally hoverflies or bees land on the
flowers and collect pollen from the pale yellow anthers. The species is usually cross-
pollinated.

The berries are small and green at first, but
they ripen to a deep purple colour in August.
By early September the branches have become so heavy under the weight of their load
that the berries sag on limp, claret-coloured
stems. The berries, like the flowers, were once
thought to be poisonous. Nowadays we make
them into elderberry wine, chutney, jelly and
ketchup. The taste of the fruit can be cloying
to human palates, but large numbers of
birds such as blackbirds, pigeons, rooks,
starlings, robins and blackcaps relish the
fruits.

Seed dispersal The elder is widely dispersed
by birds swallowing the fruits and excreting
the small hard seeds. Small shrubberies spring
up around tree trunks where starlings have
roosted above.

Elder saplings grow particularly quickly—
up to a metre (3ft) in their first season. The
price of this rapid growth is that the stems
are weak and pithy; the tree is easily damaged
and after a gale the bushes become a tangle of
broken boughs. The tree also spreads itself
by means of suckers which can sprout some
distance from the parent tree.

Wood The bark of elder is brownish-grey,
deeply furrowed, corky and with very prominent lenticels (pore-like openings) through
which the stems breathe. Pieces of the thinner
branches are often hollowed out by children
in the country to make pea-shooters and
whistles.

The name elder is derived from the Anglo-
Saxon *eldrum*, meaning fire—perhaps a reference to the time before the invention of
bellows when the hollowed branches were
used for blowing on fires. The mature wood
is hard and sometimes used to make small
articles like toys.

Elder wood seems to be defenceless against
attacks of fungi. The most common is the
Jew's ear fungus, which also thrives on the
dead branches. Honey agaric and oyster
fungi are also common parasites.

Elder uses The flowers and berries have
long been used to make wine. The flowers add
a distinctive flavour to stewed fruit, and elder-
flower water is still sold as a mild skin clean-
er. The berries are rich in vitamin C. A dark
inky dye used to be made from the berries, and
green dye from the leaves. Like many trees,
elder was supposed to have magic powers.

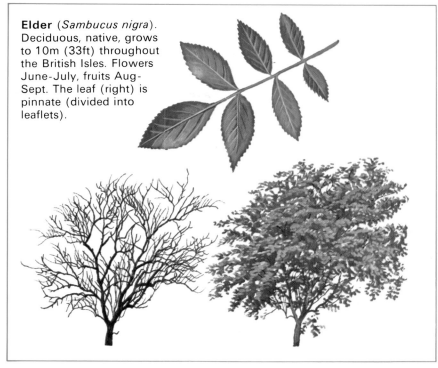

Elder (*Sambucus nigra*).
Deciduous, native, grows
to 10m (33ft) throughout
the British Isles. Flowers
June-July, fruits Aug-
Sept. The leaf (right) is
pinnate (divided into
leaflets).

Elder flowers (right) and
berries (below) have their
culinary uses, but the tree
itself has long been
credited with supernatural
powers. Invaders from
northern Europe who settled
here after the Roman
occupation are said to have
planted elders among the
rotting bodies of executed
criminals, hoping the plant
would absorb their badness
and so bring peace to their
souls.

Dog rose

The simple but beautiful dog rose, the most common wild rose growing in the British Isles, is a forerunner of many exotic garden varieties.

The dog rose is by far the most common of our wild roses. It grows extensively in hedgerows, thickets and scrub throughout the British Isles, except in the far north of Scotland. It seems to achieve its best growth along wild, straggling hedgerows that have escaped cutting for many years. Using these hedges for support as it climbs, the dog rose displays a bright cascade of large flowers in summer.

The dog rose possesses a large woody rootstock from which arise the long, arching stems armed with broad, sharp prickles shaped like shark fins. The stems grow up to three metres (10ft) long and if they are cut down to their base they are replaced by new shoots, or suckers which spring from the underground rootstock.

The formidable prickles deter grazing animals and help the plant to keep a firm hold on the bushes over which it clambers and sprawls. You can test their effectiveness by trying to pull a stem (you will have to wear gloves) away from the bush over which it is draped. It is surprisingly difficult and some-

imes impossible without enlisting the help
of other people.

The flowers are faintly scented, and are
borne singly or in groups of three or four on
side branches towards the end of each stem.
The blooms have five slightly notched petals
which are usually white with rims tinged with
delicate pink, although pure white or pure
pink flowers do occur.

Set around the middle of the flower are
clusters of numerous bright yellow stamens
surrounding the central stalked style. The
style (female part) provides a channel along
which pollen grains travel down to the ovary
to fertilise the eggs. The ovary is enclosed
within the green bulb upon which the flower
rests. After fertilisation these fleshy recept-
acles change into shiny red, flask-shaped
hips, which are a characteristic and colourful
feature of the countryside in autumn.

The fruits last well into winter and, because
they tend not to mature all at the same time,
dog rose bushes bear a mixture of ripe and
ripening hips. The mature scarlet hips are
sought by birds, especially blackbirds, fieldfares and wood pigeons, and the seeds are
dispersed in their droppings. Those that are
not eaten by birds eventually fall to the ground
and provide food for mammals such as voles
and badgers.

The hips have a number of names, including itching berries and tickling tommies.
This is because the seeds inside are clothed
with tiny stiff bristles which can irritate the
skin. They have been used by generations of
school children as itching powder – usually
being dropped down the neck of the unfortu-
ate classmate sitting at the desk in front!

The foliage which emerges in April is a
fresh bright green, but during summer the
leaves darken somewhat and acquire a glossy
surface sheen. Each leaf stalk has a number of

hips

prickles

Above: Rose hips are a
valuable source of vitamin C.
During World War II when
the disruption to shipping
created severe shortages of
citrus fruits, hips were
collected on a large scale
to make rose-hip syrup
which was given to
pregnant women and young
children.

Left: **Dog rose** (*Rosa
canina*). Native shrub
growing to 3m (10ft) in
woods and hedgerows. Rare
in Scotland. Flowers June-
July, fruits Aug onwards.

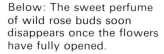

Below: The sweet perfume
of wild rose buds soon
disappears once the flowers
have fully opened.

prickles on its underside and carries from
five to seven leaflets with a sharply toothed
margin.

If you examine the leaves of dog roses –
or garden roses for that matter – you may
notice neat oval or semi-circular gaps in the
leaflets which look as though someone has
attacked the bush with a hole-puncher. This
is the remarkable handiwork of leaf-cutting
bees, nine species of which live in Britain.

Modern garden roses have a complex
ancestry because there has been much cross-
breeding between the different species. The
first roses with double blooms date to Roman
times and originated when unusual hybrids
of wild species were preserved and subsequently cultivated. Nowadays the dog rose
plays an important role in commercial rose
growing, providing the rootstocks on to
which exotic blooming varieties are frequently
grafted.

The name dog rose is sometimes said to
originate from Roman times when a soldier
was bitten by a mad dog and applied the
roots of a wild rose to heal the wound. Wild
roses assumed a special significance in the
15th century when there was a fierce struggle
for the throne between the Houses of York
and Lancaster. The warring factions adopted
the white rose and the red rose respectively
for their emblems. The conflict dragged on
for thirty years and became known as the
Wars of the Roses.

Bladder senna

Introduced from the Continent 400 years ago for its medical properties, the bladder senna now grows wild in Britain, particularly on waste land. Its strange pods, which explode when squeezed, provide a source of great delight for children.

Above: Although not native to Britain, the bladder senna flourishes here and has become naturalised, particularly in southern England, where it is often found growing on rubbish tips, railway embankments and other waste ground. Indeed, it will grow almost anywhere, provided there is enough light and the soil is not too waterlogged. This specimen was found on an area of waste ground in East London, less than 6km (4 miles) from the Tower of London.

Bladder senna is a vigorous deciduous shrub native to central and southern Europe, its range extending from France to Greece and Turkey, though it is absent from the Iberian peninsula. It has only fairly recently become naturalised in some northern European countries, including Britain, where it is most common in the southern counties of England.

The earliest record of a bladder senna being grown in Britain is in 1568. At the end of the following century the travel writer and horticulturist Celia Fiennes wrote approvingly of it as 'a fine tree that bears a great branch of yellow flowers' and, in 1778, the horticulturist John Abercrombie described it as 'elegant furniture for the shrubbery'.

Today, it is naturalised in Britain, favouring rubbish tips, railway embankment (especially in London) and other waste ground. Bladder senna can tolerate the poorest of soils and is capable of growing almost anywhere, provided there is enough light and the soil is not waterlogged. Indeed, it is one of the very few plants to be found growing on the crater of Mount Vesuvius in Italy. More typical sites for it on the Continent are dry slopes and open woods, preferably ones with a limey soil.

Senna look-alike The bladder senna was probably first introduced to Britain for its medical qualities. It was regarded as a useful purgative and was commonly grown for that purpose, though its effect seems not always to have been to the patient's benefit.

The medical reputation of this plant was, however, based in part on confusion between it and various species of the true senna, which were used medicinally but are quite a different group of plants. The problem of wrong identification was recognised early for, in the late 16th century, the herbalist John Gerard warned his readers 'that they are deceived that thinks it [the bladder senna] to be Sene, or any kinde thereof; although we have followed others in giving it the name Bastard Sene, which name is very improper to it'. But, in spite of Gerard's wisdom, the confusion was to remain for many years.

Nowadays, botanists classify the bladder senna in a different genus (*Colutea*) from that of the true sennas, which all belong to the genus *Cassia*. Both genera, however, belong to the pea family, bear seeds in pods and have yellow flowers – hence the original confusion. But, while the flowers of the bladder senna are typically pea-shaped, those of true sennas are much less so.

Brittle branches Bladder senna is a quick growing shrub, usually growing no more than 5m (16ft) high. It has a bushy habit and its branches, which are covered with grey flaking bark and prominent white lenticels, are brittle and easily snapped off, in a high wind for instance. The effects of such damage to bladder senna probably gave rise to the mistaken belief that the plant dies if its branches are lopped. Its Latin name, which comes from the Greek 'kulouo', meaning to amputate, also reflects this idea.

As an interesting sideline on the plant's name, Theophrastus, a Greek philosopher and botanist of the 3rd century BC, referred to a plant which he called 'koloutea', but whether this was the bladder senna we do not know.

The leaves are 8-15cm (3-6in) long and borne alternately on the shoots. Each leaf is compound, consisting of between seven and thirteen soft green leaflets arranged pinnate fashion. The leaflets are about 6mm-2cm ($\frac{1}{4}$-$\frac{3}{4}$in) long and broadly egg-shaped with a notch in their tips. They are hairy beneath when young but lose most of the hairs by the

Above: Young pods of bladder senna, photographed in June. The reddish tinges on the pods are common on this species.

Left: The flowers are bright yellow and typically pea-like, with a large standard petal (sometimes with red markings, as here), smaller wing petals to the sides and the keel beneath.

Right: **Bladder senna** (*Colutea arborescens*). Introduced deciduous shrub native to southern and central Europe. Height to 5m (16ft).

Below: Despite the ripe pods on this bush, a few flowers are still appearing and will continue to do so until the autumn.

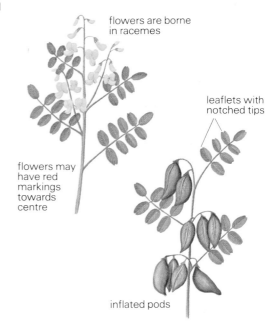

flowers are borne in racemes

leaflets with notched tips

flowers may have red markings towards centre

inflated pods

ime they mature.

In June and July, clusters of golden-yellow flowers are borne in the leaf-axils of the current year's growth, more appearing as the branches extend. The clusters are 4-10cm (1½-4in) long and carry three to seven flowers.

Each flower is about 2cm (¾in) long and has four petals arranged in typical pea-fashion. At the bottom is the keel; slightly above and to the sides are a pair of wing petals, which are slightly shorter than the keel; at the top of the flower is the standard petal, which is large and occasionally has faint red markings on its inside surface towards the centre. The calyx, which encloses the flower when it is in bud, is cup-shaped, green and covered with black and white hairs.

Exploding pods As with all plants in the pea family, the bladder senna bears its seeds in pods. In this species, the pods are about 4-7cm (1½-2½in) long, pointed and green with reddish tinges, especially at the ends. Each pod contains between 15 and 20 seeds.

A curious feature of the pods is that they are inflated and burst with a loud noise when squeezed, which makes them particularly attractive to children. Henry Philips, who in 1825 wrote a book called the 'Language of Flowers' in which he assigned qualities to different plants, made the bladder senna stand for 'Frivolous Amusement'. He commented that 'children find amusement in dancing on, or pressing these little bladders'.

Wayfaring tree

From spring through to late autumn the wayfaring tree adorns the roadsides of southern Britain. Heads of white flowers in May are soon followed by bright red berries. With the arrival of autumn the berries have turned a glossy black and the leaves are turning shades of red to provide a final touch of colour.

Below: A wayfaring tree (*Viburnum lantana*) in flower. Its requirement for a dry, well-drained and preferably alkaline soil limits its distribution in the British Isles: it is common only in southern England (except the West Country) and the south Midlands. On the Continent however, it is a common shrub throughout central and southern Europe, and extends into north Africa and western Asia.

The name 'wayfaring' tree seems an appropriate choice for this roadside plant, yet it arose through a misunderstanding. The Latin name, 'viburnum', gave rise to the French word for the wayfaring tree, 'viorne'. This was mistakenly thought by the 16th century herbalist, Gerard, to derive from the Latin word 'via', meaning a road. So he named it the wayfarer's tree – it seemed to him a suitable name because he encountered it frequently on his journeys between London and Canterbury. The name 'wayfaring' tree has stuck ever since.

The wayfaring tree grows best on chalk or limestone soils, such as those found between London and Canterbury, but it is occasionally seen growing elsewhere provided the soil is dry and well drained. It is most common in the southern counties of England and the south Midlands, although it is absent from the West Country and parts of East Anglia. In Wales it is native to a narrow strip along the south coast. It is not thought to be native to areas north of Yorkshire, although it has been introduced to Scotland, particularly in the lowlands. It is, however, entirely absent from the Scottish islands and the Isle of Man. In Ireland the wayfaring tree is not native but it has been introduced to a few places.

Woods and hedgerows are the most likely habitats in which to find a wayfaring tree. It sometimes forms small, rather open thickets and can produce suckers which, given the chance, rapidly invade grassland and other open habitats close by.

Sizeable shrub Despite its common name the wayfaring tree rarely grows into a tree. It almost always remains a shrub, though sometimes a substantial one reaching a height of 6m (20ft). It has a regular branching pattern and its buds are borne naked on the shoots – that is, the buds have no protective scales to cover the undeveloped leaves. Instead they are insulated from the frost and cold weather of winter by a coating of hairs, giving the buds a greyish, felted look. The presence of naked buds on the shoot distinguishes the wayfaring tree from the other members of its genus, *Viburnum*.

The leaves are borne in opposite pairs on the shoots. They have a rather wrinkled appearance and are oval or slightly heart-shaped with finely toothed margins. They may reach a length of 10cm (4in). The upper surfaces of the leaves, and the young twigs, are covered with the same greyish hairs found on the buds. The lower surfaces of the leaves are also covered with hairs, but here they are much thicker and woollier in appearance. While the hairs on the buds are there to provide protection against the winter, the hairs on the leaves clearly perform a quite different function because the leaves are shed in the autumn. The purpose of these is to prevent the leaves from losing too much moisture in the dry habitats that the wayfaring tree often prefers.

Stems for withies The distinctive white

Right: A flowering head of a wayfaring tree. All the flowers are similar to each other – unlike another species of *Viburnum*, the guelder rose, in which the flowers on the outside of the head are much larger than those on the inside. Each flower is about 5mm across and contains five white petals fused together. Inside this tube are five conspicuous yellow stamens. The flowers of the closely related elder have the same structure.

Above: Young berries of a wayfaring tree. The berries start off green but soon turn a bright red (right) before becoming a shiny black in early autumn. Each berry is about 8mm long and oval with a fleshy interior, inside which are embedded several seeds. The berries have too sharp a taste for humans but they are a popular source of food for birds, which devour them eagerly and so disperse the seeds. The juice from the berries was once used to make black ink.

Below: The evergreen laurustinus flowering in February. Unlike the wayfaring tree, which flowers in early summer, the laurustinus flowers from November onwards, sometimes through to April during a mild winter. Typically for a broad-leaved evergreen, the leaves are thick and glossy. Unlike the wayfaring tree the upper leaf surfaces lack hairs and the undersides have tufts of hairs in the angles between the veins.

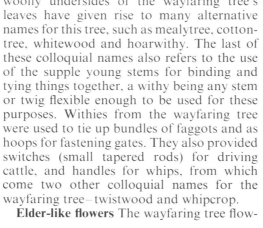

woolly undersides of the wayfaring tree's leaves have given rise to many alternative names for this tree, such as mealytree, cotton-tree, whitewood and hoarwithy. The last of these colloquial names also refers to the use of the supple young stems for binding and tying things together, a withy being any stem or twig flexible enough to be used for these purposes. Withies from the wayfaring tree were used to tie up bundles of faggots and as hoops for fastening gates. They also provided switches (small tapered rods) for driving cattle, and handles for whips, from which come two other colloquial names for the wayfaring tree – twistwood and whipcrop.

Elder-like flowers The wayfaring tree flow-

ers in May and June, each shrub producing numerous tiny white-petalled flowers borne in large umbel-like clusters up to 10cm (4in) across. Superficially the flower heads resemble those of an elder bush – the two species belong to the same family, the honeysuckle family – but the elder flowers slightly later in the year, usually in June and July.

In July the flowers are followed by fleshy oval berries, again resembling those of elder. The berries of a wayfaring tree are green when young but soon become bright red and eventually turn black and shiny when fully ripe in about September. The berries are not poisonous but they have an extremely tart taste and are not recommended for eating.

As the year advances the wayfaring tree becomes even more colourful and the leaves take on their autumn hues of red, providing a striking contrast to the clusters of shiny black berries.

Close relative Another member of the same genus – *Viburnum* – is sometimes found growing in the wild. This is the laurustinus, a species that, though not native to the British Isles, has become naturalised here in some areas.

The laurustinus is native to the Mediterranean region, particularly southern Italy and north Africa. It was first introduced to Britain during the 16th century and has been cultivated in gardens ever since, sometimes escaping to the wild.

Like the wayfaring tree, the laurustinus is a shrub, though smaller – usually between 2m (6ft) and 4m (13ft) high – and with a domed crown. It differs from the wayfaring tree in being evergreen, as its thick, leathery, dark green leaves suggest. It bears a great many branches from ground level upwards.

The flowers of the two species are similar, except that the outsides of the laurustinus petals may be tinged pink. Also, the flower heads are often smaller on laurustinus, usually 5-10cm (2-4in) across, and they appear at a quite different time of the year, opening in November and often continuing to flower through the winter until April, depending on the severity of the weather.

Although laurustinus flowers prolifically in Britain, it rarely produces fruits here. When they do appear, however, they are smaller than the fruits of the wayfaring tree, and a striking metallic blue in colour. Nevertheless, the fact that laurustinus occasionally sets fruit in Britain has allowed it to escape from gardens and establish itself in the wild.

Different specimens of laurustinus can be very variable in such features as leaf shape, size of flower head and so forth. This suggests that there are a number of different races in this species that have become adapted to different climates. Some, for example, are adapted to the warmth of the Mediterranean while others – presumably those that set fruit here – are adapted to the cooler, moister climate of Britain.

Blackthorn and cherry-plum

Blackthorn and cherry-plum may look alike at a quick first glance. But look closer, and you'll see that blackthorn is a prickly, rigid bush with tangled branches, whereas cherry-plum is an elegant tree with smooth bark and larger leaves and flowers.

Below: Blackthorn breaks into a mass of blossom in spring. As with hawthorn, it is considered unlucky to bring the blossom into the house or wear it in a buttonhole.

The blackthorn is a deciduous shrub which is one of the best protected against grazing animals: it positively bristles with stiff, spiny thorns on the twigs, branches and even the stem. It is common throughout the British Isles on most types of soil and in a wide variety of habitats. It is most conspicuous on scrublands where it forms dense, impenetrable thickets, but rarely grows taller than 4m (13ft), and on windswept coastal cliffs it is

shaped and stunted by the prevailing winds.

Blackthorn also grows in woodland but because it needs plenty of light you are unlikely to see it in the shady interior, although it thrives on the edges of woods and in clearings, along road verges, grassy tracks, hedgerows, embankments, and on commons.

The blackthorn is a rigid bush, sending out many branches which further divide to form a close network of twigs, each ending in a sharp point. The bark is usually quite smooth and blackish—hence the name—but the younger shoots are covered with fine downy hairs. The older branches are frequently thickly encrusted with lichens.

Prickly trap It is not surprising that many birds choose to nest in blackthorn bushes, their eggs and nestlings relatively secure from predators by being tucked away in their spiny fortress. The most important is the red-backed shrike, a rather rare bird which has an interesting habit of impaling its prey on to the tips of thorns. The shrike's 'larder' is a store of surplus food which is either eaten later or fed to the young.

The blackthorn's tight prickly growth would seem to make it an ideal hedging plant

Above: Sloes are hard to collect because blackthorn bushes are so prickly, but added to gin, they make a delicious drink.

Right: **Blackthorn** (*Prunus spinosa*). Deciduous, native, grows to 4m (13ft) in scrub, woods, hedges. Flowers April, sloes Aug-Sept.

Below: The remains of a lizard impaled on blackthorn. Beetles, frogs, bees and nestlings are also stored in this way and eaten by the red-backed shrike.

for creating stockproof barriers. Indeed it is, but there is one drawback: blackthorn sends up erect shoots or suckers from its roots, often several feet from the main stem. If these are not cut back they gradually spread out into the pasture, eventually forming a dense thicket that is difficult to remove. This suckering habit means that a large clump of blackthorns can result from just one plant spreading vegetatively.

Flowers The blackthorn flowers early, in March or April, before the foliage appears. Each flower is composed of five pure white petals, and they are pollinated by insects. In some years the starry blossoms cover the twigs in such profusion that you can hardly see the bark.

Many people believe that if the weather is cold when blackthorn blossom appears then it will remain cold for the whole flowering period – about a fortnight – a so-called blackthorn winter. It is easy to dismiss these age-old beliefs, but there was a typical blackthorn winter in 1981: a week of below-average temperatures in mid-April culminated in blizzards which swept across most of the country, cutting off farms and villages and causing chaos on the roads. The fact is that the flowering of blackthorn does often coincide with a cold winter.

Leaves The leaf buds are spaced alternately along the twigs and the foliage unfurls in May. The leaves are small, about 3cm (1in) long, oval in shape with finely toothed margins. A large number of moth caterpillars feed on the leaves, as do the caterpillars of two small butterflies, the brown hairstreak, and the rare black hairstreak, which is known only in a few places in the Midlands. After mating the females of both species lay their eggs on blackthorn twigs where they pass the winter before hatching early the following summer.

Sloes The flowers are succeeded by hard green fruits which ripen and swell during summer to become the familiar small, round, blackish plums called sloes. Each one is about 15mm ($\frac{1}{2}$in) across and the black skin is usually coated with a dusty bloom which gives them a bluish-grey colour. A single round stone is embedded within the greenish-yellow flesh.

Sloes are extremely sour and if you bite into one it will set your teeth on edge. However those fruits that linger on the bush for a month or so do become slightly sweeter. Sloes can be used with sugar for making wine or steeped in gin to produce sloe-gin, an excellent liqueur-type drink.

Blackthorn wood is hard and the grain forms intricate patterns of colour. The straight stems from younger bushes make handsome walking sticks. In Ireland the shillelagh, a fearsome cudgel traditionally carried for personal protection, is usually fashioned from blackthorn. Shillelaghs are still made today for sale as tourist souvenirs.

The cherry-plum or myrobalan is a small deciduous tree growing to about 8m (26ft) in height. The trunk, which is covered with smooth blackish bark, sends out slender branches to form a rather narrow, rounded crown. As a young bush it can easily be confused with blackthorn but the twigs are much less thorny and the leaves are generally larger – up to 7cms (3in) long.

The cherry-plum is native to Asia Minor and it is not known for certain when it was introduced to the British Isles, but it was recorded growing here in the 16th century. It has a rather local distribution, more or less limited to south and eastern regions of England. In some districts it was widely used as a hedge plant, for it tolerates heavy cutting and does not sucker freely like the blackthorn, so is easier to control and maintain. It is also locally planted in shelterbelts around orchards but elsewhere it grows wild in overgrown hedgerows and waysides.

The white flowers are a larger version of blackthorn blossom, about 2cm ($\frac{3}{4}$in) across, but not produced in such quantity. The flowers appear in April, before the leaves unfold, but they are easily damaged by frost and so rarely produce much fruit in the British Isles. In September, if the spring has been mild, the tree becomes laden with reddish 'cherry-plums' each about 2.5cms (1in) in diameter and hanging from a 2cm ($\frac{3}{4}$in) long stalk. They are delicious to eat.

Above and below: Cherry-plum is usually planted along hedgerows although it is occasionally naturalised. It is widely believed that an ancient hybrid between blackthorn and cherry-plum gave rise to all our domestic plum trees including bullaces, damsons and greengages.

Left: **Cherry-plum** (*Prunus cerasifera*). Deciduous, introduced, grows to 8m (26ft) in hedgerows. Flowers March, only fruits in good years.

Ash

Strong, yet graceful, the common ash (below) grows easily throughout the British Isles. It is particularly associated with limestone areas where it flourishes in steep hillside woods, in hedges and between rocky, inhospitable-looking crevices.

The ash is one of our commonest native trees. Although it does not achieve the grandeur of oak nor the majesty of beech, it is nevertheless a handsome species, noted for its graceful foliage and sturdy trunk clad with pale grey bark that becomes deeply furrowed with age.

The crown is rather loosely branched and the foliage relatively light so that the tree does not cast deep shade and a wide variety of plants grow beneath it. In winter, without the benefit of its leaves, the ash reveals its uneven branching and stout twigs which combine to produce a rather shapeless silhouette.

The ash is native to Britain and most of Europe. It is widespread throughout the country in oak woods, copses, in hedgerows

Ash (*Fraxinus excelsior*). Deciduous, native, grows to 25m (100ft), lives up to 200 years. Common throughout the British Isles in scrub, oak woods, hedgerows. Forms woods on chalk or limestone soils. Flowers May-June, fruits Oct-Nov.

keys

Ash keys gradually change colour from green to brown in winter when they ripen. Each key holds one seed at the base of the twisted wing.

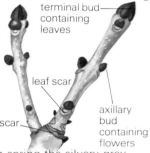

terminal bud containing leaves

leaf scar

scar

axillary bud containing flowers

In spring the silvery grey twigs are characterised by velvety black buds 5-10cm long containing leaves and flowers.

Male and female flowers emerge before the leaves and may be found on the same twig, on different twigs or often on different trees.

Right: Ash keys ripen in early autumn. The name dates from medieval times when door keys were fashioned in the shape of ash keys. Ash trees rarely bear fruit until they are over 40 years old.

and along river banks. Woods dominated by ash tend to occur on steep limestone hillsides. Pure ash woods are often associated with outcrops of carboniferous limestone and fine examples occur in such widely dispersed parts of the country as the Mendip Hills, the Pennines and Cumbria.

Limestone pavements But by far the most interesting ash woods grow on limestone pavements, the largest areas of which are in the north of England around Morecambe Bay, Great Asby, Ingleborough and Malham. These pavements are platforms of rock which were carved and smoothed by the scouring action of glaciers during the last Ice Age over 10,000 years ago.

Huge flat blocks of limestone clints are separated from each other by crevices called grikes which are 2-4m (6-13ft) deep and up to 50cm (1½ft) wide. Ash is the dominant tree and forms open woods which allow a profusion of shrubs, such as hazel, blackthorn and bird cherry, and wild flowers, such as red campions, wood anemones and lilies of the valley, to mention just a few, to grow in the

light underneath. In addition, rather like a natural rock garden, a tremendous variety of ferns and mosses thrive in the damp shade of the grikes.

Recognising the ash is easy because the twigs in winter and the foliage in summer are so distinctive. The smooth pale-grey twigs bear pairs of opposite buds along their length and are each tipped with a large, robust black bud. The buds owe their velvety texture and appearance to a coat of minute black hairs covering the bud scales.

The leaves are compound; 3-6 pairs of toothed lance-shaped leaflets are arranged along the leaf stalk which is itself tipped with a single terminal leaflet. The form of ash leaves is unlike any other British wild tree except for the totally unrelated mountain ash or rowan (*Sorbus aucuparia*). But because the species are different in every other respect, there is little danger of the two being confused.

Flowers Early in April the axillary buds break into flower, well before the emergence of the leaves. The purplish-green flowers that hang like tassels from the bare twigs are

Above: Ash growing out of a limestone pavement near Malham in the Yorkshire Dales. Ash is one of the last trees to leaf out and one of the first to shed its leaves in autumn, often while they are still green.

pollinated by the wind.

Generally ash flowers are bisexual, ie the male and female parts are produced together. The female organs are called pistils; the male organs are the pollen-producing stamens. However it is not unusual to find ash trees with flowers that are all male or all female. And what's more, the ash tree can undergo a sex change from year to year. A male tree last year may be female this year, and perhaps bisexual the next.

Short-lived leaves The ash is one of the latest trees to burst into leaf and is usually not fully covered until May. Generally the ash 'leafs out' later than the oak, but not always. The timing is the subject of a country rhyme which claims to forecast the weather we can expect in the coming months:

Oak before ash . . . we're in for a splash;
Ash before oak . . . we're in for a soak!

The ash loses its leaves quite early in autumn so it has a short cycle of summer growth. The leaves are highly sensitive to cold and are frequently shed at the first hint of

frost. Usually the leaflets fall before the leaf stalk. Occasionally the leaves turn pale yellow, but more often they fall while still green, making the tree one of the least spectacular in the autumn.

Keys Following fertilisation of the flowers, the fruits of the ash (samaras) hang in clusters popularly known as keys, which are green at first and ripen brown during summer. Each key consists of a slightly twisted vane attached to a single seed. The twist helps to give the winged seed a spinning motion, keeping it airborne for as long as possible while it is transported. In autumn gales ash keys may be blown several hundred metres.

Bunches of ash keys last well into the winter and are thus important for birds as food becomes scarce. The amount of seed produced varies from year to year. A heavy ash seed crop may please orchard owners. It has recently been suggested that bullfinches, chief enemies of juicy young buds on fruit trees, are less of a pest when there are plenty of ash seeds available nearby.

Valuable timber Ash has always been a highly prized firewood because it burns 'green', that is when it has been freshly cut. This makes it an excellent fuel, as was celebrated by Walter de la Mare:

Of all the trees in England,
Her sweet three corners in,
Only the Ash, the bonnie Ash,
Burns fierce while it is green.

A great advantage of ash timber is that it is so tough and elastic and it can withstand stress, strain and sharp knocks. It is easily the best native timber for any sort of long handle which has to resist sudden shock. Axes, picks, mallets and various garden tools invariably have ash handles. Similarly it is used for sports equipment such as oars, hockey sticks and parallel bars.

Ash was widely planted in hedgerows because the wood was useful on farms, and in woodland ash trees used to be coppiced to provide poles. But ash wood is no good for fencing because it quickly rots in the ground. Ash poles are still specially grown in nurseries to make walking sticks. The young ash plants are cut back and replanted on a slant. Subsequent regrowth from the stump is vertical and so a stick with a bent handle is produced.

In the past ash was used for weapons, especially for the shafts of spears and lances. The Anglo-Saxon word for ash is *aesc*, which was also used to mean spear.

The ash played an important role in ancient Nordic mythology from Scandinavia where it was regarded as the 'tree of life'. From a huge ash tree, whose crown reached up to heaven and whose roots penetrated hell, the gods ruled the world. To watch over earthly affairs, they were helped by an eagle perching on the topmost branches. In turn the eagle was assisted by a squirrel, which spent its time scampering up and down the tree and reporting on what was happening below.

Silver and downy birches

Few trees match the style of the birch. The narrow trunk, silvery bark and slender branches ending in a mass of drooping twigs have the outline of a fountain that produces a cascade of delicate leaves. No wonder it has become known as the Lady of the Woods.

There are three native species of birch in the British Isles but only two, the silver birch and the downy birch, are common. They thrive particularly well on acid soils, but rarely grow on chalk. The silver birch grows best on dry sandy or gravelly soils such as those of the heathlands of southern England, but the downy birch prefers wetter soils and a cooler climate and so is most common in the uplands of Scotland, Wales and Ireland. However, their ranges overlap considerably and they are often found growing in the same areas, exploiting local variations in the wetness or drainage of the soil.

Differences in detail In general form the silver and downy birch are very similar and can be described together, although they differ in a number of details.

The silver birch, as its name suggests, has much whiter bark, whereas the bark of the downy birch is more variable, ranging from silver-grey to brownish in colour. The only way to distinguish the two species from a distance is by the colour of the bark. A characteristic of old silver birches is the patches of rough, knobbly black bark replacing the white bark at the base of the trunk. In downy birches the bark remains more or less smooth right down to the ground.

Secondly, unlike downy birches, silver birches typically have hanging or 'weeping' twigs–a feature that has been exaggerated by selective breeding to produce ornamental

Below: Birch woodland in early autumn with young oak and sycamore, and a ground-covering of bracken.

varieties that grace many parks and gardens. And the twigs of the silver birch are smooth, whereas those of the downy birch are covered with short fine hairs.

Leaves, flowers and fruits The foliage appears towards the end of April, the leaves unfolding from small, pointed buds that are arranged alternately along the thin, purplish-brown twigs. The bright green leaves, about 3cm (1in) long, are usually triangular in outline but the shape may vary from diamond to oval. Their margins are rather unevenly toothed and they taper to a sharp point. They are borne on slender stalks which allow them to twist and flutter in the breeze. The leaves of young birches are often much larger than those on full grown trees because they grow much more vigorously. After a heavy shower in late spring the air in a dense stand of birch has a delicate fragrance from the aromatic resin washed from the unfurling leaves and from tiny warts on the twigs.

In autumn the leaves turn bright yellow, before falling in October to leave the trees bare, but still beautiful, their trunks gleaming white in the pale wintry sunlight.

Birch flowers are catkins and both sexes are borne on the same tree. The males develop during autumn and by April or May have turned into a dangling catkin about 5cm (2in) long, covered with reddish brown scales which separate to release their pollen. The female catkins appear with the unfolding leaves. They are held erect on the twigs, 2-3cm (1in) long, and are made up of overlapping green

Above: **Silver birch** (*Betula pendula*). Deciduous, native, grows to 25m (80ft) throughout the British Isles, on light soils, heathland, may form pure woods in the Scottish Highlands. Rare on chalk. Flowers April, fruits July.

Above right and below: **Downy birch** (*Betula pubescens*). Deciduous, native, grows to 20m (65ft) in similar areas to the silver birch though it prefers wetter, colder conditions.

scales, each shielding an ovary from which two purple stigmas protrude to catch pollen grains wafted on the wind.

After fertilisation the female catkins expand into club-shaped cone-like structures that slowly disintegrate in autumn to release the tiny winged fruits. These are so light they may be carried for considerable distances by strong winds.

Birch woods are a favourite haunt of redpolls and siskins, winter visitors from Scandinavia, which feed on the seeds scattered on the ground.

Hardy pioneer The birch is an extremely hardy tree and has established itself in some northern-most forests at the frontier of the treeless tundra. The pollen record shows that birches and pines were the first trees to advance into the British Isles when the climate warmed after the last Ice Age. Both species formed vast forests but were confined to the better-drained uplands.

Today the birch is found in most woodlands on the poorer soils, from English oak woods to Scottish pine woods. It also forms pure birch woods – you can see good examples on the sandy heaths of southern England and the steep hillsides of Scotland.

The birch is an aggressive colonizer of forest clearings, ungrazed heaths, and areas which have suffered recent burning. Its tiny winged seeds spread in profusion and germinate quickly to invade new areas. The pioneer trees form dense thickets of fast growing saplings that develop into pure birch stands up to 25m (80ft) tall at maturity.

Fungi associates Birch trees have a remarkable relationship with the fly agaric fungus which sends up its striking red toadstools in autumn. The fungus is attached to the tree's roots and both benefit from this association: the fungus speeds the entry of soil nutrients into the root system of the tree in return for sugars manufactured by the tree.

You may also find the bracket fungus clamped on to the trunks of older trees. It is a parasite, feeding on the tree's sap but giving nothing in return. Indeed, this fungal

Right: Not birds' nests among the branches of a mature silver birch, but witches broom, a growth deformity.

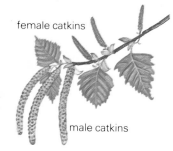

female catkins

male catkins

The ripe seeds in the fruiting catkins have large wings – 2-3 times as wide as the seed in the silver birch (above) and 1-1½ times in the downy birch (below), allowing them to spread to great distances.

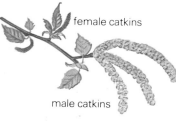

female catkins

male catkins

Below: A large gall growing on the trunk of a silver birch may damage but is unlikely to kill the tree.

Below right: The small bracket fungus (*Trametes versicolor*) thriving on a dead birch tree. The fungus may continue to feed on the rotting wood for many years.

assault so weakens the tree that it soon perishes, and the fungus continues to feed on the dead wood. Although the birches' death is often hastened by fungal attack, birches do not live for a long time anyway – rarely exceeding 80 years. Dead or dying trees are favourite nesting sites for woodpeckers whose bills can easily tunnel holes into the wood softened by decay.

Witches broom Many birch trees appear to have large birds' nests among their branches. In fact these untidy tangles of twigs are galls, a growth deformity caused when the buds are attacked by either a fungus or a tiny mite. A dense mass of twigs sprouts at the point of attack to form the so-called witches broom. (Actually birch twigs are cut and

bundled to make the sort of broom that witches are supposed to fly around on at night. They are also used for steeple-chase fences to fill out the jumps.)

Bark and timber The thin paper-like bark is shed in strips as the tree grows, and is replaced anew from underneath. Birch bark is remarkably resistant to decay – the bark on a fallen log remains for months after the wood inside has rotted to a soft pulp. It is also waterproof, and has been used in parts of Europe for roofing. Birch bark makes excellent kindling for camp fires and the wood itself burns very well. In parts of Scandinavia and Central Europe birch wood is still the main winter fuel.

Birch timber is a pale creamy brown colour and has been put to a wide variety of uses: for instance, the making of carts and packing cases, and smaller items such as floor tiles, cotton reels, spools and bobbins for the textile trade. But although it is a hard wood, it does not last long out of doors.

In spring there is a copious flow of sugary sap through the trunk and in some country districts this is collected by tapping the trees; the liquid is fermented into wine.

Dwarf birch There is a third species, the dwarf birch (*Betula nana*), an arctic-alpine shrub less than 1m (3ft) tall which grows at a few sites in the Scottish Highlands. It also has the distinction of being the only woody species to grow in the frozen wastes of Greenland – the world's northern limit for woody plants. Here it takes the form of a low wiry bush, spreading close to the ground, its growth stunted by the icy blasts of Arctic gales. Its leaves are smaller and rounder in shape than those of the other two species. A few specimens occur in Northumberland, but it is generally a rare species.

Deciduous trees of parks and gardens

Some seven to eight thousand years ago, as the ice of the last Ice Age melted, the sea swept through the Straits of Dover (until then dry land) and cut the British Isles off from the rest of Europe. At that time Britain had just 32 species of broadleaved trees, three species of conifers and an assortment of shrubs. Yet today, almost 1,500 species of trees grow in this country. Basically, all these additional tree species are due to the acquisitiveness of early travellers and gardeners for whom plants from far-away places were a great attraction, and to a large extent this is still the case today.

Some garden plants have been in cultivation for many hundreds of years. The mulberry, for example, is thought originally to have been an eastern species, but it has been known in cultivation for such a long period that its origins are obscure. Similarly, Cornelian cherry has been a cultivated plant since at least the 16th century, bringing early colour when no native trees are in flower. Botanical expeditions eastwards have sent back many fine trees, particularly several species of magnolia and forsythia–all fine decorative plants. The plant for which the East is known best, however, is the cherry, and particularly the cherries of Japan–the country and the plant have more or less become synonymous. The Orient has also been instrumental in producing the typical street tree of London, the London plane. This is thought to be a hybrid between two species– *Platanus orientalis* and *P. occidentalis.* These are normally separated by several thousand miles, but the hybridisation occurred in cultivation, giving a fertile offspring that loves grimy streets!

The New World also has provided its fair share of plants which have been received gladly into cultivation. Several magnolia species are found in North America, including the large flowered evergreen *Magnolia grandiflora,* and several species of hickory have been introduced from North America as timber trees. Several species of oak have also been introduced, sometimes for timber, and in other cases for ornamental reasons.

The prerequisite for a garden or park tree is that it must produce attractive flowers, fruit, leaves or bark, or that it is in itself striking. Large trees, like oaks, walnuts or horse chestnuts, make fine specimen trees in large park areas. It is the fortunate few, however, who have gardens which can do such large trees justice. Nevertheless, the smaller bushes and trees come into their own in more typical gardens, and in the flowering season it is hard to come across a suburban garden that does not possess an ornamental tree of some description. Many of these small decorative trees have the very pleasant habit of surprising the gardener with an elegance and grace not thought possible. It is one of the bonuses of growing trees.

Opposite: In Britain's National Arboretum at Westonbirt, Gloucestershire, Japanese maples make a brilliant display of leaf colours every autumn.

London plane

The London plane, the most characteristic tree of London's streets and parks, also thrives in other towns and cities. You can recognise it immediately for the mottled bark that it sheds in great slabs, so ridding itself of pollution and dirt.

Opposite: A typical view of a London plane, growing here in Fitzroy Square in central London. London planes thrive in cities not only because they can withstand pollution, but also because they are tolerant of the periodic rigorous pruning which is necessary to prevent the branches obstructing overhead wires and high vehicles like buses.

Below: **London plane** (*Platanus x hispanica*). Deciduous, introduced, grows up to 35m (115ft), lives up to 200 years. Common especially in London but also planted in other towns and cities in the southern half of England. Flowers May, fruits late summer-early autumn.

One tree above all dominates the London landscape–the London plane. Planes make up over 60% of London's planted trees, lining streets and avenues, and gracing parks, squares and gardens. It is an unmistakable species, with distinctive peeling bark, shining green summer foliage, and dangling seed-balls in winter.

Opinions differ about the origins of the London plane. One idea is that it grew from a cross between the oriental plane (*Platanus orientalis*) which grows wild in Turkey and Greece, and the western plane or buttonwood (*P. occidentalis*), a native of North America where it is the tallest deciduous tree. Other theories, and indeed the current one, favours that it is merely a variety of the western plane. This hybrid theory suggests that it was crossed in Spain or the south of France in 1650, and first planted in England in Ely and Barnes, Surrey in about 1680.

The London plane grows vigorously and is resistant to air pollution. This has made it increasingly popular as an ornamental tree in towns and cities. Most of London's planes were planted at the beginning of the 20th century but some, such as the giants around Berkeley Square, are about 200 years old.

Outside London the plane has been widely planted in parks and along roads in southern England and the Midlands. Further afield, it has been cultivated in many European cities, notably in Paris.

New bark for old The London plane is a handsome tree, reaching a height of 35m (115ft) or more. The tallest on record–48m (145ft)–grows at Blandford in Dorset. Numerous side branches sprout from the contorted and arching main limbs, dividing to form intricate layers of drooping twigs. The trunk is tall, massive and smooth apart from occasional bumps and wrinkles.

The bark, the tree's most striking feature, flakes off in sheets, leaving the trunk dappled with various shades of brown, grey and yellow. As the tree grows, it breaks out of its old 'skin', shedding the older grey or brown bark to reveal the new yellowish bark beneath.

It is thought that this bark-peeling habit has helped the London plane to tolerate city life. All trees 'breathe' through pores in their bark, and in an urban environment these soon get clogged by dust and soot. But as the London plane constantly replaces old bark with new, its trunk does not become so coated with the grime that harms other trees. In effect the plane regularly renews its air filter.

Glossy leaves, green catkins Rain water washes off accumulated dirt from the smooth glossy surfaces of the leaves. These large leaves, which cast a pleasantly cool shade in summer, are alternately placed along the twigs and unfurl from cone-shaped buds which are almost completely encircled by a

Right: The distinctive bark of the London plane. The outermost layer is dark from continued exposure to dirt and pollution. It flakes off to reveal large, pale and as-yet unpolluted patches of bark.

scar left by the previous year's leaf-stalk. They appear in mid-May and are at first covered with a woolly brown down that is later shed as they unfold and expand. The leaves display great variation from tree to tree but generally they are made up of five broad lobes, each with a deeply cut margin.

The base of the leaf-stalk is hollow where it joins the twig, and encloses the developing bud that lies dormant through winter before sprouting the following spring. The upper surface of the leaves is a rich shining green, while the underside is less bright and more yellowish in colour.

The London plane is a wind-pollinated tree that flowers in May and June. The round flower heads are made up of tightly packed green flowers which are either all female or all male, although both sexes are carried on the same tree. The flower heads hang on the tree throughout winter and start to disintegrate the following year, releasing hundreds of seeds.

Tough timber Although the London plane is planted purely for ornament it yields a timber that is highly regarded by craftsmen. The pinkish-brown wood is tough and hard and has been widely used by manufacturers of keyboard instruments, and cabinet makers. London plane timber is sometimes called lace-wood because of the intricate patterns made by the grain, and is cut into thin sheets of veneer for use on high quality furniture.

Male and female flower heads

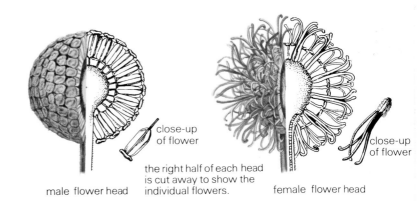

close-up of flower

close-up of flower

male flower head

the right half of each head is cut away to show the individual flowers.

female flower head

Right: The leaves and ripening fruits of the London plane. The fruits usually dangle singly or in pairs on stalks up to 10cm (4in) long throughout the winter. The seeds are not reliably fertile and London planes are generally raised from cuttings.

Below: In autumn the leaves turn various shades of yellow before falling to the ground, and for a few weeks London's parks become a mass of golden colour.

Magnolia and tulip tree

Arguably, no other tree grown in Britain bears such spectacularly beautiful flowers as the magnolia and its less well-known relative, the tulip tree. Yet these same flowers have one of the most primitive structures of any in the world.

Above: The magnolia that has been cultivated the longest is probably the yulan tree (*Magnolia denudata*), which has been grown in the gardens of its native China since the Tang Dynasty (618-907). The Chinese used the buds for medicinal and culinary purposes but in Britain, where it was introduced around 1790, it is grown purely as an ornamental. A deciduous tree growing to a height of 18m (60ft), it bears copious white flowers before the leaves open.

Magnolias and tulip trees both belong to the same family, the magnolia family or Magnoliaceae, a group generally considered to be one of the most primitive families of flowering plants. Today, the trees and shrubs of this family are confined to America and south-east Asia, but the fossil record shows that the family was once distributed throughout the whole of Europe and as far north as northern Alaska and Greenland. Fossils of leaves and flowers looking like those of magnolia have been found in rocks 100 million years old, and there can be no doubt that magnolia-like plants were a feature of the landscapes through which dinosaurs roamed.

Magnolia species The genus *Magnolia* is named after Pierre Magnol (1638-1715), who was professor of botany and medicine at Montpellier in France. Of the 80 or so species occurring today, about a third are native to the south-east United States, Mexico, Central America and the northern part of South America. The remainder come from the area bounded by the Himalayas, Japan and Java. More than half the species are tropical but, in spite of most being montane, they do not grow successfully out of doors in Britain. Only those magnolias from temperate latitudes are hardy here.

Evergreen magnolias While the majority of magnolias are deciduous, some of the most impressive are evergreen. One such is *Magnolia grandiflora,* a species introduced to Britain from the southern United States in 1734. In its natural environment it grows to a height of 30m (100ft). In Britain, however, it never develops its full magnificence and is often seen as a small shrub or tree growing against a south-facing wall. It bears creamy-white flowers up to 30cm (1ft) across with purple stamens.

The white laurel (*M. virginiana*) was the first American magnolia introduced to Britain, in 1688. A semi-evergreen species from the eastern United States, it bears rounded creamy-white flowers with a heavy fragrance–in contrast to the lightly scented flowers of *M. grandiflora.*

Another evergreen species from the eastern

Left: Magnolia 'Leonard Messel', one of a great number of cultivated varieties that have been developed for gardens. Like many other deciduous magnolias, 'Leonard Messel' flowers in spring before its leaves unfurl.

Below: The star magnolia (*M. stellata*) from Japan is the earliest of the outdoor magnolias to flower in Britain, its fragrant flowers with 12-18 white tepals appearing in March. A similar-looking species is *M. kobus*. It, too, has white star-shaped flowers but is a larger tree. It was introduced from Japan in 1709.

Left: In many species of magnolias the fruits ripen to a collection of brightly coloured seeds—as in *M. mollicomata*, one of the less familiar species of magnolias in Britain. In all magnolias, the seeds, whether brightly coloured or not, develop a fleshy outer layer after fertilisation. This layer serves to attract birds, which help to disperse the seeds. In tulip trees the seeds are smaller and do not develop such a fleshy outer coat.

United States is the umbrella tree (*M. tripetala*). Introduced in 1752, it too has strongly scented flowers.

Deciduous species Among several deciduous magnolias grown in Britain is the yulan tree (*M. denudata*), a species that has been cultivated in its native China since at least a thousand years ago.

Also from China is *M. liliflora*, which forms a large bush bearing purplish-white flowers. In 1820 a hybrid was produced from these two deciduous species. Known as *M. × soulangiana*, cultivars from it are widely planted today.

Primitive structure Why do botanists consider magnolias to be so primitive? The answer lies partly in the structure of their flowers and leaves.

When a magnolia flower opens, the enclosing bud scales drop off to reveal single blooms, typically creamy to purplish-white in colour. Although prized for their beauty, these flowers do not possess true petals, nor do they have sepals (the outer green 'floral leaves' found on many other flowers). Instead, the coloration is provided by whorls of structures intermediate in form between petals and sepals, and known as tepals. In some species the tepals in the outermost whorl are reduced and resemble sepals, while those towards the middle are more petal-like. All these features are considered to be primitive.

The whorls of tepals surround the stamens, which in turn surround the carpels – the female part of the flower consisting of an ovary containing the ovules (the unfertilised seeds) and their attendant styles and stigmas. Both the stamens and the carpels are arranged in a conspicuous spiral, another feature considered by botanists to be primitive.

The stamens bear anthers consisting of two pollen sacs, which split open longitudinally to release the pollen grains. The shape of the pollen grains provides another clue to the primitive nature of magnolias. The grains of most other dicotyledons have three pores or furrows in their outer wall, whereas those of magnolias have a single longitudinal furrow along one side. Some of the oldest fossilised pollen grains thought to belong to flowering plants have the same furrow.

The leaves also share certain features in common with those of primitive flowering plants, particularly in the way that some veins loop round to meet each other near the margins whereas others peter out beforehand. In some species the courses and thicknesses of the veins are highly variable.

Tulip trees Many of the primitive features of magnolias are also found on their close relatives, the tulip trees, genus *Liriodendron*. The more common one in Britain, *L. tulipifera*, was introduced to Europe from its native eastern North America in the 17th century. The other species, *L. chinense*, was discovered in the mountains of central China in 1875. It is a smaller, more compact tree than *L. tulipifera*

cone-like fruit

carpels containing seeds

Magnolia fruit

Left: The fruit of both a magnolia (shown here) and a tulip tree is a cone-shaped collection of carpels, which split open when ripe to expose the seeds.

Below: The leaves of a magnolia and a tulip tree show the same primitive pattern of veins. A series of veins, called secondary veins, branch off from the midvein and loop round near the margin to join one another. Some, called intersecondary veins, peter out before the margin.

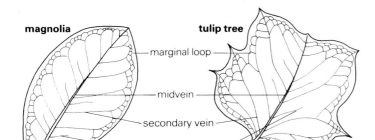

magnolia

tulip tree

marginal loop

midvein

secondary vein

intersecondary vein

Vein patterns

Left: A close-up of the cultivar *M. grandiflora* 'Exmouth Variety' clearly shows the structure of a typical magnolia flower. Whorls of white petal-like tepals surround the cream-coloured stamens, which in turn surround the female carpels. Both the stamens and the carpels are arranged in a spiral, a feature regarded by botanists as primitive.

Below left: The flower of a tulip tree has obvious similarities to that of a magnolia, but there are also some important differences. The six greenish structures surrounding the stamens and carpels are petals, not tepals. The orange-white marks at their bases are nectaries. Behind the petals lie three greenish sepals, one of which can be seen here.

Right: The tulip tree *Liriodendron tulipifera* grows well in our climate, reaching a height of 25m (80ft).

The leaves of tulip trees are readily identifiable by their bizarre shape, for their apex consists of two pointed lobes.

The trees flower between May and August, with most blossoms appearing in June and July. While the stamens and carpels resemble those of magnolia flowers, the petals and sepals are better differentiated in *Liriodendron*. The flowers bear a superficial resemblance to tulips—hence the trees' common name—but the two plants are unrelated. Each flower has a whorl of three sepals reflexed (bent back) from the main flower. There are six petals, about 5cm (2in) long, greenish-white outside and yellowish inside.

After fertilisation each carpel forms a winged seed on a short stalk. The fruits are borne in large numbers on a dense, cone-like structure, but in Britain the fruit rarely ripens.

Diverse distribution One further reason for considering the magnolia family to be primitive is the present distribution of its members in two widely separated regions of the world—America and south-east Asia. It is unreasonable to expect that the numerous features characterising these plants evolved independently on both sides of the Pacific Ocean.

Instead, the occurrence of magnolia-like fossils in a great many countries supports the idea that the family was once much more widespread. But, as climates changed and perhaps the tolerances of magnolias and tulip trees to their environments altered, so the distribution shrank and split into two. It may be, therefore, that today's plants are but a remnant of a previously more diverse and possibly more spectacular group.

Cherry and Portugal laurels

Two species so often seen growing in suburban gardens, the cherry laurel also grows in the wild and has been much planted to provide game cover on country estates, while the Portugal laurel is only ever seen in cultivation in this country.

Neither the cherry laurel nor the Portugal laurel are true laurels, despite their names. True laurels are members of the laurel family, of which the sweet bay (*Laurus nobilis*), from which we get our bay leaves, is the most familiar. The cherry and Portugal laurels, on the other hand, are included among the cherries because of their five-petalled flowers and their dark purple, cherry-like fruits. But the fact that they are both shrubby and have oval, evergreen leaves somewhat similar to those of the sweet bay led to their being called laurels, as indeed were several other broad-leaved evergreen shrubs.

Cherry laurel This species is one of our most familiar broad-leaved evergreens. It is

native to forests bordering the southern part of the Caspian Sea in Iran, where it is often seen growing in association with the oriental beech. It is also found in the Caucasus mountains of the USSR, the mountains of central Turkey and west into the European part of Turkey and Bulgaria. There is also an isolated population in Yugoslavia.

The cherry laurel has been cultivated in southern and western Europe for centuries, certainly since the 16th and 17th centuries, and is now naturalised in many of these countries, including Britain and Ireland.

In Britain, the cherry laurel is most commonly seen as a widely branching shrub between 1.5m (5ft) and 3m (10ft) tall. The leaves are arranged alternately and are large (up to 20cm/8in long) and thick with minutely toothed or entire margins.

The flowers of cherry laurel are similar to those of other species of cherry, each flower having five separate petals and a cluster of protruding stamens. Usually produced in April, the creamy-white flowers are up to 8mm across and strongly (though not pleasantly) scented. The flowers are borne on elongated heads called racemes, like the flowers on the closely related bird cherry.

As the fruits of the cherry laurel begin to develop, the similarity between it and other species of cherry is again apparent. Each fruit is globose (ie, globe-shaped) and up to 1.5cm ($\frac{5}{8}$in) across, turning from green to red and becoming blackish-purple around September. Like an ordinary cherry, the fruit has an outer fleshy layer and a central stone; it closely resembles a small sloe but you cannot eat it for it is poisonous.

The Portugal laurel This species was introduced to Britain in the middle of the 17th century. It is native to Portugal and Spain, its range just extending into south-western France. The Portugal laurel also occurs on the islands of the western Atlantic, most notably in the famous evergreen forests in the mountains of the Canary Islands. It also occurs in the Azores, where it is distinguished as a separate sub-species because plants from there have relatively wider leaves, shorter racemes with fewer flowers and shorter fruit-stalks. The sub-species was introduced to Britain in 1860 and is sometimes cultivated here.

The Portugal laurel is generally taller than the cherry laurel, sometimes growing to become a small tree. It is usually between 3m (10ft) and 6m (20ft) high, though it may reach a height of 15m (50ft). It has smaller leaves (up to 13cm/5in long), the margins of which are more conspicuously toothed.

In flower, the two species are easily distinguished, particularly as the Portugal laurel usually flowers in June, which is two months after the cherry laurel. Instead of the cherry laurel's short upright heads bearing some 30 flowers, the Portugal laurel has a profusion of spreading or pendulous elongated heads, each

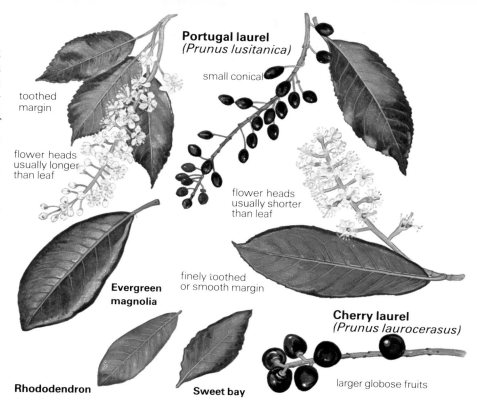

Portugal laurel
(Prunus lusitanica)

small conical

toothed margin

flower heads usually longer than leaf

flower heads usually shorter than leaf

Evergreen magnolia

finely toothed or smooth margin

Rhododendron

Sweet bay

Cherry laurel
(Prunus laurocerasus)

larger globose fruits

with up to 100 flowers. These have a scent that has been likened to that of the hawthorn. The inflorescence of a Portugal laurel is usually much longer than the leaf from which it arises, whereas on the cherry laurel the inflorescence is usually shorter than the leaf.

The fruits of the Portugal laurel are similar to those of the cherry laurel, though slightly smaller and more conical. They ripen through red to a dark purple.

Wild and cultivated Of the two species, only the cherry laurel is naturalised in Britain. Since it occurs as an understorey to beech in its native lands, it is not surprising that cherry laurel grows quite happily in the shade in this country. Indeed, it is one of the most useful

Above: Leaves, flowers and fruits of the cherry and Portugal laurels, with the leaves of other common evergreen shrubs for comparison.

Opposite page: Usually seen as a shrub, cherry laurel is sometimes encountered as a tree, as in this large specimen with its twisted and much fluted trunk.

Below: Cherry laurels flower in April, bearing upright racemes of creamy-white flowers.

evergreens for such situations and is planted to provide protection for gamebirds in coverts. The spreading lower branches give the birds shelter from the wind, rain and snow, and the berries supply food at a time of scarcity. The seeds from these woodland plants germinate readily and have allowed the cherry laurel to become naturalised in this country.

In cultivation, the cherry laurel is probably seen at its best when it is grown on its own in the lightest shade, with plenty of room for it to expand. The tallest garden specimens are to be found in the west of Britain, where the damper climate allows specimens to form trees some 8m (27ft) tall, though exceptional plants of 14m (47ft) tall have been recorded.

On lime-rich soils, the cherry laurel does not fare so well, its leaves tending to become yellow and fall off, and under these circumstances the Portugal laurel is the more appropriate species to plant. Both species are generally hardy in Britain, the Portugal laurel slightly more so.

Above: The Portugal laurel flowers in June, two months after the cherry laurel. The individual flowers are similar in the two species but on the Portugal laurel many more are borne on the flower heads, which tend to spread out horizontally or even hang down.

Right: Of the many cultivars of cherry laurel, one of the best known and most suitable for small gardens is 'Otto Luyken', a low-growing shrub, seen here in full flower.

Below: Berries of the cherry laurel, ripening from green through red to become dark purple at maturity. Portugal laurel berries are similar, though smaller and more conical.

Killing jars Back in the days when budding young naturalists were taught that before nature's diversity could be appreciated it must first be killed and preserved, every schoolboy knew that a few crushed cherry laurel leaves in a jam jar made an excellent 'killing jar' for butterflies: the insects remained relaxed long enough for the wings to be spread out and set.

This property arises from the fact that all parts of the plant, but particularly the leaves and fruits, are poisonous because they contain hydrocyanic (prussic) acid. In spite of this, a distillation (presumably weak) of the young leaves was once used to treat respiratory disorders and dyspepsia.

Sweet bay

Few plants are surrounded by as much mythology and symbolism as the sweet bay. Though not native to Britain, the sweet bay has been grown in this country for centuries and is the source of one of our most popular herbs: the bay leaf.

Sweet bay (*Laurus nobilis*). Evergreen shrub or small tree, native to the Mediterranean. Naturalised in some parts of southern England, but more often seen as a garden shrub (see below). Height to 15m (50ft) but usually smaller.

Common names are often an unreliable guide to whether plants are related to each other. For example, the sweet chestnut and the horse chestnut sound as if they should be closely related – but they are not. They are related only in so far as both are broad-leaved trees but, because their nuts are similar, they were long ago both called chestnuts.

The same situation exists with the word 'laurel'. True laurels are members of the laurel family (Lauraceae) but the term has been indiscriminately applied to a wide range of broad-leaved evergreen shrubs, so that we now have the cherry laurel, which is related to cherry trees, and the spurge laurel, which is actually a species of *Daphne*. There is only one true species of the laurel family commonly grown in Britain and that is the shrub (or small tree) known variously as bay, sweet bay, bay laurel or poet's laurel.

Northern outlier Sweet bay is one of the few members of the laurel family to grow well in the British Isles. Most are native to the warm temperate or tropical zones. For example, the most economically important member of this family, the avocado pear, comes from Central America.

The sweet bay is native to the Mediterranean region and has been cultivated in the British Isles since about the 16th century, or possibly earlier. It is moderately hardy in this country, apart from in the far north-east, and has become naturalised in parts of southern

Above: Male flowers are pale yellow and consist of four petals and four sepals surrounding about a dozen stamens.

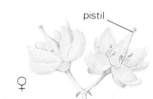

Above: Female flowers resemble the males closely, the only difference being that the petals and sepals surround a single pistil.

Above: Bay leaves with immature fruit. The leaves have wavy margins and a parchment-like texture.

England. However, it is usually seen as a bush growing in gardens, though it is also common as a potted plant.

Sweet-smelling leaves The part of the sweet bay most familiar to people is the leaves. These are, of course, the well-known bay leaves, one of our most popular kitchen herbs. They have a distinctly sweet smell (hence the description 'sweet' in the name sweet bay). Bay leaves are used either fresh or dried for flavouring a variety of dishes, especially stews and soups.

The leaves of sweet bay are evergreen and persist on the plant for two or three years. They have an oddly stiff, yet brittle texture, rather like parchment. The upper surface is slightly glossy and mid-green to dark green, except along the midrib and other veins, which are pale and translucent – if a bay leaf is held up to the light the delicate network of veins shows up clearly. The leaf margins appear toothed at first sight but, in fact, they are simply crinkled and wavy.

Sweet bay occasionally has just a single stem but more often it has several and is shrubby. The bark is very dark, almost black, and generally smooth or slightly wrinkled, though it may become cracked near the base.

Segregation of the sexes The male and female flowers of sweet bay are borne on separate trees. They appear in clusters in the leaf axils on the previous year's wood. Each cluster contains between two and five individual flowers, which open in the spring to reveal four pale yellow petals. In the case of male flowers, these surround a dozen stamens; on female flowers they surround a single pistil.

Usually just one female flower in each cluster develops into a fruit. This is a small round or oval berry, which is green when young but becomes black or dark brown and wrinkled by the time it reaches maturity during winter. When mature, bay berries are about 1cm ($\frac{1}{2}$in) long. The word 'bay' comes from the French word for berry, 'baie'.

In common with all other true laurels, the sweet bay undergoes what is known as hypogeal germination. All flowering plants have one or two leaves present in embryonic form inside the seed. These are the cotyledons, or seed leaves, and are usually the first leaves to appear above the ground when the seed germinates. In hypogeal germination, however, the cotyledons stay inside the seed below ground. When a sweet bay seed germinates, it sends up a narrow shoot above ground, from which emerge true leaves which are scale-like at first but soon grow to resemble the adult leaves.

Myths and legends Man has long held the sweet bay in special regard. The ancient Greeks knew the tree as Daphne because, in their mythology, it was believed that the nymph Daphne turned into a bay tree to escape from Apollo, the Greek god of music, poetry and healing. In remembrance of the

Above: Bay berries are green when young but darken as they mature. By the time they ripen in the winter, they are black and wrinkled. The berries are borne in the leaf axils, usually just one to an axil.

Right: In June, sweet bay bears clusters of pale yellow flowers, between two and five appearing in each leaf axil on last year's wood. Male and female flowers are borne on separate plants; close examination is needed to tell the sex of a flower and therefore of a particular bush. These flowers bear clusters of stamens and so are males.

nymph, Apollo declared the bay to be sacred to himself and symbolic of his own attributes.

With the decline of ancient Greece and the ascendancy of the Roman Empire, bay's traditional associations were transferred to Rome. The Romans called sweet bay 'laurus', from which the modern word laurel derives. They used to award both their conquering warriors and their poets with laurel, the former being crowned with laurel leaves and the latter being presented with branches of laurel in fruit (the modern position of Poet Laureate originates in this ancient custom).

The association of laurel with honour and glory has continued ever since. Napoleon incorporated a golden spray of laurel foliage into his crown; there is the expression 'to rest on one's laurels'; and the modern word 'bachelor' derives from the latin 'bacca-laureus', meaning laurel berry. Originally, the word bachelor referred to one who studied, as in Bachelor of Arts and so on. But, because students used to lead a monastic life and did not marry (and were male), the word came to mean an unmarried man.

Potted bay trees
Bay makes an ideal pot plant since it is one of the few evergreen plants that can withstand having its roots confined in a tub. Potted bay trees, perhaps clipped into an unusual shape, are often seen decorating the entrances of smarter restaurants.

Horse chestnut

The dazzling flowers of the white horse chestnut are a sure indicator of summer. Perhaps more than any other tree, the horse chestnut vividly reflects the changing seasons: the fat sticky buds of winter open in spring to reveal downy green leaves, and shiny brown conkers litter streets and parks in autumn.

Below: The horse chestnut in May—a cascade of brilliant white flowers. The tallest specimen in the British Isles—38m (125ft) high—is at Petworth House in Sussex.

White horse chestnut
(*Aesculus hippocastanum*)
Deciduous, introduced, grows to more than 30m (100ft), lives up to 100 years. Cultivated in parks and gardens, occasionally grows wild, on rich well drained soils.

The white horse chestnut is an impressive tree at any time of the year—and in flower it is truly magnificent. With its wide-spreading branches and typically rounded crown it presents a towering mass of luxuriant foliage throughout the summer and a glorious blaze of colour in early autumn.

Growing wild in hilly regions of Greece, Bulgaria and Iran, the horse chestnut was introduced into Great Britain early in the 17th century. Since then it has been widely planted as an ornamental tree in gardens, parkland and often in long avenues. The horse-chestnut avenue in Bushy Park, Hampton Court, is a fine example which in Victorian times drew large crowds to admire the trees in flower. It is also planted in and around fields to provide shade for farm animals. The foliage is palatable to cattle and horses who stretch to eat all the leaves they can reach while sheltering beneath the tree. The base of the crown forms a conspicuously straight line parallel to the ground.

A curious feature of the horse-chestnut is its slowness to establish itself in the wild, despite its apparent adaptability: it is a hardy tree able to grow on most soils and its seeds (or conkers) germinate freely, yet it seems unable to compete easily against many of our native plants which often crowd it out. This is in stark contrast to other introduced species, such as sycamore, which spread rapidly into woods and plantations.

It is impossible to confuse the white horse chestnut with any other tree, including other chestnuts. The red flowered horse chestnut, which is less widespread, is a result of a cross between the common species and red buckeye, a native of North America. It differs by having red flowers, smoother fruits and generally smaller leaves. The totally unrelated sweet chestnut is clearly distinguished by its yellow flowers, spirally-twisting bark, long saw-edged leaves and more spiny fruit cases.

Bark and timber The horse chestnut's grey-brown bark, which is initially smooth, becomes rough and scaly with old age; the oldest dated specimens in this country were planted in 1664. The tree itself is of little

Left: The horse chestnut bears up to 100 male or bisexual flowers on each candle. The centres of each flower change from yellow to red after pollination.

Below: Under the spreading horse chestnut in autumn you find golden leaves—the largest of any tree in Britain —and conkers that children use in the game originally known as 'conquerors'.

practical value. The cream-coloured wood is soft and weak, making it unsuitable for most purposes, although it is used to make toys and trays. It does not burn well; but in medieval times its charcoal went into the manufacture of gunpowder.

Sticky buds The fat buds, which form during the previous summer and are so prominent in spring, are coated in shiny resin; this protects the new season's shoots from attack by insect pests. The sticky resin gums up these insects, immobilising them and preventing them from chewing into the delicate buds.

If you collect the winter twigs in bud and place them in a jar of water, you can watch the buds burst into leaf. In early spring the buds swell and break open on the tree, the bud scales peeling back as the growing tip emerges. The young leaves are pale green and clothed in white, furry down which gives protection throughout the winter, although the down is soon shed as the leaves expand. Large horseshoe-shaped scars are left on the twigs where previous years' leaf stalks were attached.

The leaves are among the first of any tree to appear in spring and also among the earliest to colour and fall in autumn—changing to yellow and deep gold before dropping. Growing up to 20cm (8in) across, the largest leaves of any tree found in Britain—indeed in Europe—they are made up of from five to seven pear-shaped leaflets borne on a long, stout stalk. When the tree is in full leaf it forms a dense, shady canopy which shows beautifully how leaves can be arranged to reap the maximum benefit from incoming sunlight. Moreover, the leaves can twist on their stalks during the day and position themselves to catch the sun, so avoiding being shaded by their neighbours.

Candles The flowering spikes, or candles, blossom in mid-May, although they emerge earlier with the young leaves. Made up of four or five petals, the white flower is tinged with yellow blotches that turn red after the flower is pollinated. Hard-working bees pick up and transfer pollen from the seven red-tipped stamens that protrude from each flower to the stigmas of other flowers. Two other horse chestnuts, the Japanese and the Indian, also have white/yellow candles. The Indian flowers later than the white horse chestnut.

Conkers form inside a tough, spiky capsule and are protected by a lining of soft white padding; as they ripen they change colour from white to rich, glossy brown by early October. If they do not fall with the capsule, or are not knocked down with sticks thrown by children, they will be released as the three segments that make up the capsule dry and peel away from the swelling seeds. During October most playgrounds and classrooms become littered with broken horse chestnuts, the aftermath of energetic conker duels—a game first popular in the 19th century.

It has been suggested that horse chestnuts

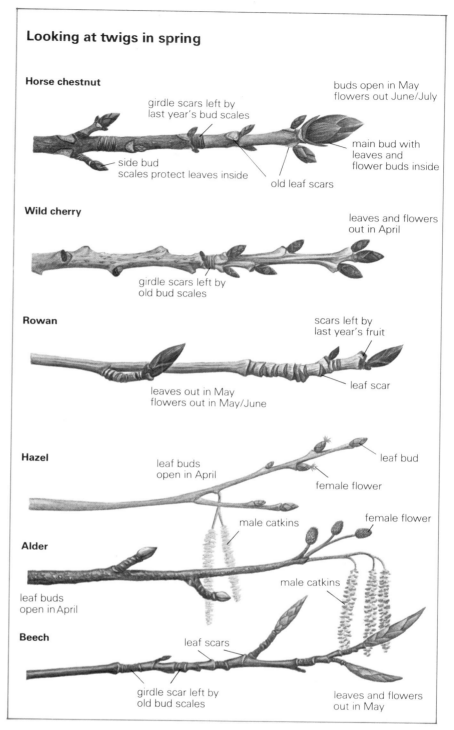

Looking at twigs in spring

Horse chestnut
girdle scars left by last year's bud scales
buds open in May flowers out June/July
side bud
scales protect leaves inside
old leaf scars
main bud with leaves and flower buds inside

Wild cherry
leaves and flowers out in April
girdle scars left by old bud scales

Rowan
scars left by last year's fruit
leaf scar
leaves out in May flowers out in May/June

Hazel
leaf buds open in April
leaf bud
female flower
male catkins

Alder
female flower
leaf buds open in April
male catkins

Beech
leaf scars
girdle scar left by old bud scales
leaves and flowers out in May

were so called because the conkers were a remedy for horses with a cough. This is, in fact, unlikely, for horses refuse them owing to their very bitter taste; but deer and sheep will eat them.

Protect a tree As has been mentioned above, horse chestnuts may germinate and then soon become overwhelmed by other vegetation. However a sapling usually flourishes if it is moved to deep, preferably loamy, moist but well-drained soil and a sunny position. Keep it free from smothering plants and protected from livestock and it will have a good chance of survival. And you will have contributed another beautiful summer sight for the next generation to enjoy.

Even before the leaves of broadleaved trees appear, you can identify a tree by the marked characteristics of the twigs. Look at their shape and colour, the position of the buds, their distinctive markings—old leaf scars and 'scale-scars' from old buds. The distance between one scale-scar and the next tells you how far the twig has grown in length in a year.

Holm oak

It is surprising to discover that many of the hundreds of oaks found throughout the world are not deciduous, but are evergreen. Among all these evergreen species, only one, the holm oak, is at all common in Britain.

Above: In this country holm oaks are usually found planted as town trees, for which their resistance to pollution makes them particularly well adapted. In the south-west of England, however, where the winters are milder than elsewhere, holm oaks have become naturalised.

The holm oak is not native to the British Isles. It comes from the Mediterranean countries and was introduced here from the Cape Finisterre region of Spain at the end of the 16th century. Most likely, it was brought over here by merchants and sea captains, either in the form of seedlings or as acorns.

The tree proved successful in this country, especially in the milder climate of south-west England where it has become naturalised. In the rest of the country it is found primarily in town parks and gardens. It is particularly useful as a source of shelter in coastal areas, where its thick leathery leaves are well able to resist the drying effects of sea winds.

The name 'holm oak' comes from the old word for holly, 'holm', because the leaves of the two trees are somewhat similar. But there are several other names for this tree, including the evergreen oak, the live oak and the holly oak. Its botanical name, *Quercus ilex*, also refers to its holly-like leaves, *Quercus* meaning oak and *ilex* being the generic name for holly.

Variable leaves The leaves may have smooth margins, or may be toothed and resemble holly leaves. Frequently the leaves are also curved downwards slightly.

The colour is less variable than the shape, being dark green above and buff-grey below. The undersides are covered with tiny white hairs, as are the leaf-stalks and the young twigs.

The tough leathery leaf surface makes the holm oak unusually resistant to pollution because any dirt falling on it is easily washed away by rain. Its felted underside also helps to keep out pollution by preventing the stomata from becoming clogged up. (Stomata are pores found in the leaf surface that allow gases to be exchanged between the leaf and the atmosphere.) This is why the holm oak grows well as a town tree.

Usually the holm oak sheds its previous year's growth of leaves in May and June, but in severe winters frost may cause the leaves to turn brown by the spring. In this case, the leaves are shed early, but the tree quickly becomes green again as the dormant buds in the leaf axils are stimulated to grow.

Flowers and fruit The male and female flowers are borne separately, though on the same tree. Male flowers are borne in catkins 4-7cm (1½-3in) long. They are inconspicuous at first but become more noticeable as their yellow pollen ripens in mid-June. Female flowers are solitary and inconspicuous. After pollination by the wind, they develop a typical acorn cup at their base in which the fruit slowly forms.

The fruit of a holm oak is an acorn. Its acorn is smaller than that of our deciduous oaks. When young it is green, sometimes turning reddish-brown when fully mature. The cup is stalked and scaly, bearing silvery-grey closely matted hairs.

In the south of England the acorns germinate quickly where they fall, but in the north and Midlands, where the climate is colder, the seed is not always viable. In these parts, you often see holm oaks grafted on to stocks of common oak.

As with all oaks, the acorns make good fattening food for pigs, although the old practice of turning out pigs into oak woods has largely died out in this country–certainly holm acorns are no longer used for food. But there is a record of pigs feeding on holm oak acorns in Surrey during the 17th century.

Timber for the Romans In its native lands the holm oak was once used extensively for making the wheels of carts and carriages, and for constructing a wide range of agricultural implements. Using the wood for wheels may well be a tradition dating back as far as the Romans. Certainly, they found it particularly suitable for this purpose on account of its hardness, durability and weight. Today, the timber is not much used around the Mediterranean, though in Algeria it is still used in carriage building and in all forms of joinery.

In Britain, the timber has never been used much, except as a source of fuel. This is probably due to the fact that common oak timber was, until recently, easily obtainable. Nevertheless, holm oak wood is very durable when used for outdoor purposes such as gateposts and stakes because, like other oaks, it contains tannic acid which preserves the wood.

There are a few instances of the wood being used in this country for construction. For example, at Munden in Hertfordshire the panelled walls of the library were made from

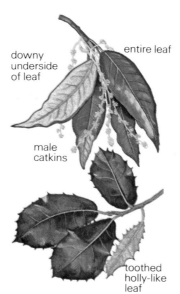

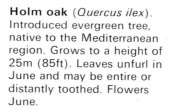

downy underside of leaf

entire leaf

male catkins

toothed holly-like leaf

Holm oak (*Quercus ilex*). Introduced evergreen tree, native to the Mediterranean region. Grows to a height of 25m (85ft). Leaves unfurl in June and may be entire or distantly toothed. Flowers June.

Right: The bark of a young tree is smooth and dark green, gradually becoming scaly and fissured with age.

a single tree grown on the estate. The grain is very hard and close, and slightly darker than the wood of common oak.

Oracle for the Greeks Many trees have folklore attached to them and the holm oak is no exception. The ancient Greeks used the leaves as oracles during their ritual ceremonies. They regarded them as infallible. Crowns made from holm oak leaves were used to honour prominent citizens, and the acorns were regarded as symbols of fertility, a belief shared with other cultures. Greek women used to wear imitation acorns made of gold in the hope that they would make them fertile. They used to make these golden acorns into pendants and necklaces.

Above: The acorns of a holm oak are enclosed in a felted scaly cup. They are green when young, sometimes turning brown as they mature.

Because it bears acorns (and catkins) botanists classify the holm oak with the other oaks, even though to most people its evergreen unlobed leaves are quite different from the more common oak leaf. This is because botanists recognise the genus *Quercus* (ie oaks) mainly by its flowers and fruits.

Turkey oak

mossy cups

stipule

pointed lobes

Sessile oak

smooth stalked cups

rounded lobes

English oak

round lobes

smooth stalked cups

Turkey and Lucombe oaks

At a glance, the Turkey oak and its close relative, the hybrid Lucombe oak, may seem much the same as our own native oaks. But take a closer look and the difference soon becomes apparent in their strange mossy-cupped acorns that take two years to mature.

Above: The long ascending branches stemming from a fairly short stout trunk to form a broad domed crown give the Turkey oak its typical shape.
In Britain, the Turkey oak is a fast-growing vigorous tree, able to flourish on a wide range of soil types, and has become a popular ornamental species for parks and gardens. It grows especially well in southern England, where it has become naturalised in woods and hedgerows.

Britain has only two native species of oak, the English or pedunculate oak and the sessile oak, but on the mainland of Europe there are many more oak species. All can be found growing in parks and public gardens in this country, but only a small number have become naturalised here. One of the few to do so is the Turkey oak.

This tree is native to south-east Europe and Turkey, to which, presumably, it owes its name. It was introduced to Britain around 1735 and soon proved to be extremely hardy and fast-growing here. However, hopes that it would prove to be a valuable source of timber were dashed when it was discovered that the timber from Turkey oaks grown in

Britain was brittle and not at all durable.

Nevertheless, it soon became popular as an ornamental tree in parks and gardens throughout much of the British Isles. It grows especially well in southern England where, with the help of birds and mammals collecting its acorns, it has spread to the wild and become established in hedgerows and woods.

One of the reasons for the Turkey oak's success in this country is its tolerance of different soils. It grows equally well on light sandy soils and heavy clays, provided they are well drained. But it does not thrive in exposed windy places, for the brittleness of its timber makes its branches liable to snap off suddenly during a strong gale.

Fast grower The Turkey oak is a handsome upright tree with a spacious domed crown. It grows faster than any other species of oak to be found in Britain and the tallest are around 40m (130ft) high. This is almost as high as our tallest native oaks, yet our Turkey oaks are all less than 250 years old, which is comparatively young.

The bark of a Turkey oak is much darker than that of our native oaks. In old age it becomes rugged and cracked by deep fissures. The slender twigs have a coarse, knobbly appearance due to numerous small brown buds that are arranged alternately in a spiral around the length of the shoot. The buds are enclosed in a fine down and almost hidden by

Right: The Lucombe oak generally forms a broader, squatter tree than does the Turkey oak. In all but the harshest winters it retains its leaves until spring.

Left: The Turkey oak differs from our native oaks in both leaves and fruits. Its leaves are generally more slender with pointed lobes and its acorns are borne in mossy cups. At the leaf-bases are long stipules. Our native oaks have smooth-cupped acorns and lack stipules.

Lucombe oak
(Quercus lucombeana)

Turkey oak
(Quercus cerris)

dark whisker-like strands. These are the shrivelled remains of stipules that were hanging from the base of the leaves earlier in the year. Among oaks, only the much rarer chestnut-leaved oak shares this strange feature.

The foliage unfurls early in May. At first, the pale green lower surface of the young leaves is covered in a grey woolly down, but this is shed by the time the leaves have expanded fully. The lower surface remains pale green but the upper surface is a much darker green and quite glossy.

The shape of the leaves varies greatly but they have the familiar lobed outline of our native oaks. However, the lobes tend to be narrower and more pointed. The Turkey oak retains its leaves long into the autumn and, on a young tree, they may even persist in a withered condition throughout the winter.

Catkin flowers The flowers of the Turkey oak are similar in structure to those of the common oak. The male flowers consist of catkins about 5cm (2in) long, hanging in dense bunches. In May they ripen and become tinged with red before opening to release clouds of pollen. The female flowers are inconspicuous round structures about 5mm ($\frac{1}{4}$in) across. They appear at the base of the leaves on new shoots.

Following fertilisation the female flowers develop into small acorns that are characterised by their curious mossy-looking cups (properly known as cupules). Indeed, in some parts of the country it is more commonly known as the mossy-cupped oak. These distinctive acorns remain on the tree, slowly ripening, for two years.

Lucombe oak In 1762 an Exeter nurseryman named William Lucombe noticed that two species of oak he had planted close together cross-pollinated to produce a hybrid oak. The two species were the Turkey oak and the cork oak, a Mediterranean species whose bark is harvested as a source of cork. The hybrid was named the Lucombe oak in his honour.

The Lucombe oak turned out to be very hardy and exceptionally vigorous, forming a superb ornamental tree for parks and gardens.

The tallest on record in Britain is a 38m (125ft) tall tree growing at West Dean in Sussex.

The trunk of a Lucombe oak is shorter than that of a Turkey oak, and its widely spreading boughs form a broad ample crown. The bark is thick and rugged, in mature trees becoming deeply furrowed. The leaves, flowers and fruits are all similar to those of the Turkey oak – in particular the Lucombe oak has the same mossy-cupped acorns – though the leaves are a much darker green on the upper surface. One major difference, however, between the two trees is that the Lucombe oak is almost an evergreen tree, as indeed is the cork oak.

Turkey oak (*Quercus cerris*). Deciduous tree, native to south-east Europe and Turkey. Height to about 40m (130ft).

Lucombe oak (*Quercus lucombeana*). Semi-evergreen hybrid between the Turkey oak and the cork oak. Height to about 30m (100ft).

Below: A Turkey oak about to flower. The catkins are male; the female flowers are small and borne at the bases of the leaves.

American oaks

The red oaks are a group of New World oaks often seen growing in British parks and gardens. These trees are notable for their superb display of autumn colours, as shown here in the tree after which the group is named – the red oak itself.

The oak has for long been considered the national tree of England yet, of the approximately 450 species of oak to be found throughout the world, only two are native to this country. These are, of course, the English oak and sessile oak. Yet there is a great number of oaks native to the New World, being found in either North America, Mexico or Central America.

Being such a large and variable genus, the oaks are grouped by botanists into various catagories called sections. Most oaks seen in Britain, including our native oaks, belong to the section Quercus, or white oaks. This is the only section with representatives in both the Old and the New Worlds. Among the New

the holly oak, and red oaks even include trees with willow-like leaves, having only a terminal filament.

Red leaves in autumn One of the most important members of the red oak section, and the most commonly planted in this country, is the red oak itself. The name refers primarily to the colour of its leaves in autumn (a feature shared with many other trees in the red oak section), though its inner bark and its young winter shoots are both also red. The red colour of the inner bark is not a feature that can often be checked, though the occasional wind-damaged branch may show it. In this case it can be seen that the dead outer layer of bark is dark grey-brown, but beneath this is a soft living layer of pale red bark.

The red oak is native to the eastern half of North America, extending from southern Canada and Nova Scotia down to Georgia and Louisiana in the south. It was introduced into Britain early in the 18th century and has since become the most popular of the American oaks in this country, being widely planted in parks and public gardens for its ornamental value.

Broad domed crown The red oak forms a tall tree, in Britain growing to a height of 30m (100ft), with a broad domed crown on top of a short stout trunk. The grey-brown bark is often broken into small plates on mature trees, but on young trees it is smooth and silvery grey.

The leaves of a red oak are highly variable. Their size may range from 12-22cm (5-9in) long by 10-15cm (4-6in) wide, the number of lobes may vary between seven and twelve, and the depth of these lobes may be between half and quarter of the distance between the leaf-margin and the midrib. The number of bristly filaments on each lobe also varies: there is

World oaks, however, especially those planted in Britain, most belong to a separate section, called Erythrobalanus, or red oaks.

Red and white oaks The red oak section differs from the white oaks in several respects. The acorns take two years instead of one to ripen, the inner surface of the acorn shell is hairy or downy instead of being hairless (though some white oaks have slightly hairy inner surfaces), and the bark is much smoother, particularly on young trees. The two groups also differ in the shape of the flower: on white oaks the style is very short or even absent, whereas on red oaks it is elongated.

There are important differences between the two groups in the shape of the leaves, though this is not a reliable guide to telling them apart. In general, however, red oaks have sharply pointed lobes ending in a fine filament—a continuation of the veins. White oaks, on the other hand, have rounded lobes—to us, the typical oak-leaf shape. Both groups include members with prickly leaves, such as

Above: When they first emerge, the leaves of a red oak are bright yellow. This colour can persist for up to a few weeks before they darken to their summer matt green.
Notice how this tree exemplifies the typical shape of a red oak: a broad domed crown with strongly ascending branches on top of a short trunk.

Right: A red oak just about to flower. The male flowers are borne in catkins (not yet open here), while the female flowers resemble small tufts and sit in the leaf axils. The flowers appear in May, just after the leaves have unfurled.

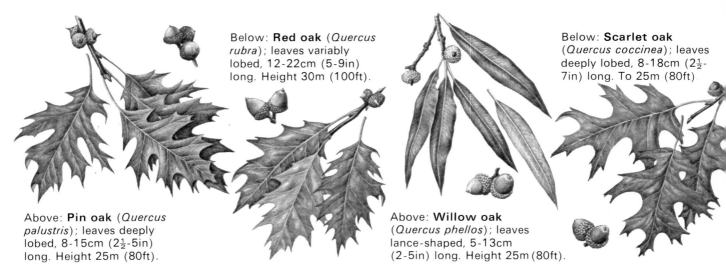

Below: **Red oak** (*Quercus rubra*); leaves variably lobed, 12-22cm (5-9in) long. Height 30m (100ft).

Below: **Scarlet oak** (*Quercus coccinea*); leaves deeply lobed, 8-18cm (2½-7in) long. To 25m (80ft)

Above: **Pin oak** (*Quercus palustris*); leaves deeply lobed, 8-15cm (2½-5in) long. Height 25m (80ft).

Above: **Willow oak** (*Quercus phellos*); leaves lance-shaped, 5-13cm (2-5in) long. Height 25m (80ft).

always one at the tip of each lobe but there may be one or more on the sides.

One of the red oak's most spectacular features is the colour of its leaves. When these first open in spring they are a bright yellow and stay this colour for several days, or even weeks. Then they become a dull matt green until late in the year, when they turn a variety of colours, from a deep red to yellow or russet-brown.

Flowers and fruits In May, the male and female flowers appear. In typical oak fashion the male flowers appear as slender yellow catkins, whereas the female flowers are extremely tiny and insignificant.

The flowers are followed by acorns. At the end of the first year these are still small and squat, but by the time they have ripened a year later the acorns have become elongated and are borne in shallow cups.

Fast-growing shoots The red oak is one of our fastest-growing trees, with shoots up to 2.5m (8ft) long appearing in a single year. In North America, this quality makes the tree a useful source of timber but, so far, it has not been widely planted in Britain for this purpose.

The Forestry Commission have planted some red oaks around the edges of their conifer plantations to act as a screen and provide some diversity. Like our native oaks, the red oak does not cast too dense a shade, so allowing other plants to grow beneath. Thus they provide an attractive border to what is typically an otherwise rather monotonous conifer wood.

Less familiar red oaks Several other members of the red oak section have been introduced to Britain, though on a smaller scale than the red oak itself. Perhaps the most attractive of these is the scarlet oak. This tree is similar in many ways to the red oak, but can be distinguished at a distance by its smaller stature (up to 25m/80ft tall) and its longer, more slender trunk.

Its name comes from the fact that its leaves turn a much more pronounced red in the autumn than those of the red oak. Usually the autumn colour appears first on just one or two limbs of the tree, with the rest of the

Above: The acorns and leaves of our most common New World oaks, showing their autumn colours. All have the lobes of their leaves (if present) sharply pointed and ending in fine filaments. The acorns take two years to mature. Here, the mature acorns are shown detached, with this season's acorns still on the twigs.

Below: Bright red autumn colours are a common feature of trees in the red oak section, though in practice the colours can vary from scarlet or crimson to yellow or brown. The leaves shown here are from a pin oak.

tree remaining green—among red oaks, a feature unique to this species.

The leaves of the scarlet oak are smaller than those of the red oak, with five to nine more deeply cut lobes.

The pin oak This species is similar in most ways to the scarlet oak, though it is quite different from a distance because the lower branches droop down to form a characteristic skirt. The upper branches, however, are swept strongly upwards. The leaves have the same size, shape and colour as those of the scarlet oak, except that the lobes are cut a little deeper.

The willow oak This species of red oak is quite different from the others because its leaves are unlobed. Instead, they are long and slender and resemble willow leaves. They still have the deep red autumn colour so typical of this group, however. Although the willow oak is today one of the rarer red oaks to be seen in Britain, it was the first member of this group to be introduced here, at the beginning of the 18th century.

Mulberry

Despite the words of the famous rhyme, the mulberry grows tall enough to be considered a tree rather than a bush. We have two species in Britain: the white mulberry – so important to the Chinese silk industry – and the more common black mulberry.

Below: A black mulberry at Stourhead in Wiltshire. The squat outline is typical of this species. Indeed, many black mulberries are broader than they are tall.

Apart from the two species of mulberry that grow in this country, about 20 others are found in various parts of the northern hemisphere, mostly in eastern Asia and eastern USA. All mulberries are small attract-

ive trees with fleshy fruits looking rather like blackberries.

Mulberries are all members of the genus *Morus*, which in turn belongs to the mulberry family, Moraceae. Most plants in this family are tropical and, apart from the mulberries themselves, the other important genus in this family is the figs, *Ficus*.

Black mulberry This is the mulberry most commonly found growing in Britain, and it is the one most suited to our climate. No one knows for sure when it was first introduced to this country – possibly around 1500 but more likely long before that. It has been cultivated in southern Europe for untold centuries, with the consequence that its native distribution is not known for sure. Some people suggest that it was introduced long ago to Europe from China via the old trading routes. Others believe that it is a 'lost' native of south-east Europe.

Both parts of its Latin name, *Morus nigra*,

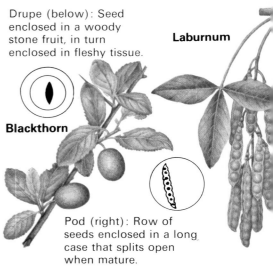

Drupe (below): Seed enclosed in a woody stone fruit, in turn enclosed in fleshy tissue.

Blackthorn

Laburnum

Pod (right): Row of seeds enclosed in a long case that splits open when mature.

refer to the colour black. The word *Morus* comes from the Greek for black, a reference to the fact that the tree's fruits change colour as they ripen from white to reddish-black. The Greeks believed that this colour change occurred because Pyramus and Thisbe died beneath the shade of a black mulberry and the tree absorbed their blood. The other part of its name, *nigra*, comes from the Latin for black.

Short and wide The black mulberry is a short tree, growing to no more than 10m (33ft) high, and is often much wider than it is tall. The trunk is short and frequently leans, and the branches are twisting, giving the tree a rugged appearance.

The leaves are roughly heart-shaped with pointed tips and serrated margins, but they can vary considerably. On very vigorous shoots, particularly those on young or coppiced trees, the leaves can be deeply lobed like fig leaves. Indeed, the leaves can be so radically different that nurserymen selling black mulberries are sometimes falsely accused of

Above: On both species of mulberry the male and female flowers are borne on separate catkins, which appear in late spring. Male and female catkins are similar, except that the males are about twice as long; both are yellow-green and difficult to distinguish among the foliage. This picture shows a black mulberry in flower.

Below: The bark of a black mulberry is orange-brown with deep stringy fissures, though in western parts of the country it is often obscured by lichen, as here. On old white mulberries, the bark is similar, though on younger trees it is usually a dull grey or pinkish-brown.

having supplied the wrong tree. One sure way of identifying a black mulberry leaf is by its rough hairy texture. On some trees the leaves can become quite large–up to 20cm (8in) long.

Flowers and fruits The flowers appear in late spring as small insignificant yellow-green catkins borne on hairy stalks in the leaf axils. The male catkins are about 2.5cm (1in) long and the females are half that length.

The fruits are much more interesting. At first they are green, becoming white and then orange or scarlet by midsummer. They continue to darken as they ripen, eventually turning a dark blackish-red. Ripening is progressive, so that mature and immature fruits are to be found on the same tree at the same time.

Until they become nearly black, the fruits are sour but, with the final colour change, they develop their pleasant sweet-and-sour taste. When mature, they are oval or round, and up to 2.5cm (1in) long.

Technically, mulberry fruits are not simple but comprise a cluster of separate fruits. The

normal leaf shape

lobe

sinus

The leaves of a black mulberry are usually rounded (top), but they may sometimes be lobed with one, two or four broad rounded sinuses (bottom).

Food for silkworms

The white mulberry has one very important use: as food for silkworms. This tree is by far their favourite food and it has been cultivated in China for this purpose for centuries. The Chinese grow fields of white mulberries, each year progressively stripping off the leaves to feed to the silkworms. The silk is made from the cocoon which the silkworms spin prior to pupating.

Several attempts have been made to establish a silkworm industry in Britain, the first being by James I in the 17th century. However, all such attempts have so far failed.

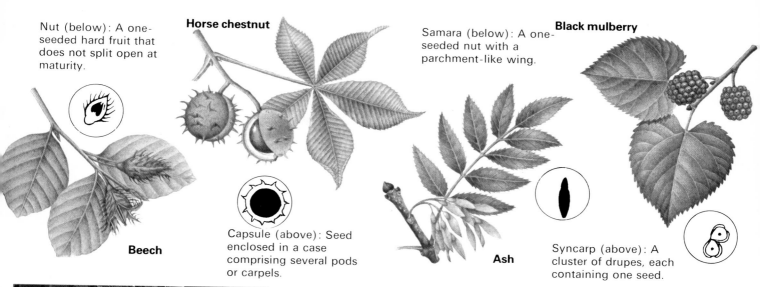

Nut (below): A one-seeded hard fruit that does not split open at maturity.

Horse chestnut

Black mulberry

Samara (below): A one-seeded nut with a parchment-like wing.

Beech

Capsule (above): Seed enclosed in a case comprising several pods or carpels.

Ash

Syncarp (above): A cluster of drupes, each containing one seed.

Above: Mulberry fruits are clustered in an unusual blackberry-like arrangement called a syncarp. But there are several other arrangements of fruit to be found on trees, the most common of which are shown here.

Left: The name black mulberry refers to its ripe fruits. Early in the season these are green. They become paler until more or less white and then darken through orange and red to a reddish-black by the time they mature in the autumn. Notice how the one tree can, at the same time, bear fruits at all stages of ripening.

Below: As its name implies, the white mulberry has much paler fruits than those of the black mulberry. On both species the fruits have the same shape but on the white mulberry they remain white for much of the summer, eventually ripening to yellow, pink or purple, but never becoming as dark as ripe black mulberry fruits.

times up to 15m (50ft) high. From a distance the two species are quite distinct, the white mulberry being much narrower and with an upright rather than a leaning trunk. Close to, the bark sometimes helps to distinguish them. The white mulberry often has a dull grey or pinkish-brown bark, with age becoming orange-brown, like the bark of the black mulberry. But the best guides to identification are the leaves and fruits.

Leaves, flowers and fruits In shape the leaves of the white mulberry are roughly similar to those found on the black species, but they have a greater tendency to be lobed and may be more rounded than heart-shaped. The texture of the two leaves, however, is quite different. White mulberry leaves have none of the coarse downiness of black mulberry leaves. Instead they are thinner, softer and hairless.

The flowers on each species are much the same but the fruits are distinctly different. Both have the same raspberry-like shape but white mulberry fruits are much paler. Indeed, for much of the summer they are almost white—hence the tree's Latin name, *Morus alba*, which literally means white mulberry.

In the autumn the fruits ripen to yellow, pink or purple, but they never reach the dark colour of ripe black mulberry fruits. Nor do white mulberries ever become as good to eat as the black ones.

whole structure is called a syncarp. The individual fruits are fleshy and contain a single nutlet. Because they do not open at maturity they are known as drupes; cherries and plums are other examples of drupes.

Commercial uses From the commercial point of view, the most important part of the black mulberry is its fruits. These make a very tasty dessert and can also be fermented into wine. Mulberry wine is said by some to taste like port; it is sometimes mixed with cider to produce a drink known as mulberry cider.

White mulberry This is the species of mulberry famous for being the staple food of silkworms in China. It is native to parts of eastern and south-eastern Asia and has been cultivated in China for silkworms for many hundreds of years. It reached Europe some time in the 12th century—the time of Marco Polo's travels—but did not arrive in Britain until about 400 years later.

The white mulberry is less common in this country than the black species, even though it grows faster and forms a taller tree, some-

Forsythias

Introduced to Britain from the Far East, forsythias have never become naturalised here, but they are among our most popular shrubs in parks and gardens due to the blaze of colour they provide early in the year as their yellow flowers open out.

Since they were first introduced to Britain during the last century, a number of forsythia species have been successfully grown here as ornamental shrubs. All but one species of forsythia – and all the species that are so popular in British gardens – come from the Far East. The odd one out is the aptly-named *Forsythia europaea*, which comes from south-eastern Europe. This shrub is the least attractive of all forsythias and so is rarely planted in Britain.

The genus *Forsythia* is named in memory of William Forsyth who was superintendent of the Royal Gardens at Kensington during the latter half of the 18th century. Forsythias are grouped together in the Oleaceae family,

which also includes several other familiar plants, such as ash, privet and lilac.

Ornamental arrivals The first species of forsythia arrived in Britain in 1845. It was introduced here from its native China by the famous plant collector Robert Fortune. Named *Forsythia viridissima*, it is the last species of forsythia to flower each year, in April producing solitary bright yellow flowers along its upright branches.

The arrival of *F. viridissima* was followed about five years later by another forsythia species, *F. suspensa*. At least one variety of this species, which is native to China, was cultivated in Japan hundreds of years ago. *F. suspensa* forms long arching shoots that reach as high as 9m (30ft) if grown against a wall, as it often is. Grown in the open, this species reaches a more modest 2.5-3m (8-10ft) high. Its flowers are borne in pairs or clusters towards the end of March or the beginning of April.

Two other oriental species, less commonly grown in Britain, are *F. giraldiana* and *F. ovata*. The former is native to China, and is the earliest forsythia to come into flower each year, usually around the end of February or the beginning of March. It grows to a height of 4.5m (15ft), which makes it one of the tallest forsythias. *F. ovata* blooms soon after. It is native to Korea and differs in several respects from the other species. In particular, it is by far the smallest and most compact of all forsythias, reaching no more than 1.5m (5ft) in height. Several dwarf cultivars (cultivated varieties) have been derived from this species. The flowers of *F. ovata* appear in pairs in early March.

Cultivars and hybrids Most forsythias growing in gardens are not true species but are cultivars bred from a hybrid, *F. × intermedia*. This hybrid was developed in Germany in 1884 from a cross between *F. suspensa* and *F. viridissima*. The cultivars, of which 'Spectabilis' and 'Beatrix Farrand' are the most popular, vary considerably, but they are all free-flowering shrubs around 2-2.5m (6-8ft) high.

lenticels (air holes)

leaves have pointed tips and toothed margins

calyx

style

corolla

bell-shaped flowers

flower buds

winter twig

Opposite and above: The hybrid *Forsythia × intermediata*. Several of the most popular cultivar forsythias have been developed from this hybrid.

Forsythia (*Forsythia* spp.). A genus of deciduous shrubs, all but one being native to the Far East. All bear yellow flowers, either in clusters or singly, appearing Feb-May. The leaves are usually lance-shaped and toothed. The maximum height of the shrub is, exceptionally, 9m (30ft).

Below: One way in which forsythia spreads is by sending out branches that bend down to the ground, where they take root.

Bell-shaped flowers A characteristic of forsythias is that they all bear yellow bell-shaped flowers early in spring before their leaves have emerged; hence their common name of golden bell. The flowers are borne either singly or in clusters on the previous year's wood. They are pale or bright yellow and have four petals united at the base.

Forsythia flowers are unusual in having two distinct forms. The difference between the two forms lies in the length of the styles, which are either long or short—there are no intermediate forms. The reason for having two sorts of style is to ensure that only cross-pollination takes place. On each bush the flowers are wholly of one type or another, but seeds set only when flowers are fertilised by pollen coming from the opposite type of flower. So it is impossible for a forsythia bush to fertilise itself.

A strange consequence of this is that forsythias very rarely set seeds in Britain, since many of the plants grown here have the same type of style. This is because they are derived by vegetative propagation from the few specimens originally brought over here (forsythias propagate vegetatively by sending out suckers or by their branches bending down and taking root where they touch the ground). The original stock of *F. viridissima*, for example, bore long-styled flowers and for many years all the cultivated specimens of this species in Britain had long styles as well. Not surprisingly, long styles were thought to be a characteristic of the species until fresh investigations in China revealed the existence of short-styled flowers of *F. viridissima*.

Lance-shaped leaves The flowers bloom for between two and four weeks. Only when they fade do the leaves emerge. They are usually lance-shaped, though sometimes oval, and vary in length from 5-15cm (2-6in), depending on the species. The leaves turn yellow in autumn but do not fall until the first frosts arrive. A plant in a sheltered position in southern England may retain its leaves well into winter, whereas an exposed plant is likely to drop its leaves much earlier.

Once the leaves have fallen the stems can be seen clearly. They are thin, light brown and covered with pale dots called lenticels, through which the plant breathes. The stems are hollow inside, apart from some pith where they meet each other.

parent plant

new plant taking root

Walnuts

Walnut trees are no longer grown in Britain for their
nuts and timber, as they used to be. Today, they
grace many a park and country garden.

No one is quite sure when the walnut tree was first introduced to Britain, although the ancient Romans very likely tried to establish it here for they were extremely fond of the nuts.

However, we know that walnut trees were definitely established in Britain by the end of the 15th century because they were mentioned in the literature of the period as growing in orchards, paddocks and gardens. There used to be large groves of walnut on the North Downs in Surrey, particularly around Godstone, Carshalton and Leatherhead, but these have now all but disappeared, having been cut down for their valuable timber. As well as being a popular wood for furniture-making, walnut was long used for making musket butts and large numbers of trees were cut down for this purpose during the Napoleonic Wars at the beginning of the 19th century.

Today, walnut is no longer planted on a large scale for commercial purposes but many fine specimens can still be seen growing in parks and gardens. It grows best in the southern counties of England, where it is not unusual to see walnut trees that have 'escaped' and are growing wild in hedgerows or copses. These were probably spread there unwittingly by rooks and jays, both of which quickly rob a walnut tree of its fruit and then drop or bury the nuts.

Distinctive bark The walnut tree owes much of its beauty to its distinctive bark. This is a very pale grey, with age becoming rugged and deeply scored by a criss-cross of furrows.

The trunk is usually short, dividing fairly low down into stout twisting branches. The crown is large and rounded.

The twigs are similarly stout and resemble those of a horse chestnut. In winter they carry small black buds arranged alternately along their length. Below each bud is a conspicuous semi-circular scar where the previous year's leaf was attached.

The buds burst into leaf early in May. When they unfurl they are a fresh olive-green colour, sometimes tinged with red. Their colour changes to a yellow-green with yellow veins as the leaf matures, and then fades during the autumn to a drab dark brown.

The leaves of a walnut tree are compound, consisting of five to nine leaflets attached to a central stalk – an arrangement known as pinnate. Each leaflet is leathery and smooth-margined – the common walnut is the only tree in the walnut family in which the leaves are not toothed. The leaflets are arranged in opposite pairs on the leaf-stalk, with one larger leaflet at the end.

Wind-pollinated flowers The walnut blossoms at about the same time as it comes into leaf, or in some years slightly earlier. Both male and female flowers are borne on the same tree, the females near the tips of the branches on the new season's shoots and the males further back along the branches on last year's

Opposite: Stout branches rising from a short trunk to a large spreading crown give the walnut tree its typical shape. Many fine specimens can be seen growing in Britain's parks and gardens.

Right: The flowers of the common and black walnut are similar to each other but the leaves and fruits show distinct differences.

Common walnut (*Juglans regia*). Deciduous tree, native to south-east Europe and Asia from Turkey to the Himalayas. Height to 25m (80ft).

Black walnut (*Juglans nigra*). Deciduous tree, native to eastern and central North America. Height to 30m (100ft).

shoots.

The male flowers are greenish catkins, about 5-10cm (2-4in) long. The female flowers are borne in clusters of two to five. They sit on short stalks and are green flask-shaped structures about 1cm ($\frac{1}{2}$in) long, each topped with two purple pollen-catching stigmas.

Walnut fruits After fertilisation the female flowers develop rapidly until, by the end of June, they have swollen into green oval fruits about 5cm (2in) across. Inside each fruit is the familiar walnut, with its wrinkled flesh enclosed in a shell. Early in the summer the shell is still soft and at this stage, with the nuts still intact, they can be pickled and

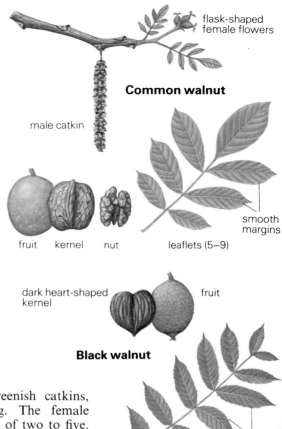

Common walnut

flask-shaped female flowers

male catkin

fruit   kernel   nut   leaflets (5–9)

smooth margins

dark heart-shaped kernel

fruit

Black walnut

serrated margins

leaflets (11–23)

Below: The pale grey, almost white, bark of the common walnut is one of this tree's most distinctive features. On young trees the bark is fairly smooth (as here) but with age it becomes deeply fissured.

Inside a walnut

The wrinkled 'brain-like' part of the walnut—the part we eat—is the embryonic cotyledons or seed leaves. When a walnut fruit matures the skin splits to release the nut (far right). This falls to the ground and, if the nut germinates, the seedling shoot and root emerge and grow, fuelled by food stored in the cotyledons inside the shell.

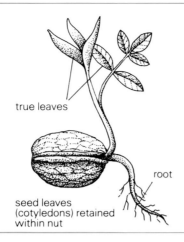

true leaves

seed leaves (cotyledons) retained within nut

root

Below: A black walnut just coming into leaf. This species has a darker bark and timber than the common walnut (hence its name) and is much less frequently encountered in this country. Yet it is the faster-growing of the two and it reaches a greater height. Both species grow best in the south of England.

steeped in vinegar with spices and seasonings. The result is delicious pickled walnuts.

If left on the tree the nuts continue to ripen. The green outside casing turns brown and then shrivels and splits open to reveal the nut inside. This usually happens by the beginning of October.

In Britain, walnut trees cannot be relied upon to produce a good crop of nuts, a late spring frost often killing the flowers and with them any chance of a crop. The best crops are collected in south-eastern England, where the climate is most favourable. But the majority of walnuts sold in this country come from France or Italy where the trees fruit freely.

Veneers for furniture Although the chief value of the walnut in Europe is as a fruit tree, it is also a very important source of timber which, being light yet durable, is highly valued in furniture-making. The grain is coarse but it shows beautiful whorled patterns in shades of brown. Walnut wood is rarely used solid for furniture-making. Instead, a piece of furniture is built from ordinary timber and then covered with wafer-thin veneers.

The timber's toughness and resistance to shrinkage made it ideal for musket butts in the past, and it is still used for the butts and stocks of fire-arms today.

Pigment for staining The characteristic brown tones of the timber are due to the presence of a special pigment, which is also found in the bark, leaves, twigs and fruits.

The leaves have a pungent fruity smell. Fishermen were advised to boil the leaves with water and sprinkle the resulting concoction over the ground—apparently, there is nothing like it for bringing worms to the surface. But the most extraordinary use for walnut leaves was recorded by John Evelyn, the distinguished 17th century diarist. He wrote that 'A distillation of the leaves with honey and urine makes hairs spring on bald heads!'

The black walnut The tree commonly known in Britain as walnut is only one among several species belonging to the walnut genus, *Juglans*. Among the other species, only the black walnut is at all common in this country.

The black walnut was introduced to Britain from North America during the 17th century. Its name comes from the fact that its timber is a rich dark brown colour. The main differences between it and the common walnut are that it has reddish-brown twigs, leaflets that are toothed—with a great number of them to each compound leaf—and bark that is dark brown or black. Its nuts are inferior to those of the common walnut, being much smaller and with a rather bitter taste.

Hickories and wingnuts

Closely related to the walnut, hickories and wingnuts are at their most ornamental in the autumn when their golden-yellow foliage (as on the shagbark hickory shown below) is complemented by decorative fruits.

In Britain the most familiar member of the walnut family (Juglandaceae) is the walnut itself, a tree that has been cultivated here since at least the 15th century for its nuts and its highly prized wood. World wide, however, the family is represented by six other genera. Three of these are confined to tropical parts of Central America and south-east Asia, and are not hardy enough to grow in our temperate climate. The remaining three genera are represented by temperate species, some of which can be seen in our parks and public gardens.

Three hardy genera These hardy members of the family can be divided into two groups. One consists of the hickories (*Carya* species),

most of which (approximately 20 species) come from eastern North America. The fruits of a hickory are similar to walnuts and botanists often separate out these two groups from the other genera and place them in their own sub-family.

By contrast, species in the other two genera (*Pterocarya* and *Platycarya*) bear a quite different form of fruit, as suggested by their common name, wingnuts. These fruits consist of long pendulous chains of winged nuts. Both genera are native to Asia and thrive in regions where the climate is similar to that found in this country.

Species in Britain Of the two groups–hickories and wingnuts–the wingnuts are more commonly seen in Britain, and of these the Caucasian wingnut (*Pterocarya fraxinifolia*) is the most widely grown. Native, as its name suggests, to the Caucasus Mountains of the Soviet Union and to Iran, this species represents the western limit of the genus. The other seven species come from China and Japan. Of these, the Chinese wingnut (*P. stenoptera*) is the most widely planted. The other genus of wingnuts, *Platycarya*, is said to be monotypic since it has only one species, *P. strobilacea*. Native to China, Japan and Korea, this graceful tree is rarely seen in this country .outside botanic gardens and arboreta.

The hickories are a less familiar group in Britain, though with their richly textured

Above: Introduced from North America in 1629, the shagbark hickory can occasionally grow to a height of 20m (65ft) or more in Britain. In the United States and Canada hickories have great importance as a commercial crop, whether for timber or nuts. The wood is tough, yet elastic,.and ideal for the manufacture of tool handles for use in forestry and agriculture. In Britain, hickories are only ever grown for their ornamental value, though in recent years the pecan–which is a hickory fruit–has become increasingly popular here.

Right: The name 'shagbark' comes from the fact that, on mature trees, the bark splits into narrow strips that lift away from the trunk at each end–giving it a shaggy appearance. This curious feature probably confers the advantage of deterring squirrels from climbing the trunk and stealing the nuts.

leaves and their sculptured barks they deserve to be more widely planted. The most commonly planted member of this group is the bitternut hickory (*Carya cordiformis*). As its name suggests, its nuts are completely inedible. Possibly the most attractive species is the shagbark hickory (*C. ovata*). The only other species seen in Britain with any regularity is the mockernut hickory (*C. tomentosa*) with its characteristically enormous grey buds and sweetly smelling leaves. This tree derives its name from the fact that its fruits are often empty.

Compound leaves Both hickories and wingnuts have compound leaves similar to those of a walnut, in which the leaflets are arranged along each side of a central stalk–a structure known as pinnate.

Hickories can often be distinguished by the size of the leaflets and their arrangement on the leaves. The shagbark hickory, for instance, has only five leaflets to each leaf. Each leaflet is usually between 12cm (5in) and 18cm (7in) long, though they can reach a length of 30cm (12in). At the other end of the scale is the pecan hickory (*C. illinoensis*), from which we get the familiar nuts of the same name. Each leaf of this tree has between nine and seventeen leaflets which are pointed, toothed and curved like a scimitar.

Wingnuts usually have more leaflets to a leaf than do hickories, often as many as 25. Consequently the whole leaf can be much longer. The leaf of the Caucasian wingnut, for example, can be as long as 60cm (2ft).

Flowers and fruits In common with the walnut, both hickories and wingnuts bear their flowers in catkins. Among the wingnuts, the most spectacular flowers are borne by the so-called hybrid wingnut, which is a cross between the Caucasian and the Chinese species. Its female catkins can be as long as 45cm (18in), the male catkins being only a third as long as this. The hybrid wingnut is much hardier and more vigorous than either of its parents something that occurs frequently with hybrids.

The fruit of a wingnut consists of a small nut bearing two leafy wings and looking rather like a cross between an ash fruit and a

Left: The rugged, fissured bark of a mature Caucasian wingnut. In its native countries the bark is used to make sandals and roof tiles, but the wood itself has little commercial value.

The walnut family

All three groups in this family have compound leaves with the leaflets arranged in the same pattern, known as pinnate. Generally, walnuts and wingnuts have more leaflets per leaf than hickories. All have male catkins but only wingnuts also have female catkins; the other two groups have inconspicuous female flowers. Wingnuts differ in their fruits as well, producing catkins of small, winged fruits rather than a single large nut.

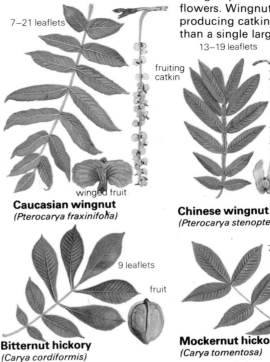

Caucasian wingnut
(Pterocarya fraxinifolia)

7–21 leaflets
fruiting catkin
winged fruit

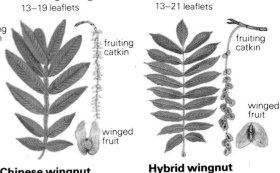

Chinese wingnut
(Pterocarya stenoptera)

13–19 leaflets
fruiting catkin
winged fruit

Hybrid wingnut
(Pterocarya × rehderiana)

13–21 leaflets
fruiting catkin
winged fruit

Bitternut hickory
(Carya cordiformis)

9 leaflets
fruit

Below: A Caucasian wingnut with its long fruiting catkins. The leaves of this tree have an intoxicating effect, and some Caucasian fishermen utilize this to stupefy their prey before catching them.

Mockernut hickory
(Carya tomentosa)

7 leaflets
fruit

Shagbark hickory
(Carya ovata)

fruit
5 leaflets

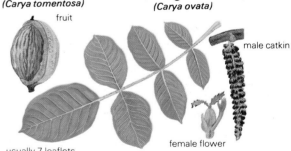

Common walnut
(Juglans regia)

fruit
usually 7 leaflets
male catkin
female flower

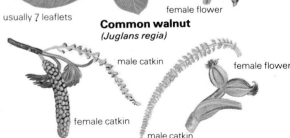

Caucasian wingnut

male catkin
female catkin

Shagbark hickory

female flower
male catkin

sycamore fruit.

In hickories, only the male flowers are borne in catkins. The female flowers are inconspicuous and borne in clusters at the tips of the new shoots. The fruit consists of an inner nut surrounded by a fleshy outer layer.

Perhaps the most foolproof way of distinguishing wingnuts (and walnuts) from hickories is to examine the pith inside young shoots. The pith of a hickory is solid whereas that of a wingnut or walnut consists of neat rows of plates that divide the interior of the shoot into chambers.

Tertiary relics In the past the British climate was very different from what it is now. Recent studies of ancient peat and sedimentary deposits have confirmed that the climate was once comparable to that of the humid tropics, similar to that found in present-day Malaysia, and the British flora was correspondingly much richer. During the Tertiary period before the last Ice Age the British land surface was dominated by trees now found in much more southerly latitudes, including hickories,

wingnuts and walnuts. Towards the end of the Tertiary, Britain's climate deteriorated dramatically with the onset of the Ice Age and these species migrated, never to return.

Although our climate is much cooler than it was before the Ice Age, hickories and wingnuts grow well in the southern counties of Britain. A particularly interesting tree can be seen in the Cambridge Botanic Garden, where there is a thicket of Caucasian wingnut that has grown from a tree blown down in 1866. Ironically, beneath this thicket fossils of the same species can be found.

Laburnum

The spectacular springtime show of yellow flowers gives laburnum (opposite) its common name of 'golden rain'. But the laburnum also has a dark side, for it is one of the most poisonous trees growing in the British Isles.

Common laburnum
(Laburnum anagyroides)

Scotch laburnum
(Laburnum alpinum)

long sparsely-flowered racemes

short densely-flowered racemes

Voss's laburnum
(Laburnum × watereri)

long densely-flowered racemes

The three major laburnums (above) differ most noticeably in their flowers. Voss's laburnum (below) is now more widely planted than the other two.

Like so many of the more colourful trees that grow in Britain, the lovely laburnum is not native to this country. It comes from the mountainous areas of central and southern Europe and was familiar to the ancient Romans. Their great naturalist, Pliny the Elder, described it as a 'tree from the Alps, with hard white wood and long yellow flowers which bees will not touch'. He was right that honey bees are not attracted to this tree, because its flowers do not produce nectar. But the wood is not white; the sapwood is butter-yellow and the heartwood is a dark chocolate-brown. Nevertheless, the name laburnum is derived from the Latin for white sapwood.

Species of laburnum From its native countries, laburnum was gradually introduced to the rest of Europe and reached Britain in the latter half of the 16th century. The first laburnum to be introduced to this country was the common laburnum (*Laburnum anagyroides*). This was followed about 30 years later by another species, *Laburnum alpinum*, which was found to grow much better than the common laburnum in the harsher conditions of Scotland. This laburnum is now known as the Scotch laburnum.

A third laburnum, now more widely planted than either of the other two, is Voss's laburnum (*Laburnum × watereri*). This is a hybrid between the common and the Scotch laburnum and is in many ways superior to them, particularly in its flowers. It also has a narrower crown, which makes it popular in small gardens.

All laburnum species flourish in the British Isles; indeed, they have become adapted to the British climate better than any other introduced tree. Not surprisingly, both the common and the Scotch laburnums became naturalised soon after they were introduced, helped also by the fact that both species set seed abundantly. The best place to see a naturalised laburnum is in wild hilly country.

Similarities and differences Apart from some minor differences, laburnums resemble each other closely. They are small trees, growing no more than 9m (30ft) high – which is why they have long been popular as street trees and for planting in small town gardens. The bark is smooth and olive-green, sometimes turning brown with age. The trunk is slender, seldom exceeding 30cm (1ft) in diameter.

The leaves are unusual in that each consists of three short-stalked leaflets – laburnum is the only tree commonly grown in the British Isles to have this leaf arrangement. The leaflets are up to 8cm (3in) long; their upper surfaces are pale green and smooth, the lower surfaces light-grey and hairy (hairless on the Scotch laburnum).

Laburnum is a member of the pea family and this is shown in the shape of its flowers. These consist of five bright yellow petals arranged in typical pea fashion – one large 'standard' petal, two 'wings' and two more connected to form a 'keel'. The flowers are borne on long pendulous racemes that vary in length from 15cm (6in) to 30cm (1ft). On the Scotch laburnum the racemes are longer than on the common, but they are also narrower and the flowers are more widely spaced. The Scotch laburnum blooms later – around the end of June, which is about three weeks

Above: Like all members of the pea family, the laburnum bears its seeds in pods. The pods, which are borne in clusters, are pale green and hairy when young.

Right: The pods turn brown and lose their hairs as they mature. When ripe they split open, twisting as they do so to force out the seeds. These are brown on the Scotch laburnum, darker brown on Voss's and black on the common laburnum.

Below: The flowers on Voss's laburnum are as densely clustered as they are on the common laburnum but they hang in much longer racemes.

In case of poisoning

All parts of the laburnum, especially the seeds, are highly poisonous. Symptoms appear an hour after ingestion. The victim suffers from a burning sensation in the mouth, nausea, severe thirst, abdominal pains, sweating and headache; in severe cases, death follows. Fortunately, it is rare for a child to eat a lethal quantity of seeds (15 to 20). Nevertheless, immediate treatment by a doctor is advisable, even if only one or two have been eaten. Wherever possible, remove any laburnum seeds growing within reach of children.

after the common laburnum.

The flowers of Voss's laburnum combine the best features of the other two: its racemes are as long as those of the Scotch laburnum, but the flowers are larger and more densely borne, like those of the common laburnum.

Peas in a pod All plants in the pea family have their fruits borne in pods. In the case of the laburnum, these pods are slender, hairy and light green when immature. They turn brown and lose their hairs as they ripen in July and August.

When the pods are ripe they twist and split along their margins, forcing out the small hard seeds–these are black on the common laburnum and brown on the Scotch laburnum. (One or two seeds at the stalk-end of the pod are often left behind if the twisting action was not strong enough to force them out. If the tree is growing in the wild this has the advantage of spreading out the interval at which the seeds are distributed, and so increasing the chances of a seed finding conditions favourable for germination.)

Deadly poisonous Although the laburnum is widely planted for its beauty it is, nevertheless, an extremely poisonous tree in all its parts–roots, leaves, flowers and seeds. The seeds are particularly poisonous and every year there are cases of young children falling ill after eating them. There are also a few cases of cattle being poisoned after browsing on the pods, though rabbits and hares seem to be unaffected.

The poisonous nature of laburnums is another reason for the popularity of the hybrid Voss's laburnum. As well as having prettier flowers than either of the other two, it produces far fewer seed pods and so attracts children less. The seeds themselves, and other parts of the tree, are just as poisonous as on other laburnums, however.

Two-tone timber Over the centuries laburnum wood has been greatly prized by cabinet makers for its hardness and its contrasting colours. The difference in colour between the sapwood and the heartwood has given rise to what is known in the furniture trade as 'oyster work'. These are small discs or roundels of wood formed by cutting across a laburnum branch to expose concentric rings of growth. The inner rings are chocolate-brown heartwood and the three or four outer rings are butter-yellow sapwood. Laburnum branches can also be cut at an angle to give oval slices. Both sorts of cut are used for decorative inlay work and veneers. Furniture carrying oyster work was particularly popular during the reign of William and Mary; today it fetches a high price at auctions.

Laburnum wood is also ideal for turning work–fruit bowls, egg-cups and so on–since it is hard, close-grained and takes a high polish. Pulleys and blocks made from laburnum last almost for ever, and the chanters on Scottish bagpipes are frequently made from this wood because it can be bored accurately.

Almonds

The sweet almond is a familiar ornamental tree and also the source of our almond nuts, yet its twin, the bitter almond, is highly poisonous and contains deadly cyanide.

The almond tree has been cultivated for so long and in so many different regions that its exact place of origin is difficult to determine. At one time, the almond was thought to have originated in the Far East, but this seems unlikely since there is no mention of it anywhere in the extensive written traditions of either India or China.

It is now thought that the almond originally came from south-west Asia, since isolated and seemingly wild specimens have been discovered growing far from human habitation in Afghanistan and its neighbouring countries. On the other hand, it is also possible that the almond once grew in North Africa – this is certainly one of the earliest regions in which the trees were cultivated.

In the Middle East, almonds are known to have been grown for thousands of years. They are mentioned in both the Old Testament and in the traditional tales of the Arabian Nights. From the Middle East, the cultivation of

Above: The almond is one of the earliest of our blossom trees to come into flower. Usually, this happens around the end of February or in early March, though it varies in different parts of the country and according to the weather. In most seasons, almonds flower before the leaves emerge, but sometimes both open together.

Above: **Almond** (*Prunus dulcis*). Deciduous tree, probably native to south-west Asia and possibly also to north Africa; introduced to Britain in the 16th century. Now widely planted in streets and gardens where it can reach a height of 8m (25ft).

Below: Almond flowers are pink when they first open but fade with age and turn white — notice how the buds about to open show pink petals here. The flowers are borne either in pairs, as here, or singly, in both cases on very short stalks so that the flowers seem to be growing out from the branches.

almonds spread to the ancient Greeks and, eventually, to Rome and throughout the Mediterranean countries. Gradually, it came to be cultivated in more northerly parts of Europe and it began to be popular as an ornamental tree. It was probably introduced into Britain during the 16th century.

Close relatives The almond belongs to a group of more than a hundred species that together make up the genus *Prunus*. Many of our favourite fruits are members of this genus, including plums, damsons, apricots, peaches and cherries. Of these, the peach is a particularly close relative of the almond; indeed, they may even have shared a recent common ancestor.

All species in the genus *Prunus* are woody plants, usually shrubs or small trees, though they occasionally grow quite tall (the wild cherry can grow to 30m/100ft high). They are similar to each other in many ways. Their leaves are always borne alternately on the branches rather than in opposite pairs. The young leaves have scale-like growths called

stipules at their bases; these usually dry out, become papery and fall off early in the growing season. The flowers are either pink or white and consist of five petals, the lower parts of which form a tube. The fruits consist of a fleshy outer layer enclosing a stone which contains a single seed. In most *Prunus* species the outer layer is edible, but not so with the almond. In the almond's case, it is the seed inside the stone that we eat.

Recognising the almond The almond is a small tree, rarely growing taller than 8m (25ft). On young trees the branches tend to be upright but, as the tree matures, they spread out so that the tree becomes bushier and develops a broad flattened crown.

The flowers open early in the year, usually before the leaves appear. Depending on the severity of our weather, the almond flowers in Britain towards the end of February or early in March, but in warmer climates, such as in the Mediterranean, it can flower as early as January. The flowers are pink, becoming paler and then white as they fade, and are 3-5cm (1-2in) across.

The leaves of an almond tree are large for a *Prunus* species – up to 13cm (5in) long and 4cm (1½in) wide. They are broad at the base and taper to a long narrow point. Their colour is dull green and their edges have small rounded teeth.

Leathery fruits The fruits are the most distinctive part of an almond tree. When young, they are yellow to grey-green, tinged with red and covered with velvet-like hairs. In Britain they take a long time to mature and may not ripen until well into the autumn, if at all. When they do ripen, the fruits are dark brown, slightly flattened and about 4cm (1½in) long. The outer part of the fruit is leathery and inedible. This splits open when ripe to release the inner stone.

Ornamental varieties The almond trees so commonly planted in streets and gardens are usually cultivars (cultivated varieties) or hybrids, of which the most popular is *Prunus* 'Pollardii'. This is a hybrid between the almond and peach and has spectacular large flowers.

Almonds, whether cultivars or hybrids, are well suited to streets and small gardens where there is often not the space to plant larger trees; they are especially liked for the splash of colour they provide early in the year.

Edible or poisonous As well as all the cultivars and hybrids of almond that have been developed, there are two naturally occurring varieties that have been known since antiquity. These look exactly the same as each other, but they differ in one crucial aspect: their nuts. In one variety they are edible but in the other they are deadly poisonous. The variety with edible nuts is called the sweet or edible almond (botanically it is known as *Prunus dulcis* var. *dulcis*). The poisonous variety is called the bitter almond (*Prunus dulcis* var. *amara*). Its bark, leaves

leaves are
toothed and
often curled

immature fruit

nut

flowers emerge
pink but
fade to white

Above left: The leaves,
flowers and fruits of an
almond tree. When young,
the fruits are yellow to
grey-green, tinged with
red and densely covered
with velvety hairs. The
fruits do not ripen until
well into the autumn,
when they turn brown and
the leathery outer layer
splits open to release the
hard inner stone. Inside
this stone is the edible
kernel.

Above: The almond is
closely related to the plum,
peach, apricot and cherry,
all being members of the
genus *Prunus*. The
similarity can be seen most
clearly in the fruit. Its
velvety grooved surface gives
it a close resemblance to
the peach in particular.

Left: The bark of an almond
tree is very dark and
cracked into small plates,
but on many varieties the
bark is lighter due to the
presence of pale bands of
lenticels.

and fruits are all rich in prussic or hydro-cyanic acid and, if eaten, cause cyanide poisoning. It has been estimated that 50 bitter almond nuts are enough to kill most adults and as few as 10 could prove fatal to a small child. Not surprisingly, the ornamental almond trees planted in streets and gardens are all derived from the sweet rather than the bitter almond.

Cultivated almonds Both varieties of almond are grown today, though the sweet almond is, commercially, by far the more important since it is the source of almond nuts. In Britain, the climate is not suitable for the production of good-quality nuts; we import almond nuts mainly from the USA, Italy and Spain.

For eating as dessert nuts, the rarer, thin-nest-shelled varieties are the most desirable, but they are also expensive since they are not cultivated on a wide scale. Many almonds are ground into a paste and used for making marzipan, or are crushed to extract oil.

A more important source of almond oil, however, is bitter almonds. The oil has first to be treated to remove the poisonous prussic acid, and then it is sometimes blended with the more expensive oil of sweet almonds to improve its quality. Whether blended or not, almond oil is an important ingredient of many cosmetic preparations, particularly hand and face creams. From almond oil, essence of almonds can be extracted for use in cooking.

Snowberry

Introduced to Britain as an ornamental, snowberry quickly proved itself hardy enough to grow here in the wild (see below). It is at its most conspicuous in winter, when it bears clusters of snow-white berries against a background of leafless stems.

Many of the trees and shrubs that are now accepted as part of the British countryside have not been growing here for long. They were introduced to Britain for their commercial or ornamental value and became naturalised. An example is snowberry. It was brought here about two hundred years ago and now thrives in hedgerows, thickets, banks and copses in many parts of the country.

Dark-berried snowberry There are several distinct species of shrub that are called snowberry. All but one come from North America, where they grow in woods and rocky areas. Despite their name, not all species of snowberry bear white berries. For example, the one species that occurs naturally outside North

America, the Chinese snowberry, has blue-black berries and is far less attractive than the white-berried types. It is only rarely planted in Britain.

The first snowberry to be introduced to Britain was the coral berry or Indian currant. It too lacks white berries—instead they are red or purple. This shrub is native to the eastern states of North America and was brought over here during the 18th century. It was followed by the white-berried species, *Symphoricarpos rivularis*, which is now commonly referred to as snowberry.

It was quickly discovered that snowberry flourished in Britain, growing well on a wide range of soils and propagating freely by means of suckers (shoots that sprout from underground roots).

Cover for pheasants In the 19th century snowberry was widely planted by landowners who were extending their gardens. They found it ideal because it spreads quickly and is easy to look after. Landowners soon discovered another advantage in planting snowberry. Copses and coverts of it provided excellent cover for game birds, particularly pheasants, and it is still being planted for this purpose today.

Snowberry is ideal for providing ground cover. It grows well in the shade of tall trees and it thrives even on poor soils. The only attention it needs is an occasional thinning out if the thickets become too dense. Without this thinning out, the pheasants escape when disturbed by running along the ground under cover; they would have no cause to fly up and so there would be no sport for the sportsman.

Slender stems Snowberry bushes consist of a dense mass of slender stems. The older stems are grey-brown and ridged, with the bark shredding in thin strips. The younger terminal branches are paler and very thin. They have scales at the points where they meet the older wood.

The leaves are oval with wavy margins. They grow in opposite pairs on the twigs and vary in size from 2cm (¾in) up to 8cm (3in) long, the largest leaves being found on the oldest wood. The upper side of each leaf is matt green; the under side is much paler and has a network of even paler veins. Caterpillars of the death's head hawk moth are sometimes seen feeding on the leaves. They usually feed on leaves of members of the potato family but find snowberry a satisfactory substitute.

The flowers are borne in clusters on the ends of the new year's growth of wood. They are small and inconspicuous—about 5mm long. Each flower consists of five white or pink petals that join together to form a tube.

Snowberry flowers appear from June through to September and are often still on the bush when the familiar white berries start to mature in the autumn. Like the flowers, the berries are of course also clustered on the

ends of twigs; the generic name *Symphoricarpos* comes from the Greek for 'fruits borne together'.

The berries are large, about 1cm (½in) across and usually contain two seeds, which are not always fertile. A curious feature of the berries is that they contain air bubbles, which make their texture spongy. When ripe the berries explode with a 'pop' if squeezed.

The berries are not poisonous but they are unpalatable to man, and birds rarely eat them—except pheasants during a harsh winter. However, berries of other members of the snowberry family are palatable and are eaten by wild animals in North America.

Garden ornamentals Snowberry has no commercial uses, apart from its connection with game-keeping, but it is grown widely in gardens for its ornamental qualities. Many of the snowberries grown in gardens are not pure species. They are hybrids produced by crossing various different species to increase the quantity of berries or to change their colour. Some hybrid snowberries bear pink and white fruit. Others are dwarf forms, useful for covering bare ground to suppress weeds or for growing small hedges.

Although the flowers are small and insignificant, they are useful in gardens because they produce abundant nectar that attracts large numbers of insects, particularly bees, throughout the summer months and well into the autumn.

Above: Landowners often plant snowberry for pheasant coverts since, left to itself, it spreads quickly to provide the dense cover that pheasants prefer.

Left: The berries are the plant's most attractive feature. They appear in early autumn (often while the bush is still in flower) and stay on the bush throughout the winter. Snowberries have a curious spongy texture and pop when burst.

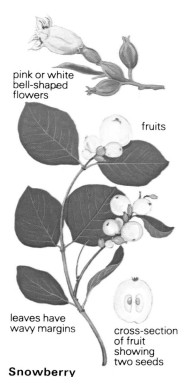

pink or white bell-shaped flowers

fruits

leaves have wavy margins

cross-section of fruit showing two seeds

Snowberry (*Symphoricarpos rivularis*). Introduced deciduous shrub, native to North America. Grows to a height of 2m (6ft). Flowers from June-Sept, followed by white berries.

flowers appear after leaves

obovate finely toothed leaves

Bird cherry

small bitter fruits in long bunches

15–40 flowers in each raceme

ovate irregularly toothed leaves

larger sweet fruits

Gean

flowers appear before or with leaves

flowers in clusters of about six

Gean and bird cherries

Of all our flowering trees the cherries are among the most popular and the most beautiful. A great many cherry trees in Britain come from the Far East, but there are two native species – the gean and the bird cherry – which, when seen flowering in the wild are every bit as pretty.

Many of the cherry trees we see around us – in gardens, parks and streets – came originally from the Far East. The majority, indeed, were introduced to the West from just one country – Japan, where for hundreds of years gardeners have been breeding cherry trees for their ornamental blossom. Rather less familiar, however, are our own native cherries, the gean (or wild cherry) and the bird cherry.

In the wild, these two species are not usually seen together as they differ slightly in their geographical distributions and soil preferences.

The gean occurs throughout Britain but is commonest in the south and favours deep moist soils. Its preferred habitats are hedgerows and the margins of woodland. The bird cherry, on the other hand, has a distinctly northern distribution in Britain, as it does in Continental Europe and Asia, the gean having a more general distribution in these parts. In Britain, the bird cherry grows on lighter, well-drained soils in limestone regions of the type found in many of the hillier areas of northern England. The natural distributions of the two species have, however, been obscured by the extensive planting of both trees as ornamentals.

Shape and size The gean is usually noticeably taller than the bird cherry. It forms a moderate-sized tree, reaching a height of about 20m (65ft), though occasional specimens may grow to become over 30m (100ft) tall. Its branches spread out widely to form a broad, rounded crown.

The bird cherry, a smaller species, is usually seen as a shrub no more than 10m (33ft) tall, though it too may grow to become a tree up to 17m (55ft) high. The branches of the bird cherry are slender and more upright than those of the gean. In both species the young branches are covered with soft downy hairs, though less so on the gean.

The bark of the gean is a glossy reddish-brown with horizontal bands of light brown lenticels; these are pores in the bark through which air passes into the trunk. On younger branches and the trunks of young trees the bark often peels away horizontally in papery strips, but on older branches and trunks the bark becomes fissured. The bird cherry has a smooth, dark greyish bark which, when crushed, releases a strongly pungent, foetid smell.

Leaf comparison Superficially, the leaves of the gean and bird cherry are similar, except that those of the former are larger – up to 15cm (6in) long, compared with the leaves of a bird cherry, which are no more than 10cm (4in) long. The leaves of both are deciduous, with toothed margins and tapering tips. The upper surfaces are dullish green and smooth; the lower surfaces are paler and often have soft downy hairs along the main veins. Before they fall in the autumn, the leaves turn an attractive red and then yellow, usually changing colour from the margins inwards.

A close inspection, however, does reveal some important differences between the leaves of the two species. The teeth of gean leaves are deep and rather irregular, while the leaves of the bird cherry are more finely

Bird cherry

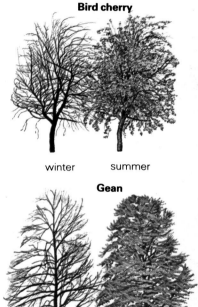

winter   summer

Gean

winter   summer

Bird cherry (*Prunus padus*). Native deciduous shrub or tree, more common in northern Britain where it grows in hilly limestone regions. Height to 10m (33ft), exceptionally to 17m (55ft).

Gean or **wild cherry** (*Prunus avium*). Native deciduous tree, more common in southern Britain, especially in woodland margins and hedgerows. Height to 30m (100ft), more usually 20m (65ft).

Opposite: A gean in spring flower.

Gean
Prunus avium
var *plena*

Bird cherry
Prunus padus
cultivar *'watereri'*

Above: Two garden varieties of our native cherries.

Above right: Gean blossoms just before the leaves show.

Below: The bird cherry flowers a few weeks later.

toothed. The two sets of leaves also have slightly different shapes. The point where gean leaves are at their broadest lies closer to the leaf base than to the tip (a shape called ovate); on the bird cherry the leaves are broadest towards the leaf tip (called obovate). The latter leaves also have rounded heart-shaped bases, and they share the same foetid smell of the bark.

Spring blossom If the leaves of the two species seem similar, the flowers are quite different. The gean flowers from April to May, the flowers opening just before the leaves appear. They are borne on short stalks in small, rather drooping clusters of about six. Each flower has five white petals–deeply notched and about 1.5cm (⅗in) long–and numerous stamens.

A gean in flower is a pretty sight but, unfortunately, the spectacle is often short lived: in fine weather the petals may remain on the flowers for little more than a week.

The bird cherry produces much larger clusters of flowers–between 15 and 40 may be present on each elongated raceme, all crowded together on short stalks. The five rounded white petals are smaller than those of a gean (less than 1cm/⅖in long) and usually have a minutely toothed margin. The flowers appear in May and are just as short lived as the gean's.

Sweet and sour fruits The two species are equally distinct in their fruits. Gean fruits are almost perfectly spherical, with just a slight depression at the stalk end. By July they have ripened to a glossy red, though a few remain yellow or become black. When ripe they are about 2cm (1in) long and sweet and juicy, sometimes with a very slightly bitter taste. They are avidly eaten by birds and were once harvested from wild trees in Britain to be sold for eating, a practice that continued until the development of modern improved varieties.

The word gean itself (which is pronounced with a soft 'g') is an Anglicised form of the French word 'guigne', meaning sweet cherry. One of the less widely used common names for this species is merry, which also has a French origin, being a corruption of 'merise', a wild cherry. As well as being eaten, gean fruits were also used to flavour brandy, as implied in another of its common names: brandy mazzard.

The fruits of a bird cherry are smaller, only 1cm (⅖in) or so across, and like the flowers are borne in large racemes. When ripe they are shiny, black and spherical, but have a sharp, bitter taste that makes them inedible. Birds, however, seem to enjoy them and devour them eagerly, as the name bird cherry suggests. Other common names for this tree include hagberry, hawkberry and hackberry, all names that emphasize its unpleasant taste.

Timber and rootstock Both the gean and the bird cherry produce an excellent-quality timber, much prized by cabinet makers for its attractive colour and fine grain. However, the wood is available only in small amounts.

Commercially, a more important use for the gean, though not the bird cherry, is as a rootstock on to which other cherries are grafted. By doing this the grafted cherry benefits from the vigorous and rapid growth of the gean's root system and trunk, while still bearing the desired ornamental flowers or improved varieties of fruit. The use of a gean rootstock is the key to the successful cultivation of many oriental cherries in Britain which, on their own root systems, would grow only very slowly, if at all, in our climate. So if you look at an ornamental cherry, or an orchard cherry, you are likely to see that it has the trunk of a gean but branches that appear quite different, being those of the grafted portion.

Garden and street trees Both the gean and the bird cherry are widely planted in their wild forms, but most specimens of these trees seen in gardens and streets are cultivated varieties, especially selected for their flowers, leaves or habit of growth.

One of the best-known garden varieties of gean is the double-flowered variety *plena* which, in addition to each flower having extra petals, also bears more flowers to a cluster than does the gean. The cultivar '*decumana*' has large leaves, up to 30cm (1ft) long, while '*nana*' is a dwarf cultivar suitable for small gardens, though it is less spectacular in flower than some of the dwarf oriental cherries.

There are just as many cultivated varieties of the bird cherry, though they are perhaps less frequently grown. The most common is '*watereri*', sometimes known as '*grandiflora*' because of its larger, more abundant flowers.

Above: The leaves of both the gean (here) and the bird cherry turn red then yellow in the autumn.

Right: The fruits of a bird cherry hang in unusually long clusters.

Growth of a cherry

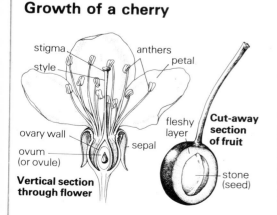

stigma

style

anthers

petal

ovary wall

ovum (or ovule)

sepal

fleshy layer

Cut-away section of fruit

stone (seed)

Vertical section through flower

At the base of each cherry flower is a receptacle containing within the ovary an ovule. The ovule (the future seed) is fertilised by male cells from the pollen grain that landed on the stigma during pollination. After fertilisation the inner layers of the ovary wall grow to form the stone of the fruit (enclosing the seed) while the outer layers form the flesh.

Oriental cherries

For hundreds of years, cherry trees have been cultivated in the Far East for their ornamental blossom. These same trees are now being planted in Britain, where they bring a welcome splash of colour to our towns and cities in spring.

'Tai-Haku'

large single white flowers

'Amanogawa'

pink semi-double flowers

Among the most attractive of all the trees in Britain are the ornamental cherries, so called because they are planted for their appearance rather than for their fruits, which are usually inedible. Ornamental cherries are becoming increasingly popular in towns and cities since many are small compact trees, ideal for growing in the confined space of a street or a small garden.

There is now a wide range of varieties to choose from, with differing flower colours and branching patterns. Even outside their flowering period, some ornamental cherries have distinct and beautiful barks and on many the leaves are brightly coloured, both in spring when they emerge and in autumn before they fall.

Oriental cherries Britain's native cherries, the gean or wild cherry and the bird cherry, have been valued for their ornamental qualities for hundreds of years, but almost all the ornamental cherries being planted nowadays originate in the Far East, especially in China and Japan. Both these countries have a profusion of cherry species growing wild which have long been cultivated for their ornamental value rather than for their fruits. In Japan, especially, flowering cherries are venerated. Temples, shrines and other holy places are planted with them; they are frequent subjects for Japanese art; and there is a host of legends and traditional stories surrounding them. Japan is famous for its massed plantations of cherries, which attract hundreds of thousands of visitors at blossom time each year.

The oriental cherries were introduced to Europe during the 19th century, when trade routes to the Far East were opened up. But many of the varieties that had been cultivated in the East for so long arrived in Britain only during this century. Their introduction and subsequent popularisation was due to one man – Captain Collingwood Ingram.

Japanese cherry The first oriental cherry to be introduced to Britain was the Japanese cherry (*Prunus serrulata*), also known as the oriental cherry. It arrived in Britain in 1822 from Canton in China, though it is more commonly grown in Japan, where varieties of this species are greatly treasured and known as Sato Zakura (Japanese for 'village cherries'). Despite its popularity in Japan, this species is actually native to China but was introduced to Japan many hundreds of years ago.

The Japanese cherry is the most widely planted ornamental cherry in Britain. Of the hundreds of varieties that have been developed around the world, at least 60 are grown here. They differ mainly in the colour and arrangement of the flowers and in the flowering period. They all have purple-brown barks with rows of protruding lenticels. The leaves, which are oval with a long tapering point and toothed margins, turn a handsome pink, red or golden-yellow in the autumn. Japanese cherries can grow as tall as 15m (50ft), but most are much shorter than this.

Common varieties The most popular variety of Japanese cherry grown in Britain is 'Kanzan', which bears masses of deep pink, double flowers in April. So many flowers are

Above: Most ornamental cherry trees in Britain are varieties of the Japanese cherry; two common ones are 'Tai-Haku' and 'Amanogawa'.

Opposite: A Sargent's cherry in blossom. This species is one of the earlier cherries to flower.

Below: 'Kanzan' is the most widely planted of all the Japanese cherries.

Above: The variety 'Cheal's Weeping' has pink or white flowers, which appear at the same time as its leaves, usually in late April. This variety often has a lop-sided shape.

Right: The Yoshino cherry, a popular hybrid flowering in March or April.

Seasonal colours

leaf opens reddish purple

spring

becomes dark green when mature

summer

turns orange or crimson in September

autumn

produced that the branches, which for most of the year are fairly upright, hang down under the weight.

Another commonly grown variety is 'Shimidsu', which has pendulous branching clusters of flowers. Each cluster consists of three to six large, white, double flowers. They open just after 'Kanzan' in late April or early May. Two other common varieties with very different habits are 'Amanogawa' and 'Cheal's Weeping'. The former has a narrow upright shape and resembles a Lombardy poplar; its flowers are pink and semi-double. The latter variety has very pendulous branches that may almost touch the ground; its flowers can be either pink or white. Both these varieties flower earlier than 'Kanzan'.

The variety 'Tai-Haku' has a most unusual history. In 1923, Captain Collingwood Ingram noticed an unusual cherry tree growing in a garden in Sussex. At first he could not identify it; but, during a visit to Japan, he discovered that it used to grow there but became extinct during the 18th century. The Japanese called it 'Tai-Haku'. Ingram later reintroduced it into its native country, but no one yet knows how it came to be growing in a Sussex garden. The flowers of 'Tai-Haku' are white and spectacularly large – up to 8cm (3in) across, which is larger than those of any other variety.

Sargent's cherry Another popular ornamental species is Sargent's cherry (*Prunus sargentii*). This is named after Charles Sar-

gent, of the Arnold Arboretum in Boston, USA, who on a visit to Japan in 1890 discovered it growing on the slopes of Mount Fujiyama. Sargent's cherry sometimes grows as tall as 20m (65ft), which is a notable height for a cherry. The bark resembles that of the Japanese cherry, except that it is smoother and glossy. The flowers open in the middle of April and are borne in clusters of two to five densely massed along the branches. The flowers themselves are pink and single.

The leaves on a Sargent's cherry are also attractive. Appearing slightly after the flowers have opened, they are reddish-purple at first and, with the pink flowers, make a striking combination of colours. As the leaves mature they turn dark green, but in autumn become a spectacular bright orange or crimson. Sargent's cherry is one of the first trees to change colour in the autumn, often as early as the beginning of September. In shape, its leaves resemble the leaves of a Japanese cherry.

Rose-bud cherry This is another species of ornamental cherry native to Japan. The rose-bud cherry (*Prunus subhirtella*)–also known as the spring cherry–was introduced to Britain in 1895. There are many varieties of this species, including those with double flowers and others with a weeping habit. But one variety in particular, 'Autumnalis', is especially popular since it flowers throughout the winter. Not surprisingly, it is also known as the winter-flowering cherry. The majority of its pale pink flowers appear in November or April, but in between these months a small number of flowers regularly appears on its otherwise bare branches.

In the wild, the rose-bud cherry can grow to a height of 20m (65ft), though cultivated trees are usually much smaller.

Tibetan cherry Not all ornamental cherries are grown for their flowers. The Tibetan cherry (*Prunus serrula*) is planted primarily for its unusual and attractive bark. In autumn the outer bark peels away in narrow bands from the trunk and branches to reveal new bark of a rich mahogany-brown colour with rings of paler lenticels. Unfortunately, the flowers are relatively insignificant for an ornamental cherry, being small and white. Since they emerge at the same time as the leaves, they tend to be obscured.

The Tibetan cherry is native to western China and was introduced to Britain in 1908. In cultivation it grows to a height of about 8m (25ft).

A profusion of hybrids These four species and their varieties cover most of the ornamental cherries grown in Britain. But there

are also many hybrids that have been developed from these and other species. One particularly common hybrid is the Yoshino cherry (*Prunus × yedoensis*), which is a cross between the rose-bud cherry and the Oshino cherry. The Yoshino is one of the earliest cherries to flower, appearing in March. The single flowers are pink or white. Many other hybrids and varieties are still being developed.

Above: The Tibetan cherry is unusual among ornamental cherries in being planted for its brightly coloured bark rather than its flowers. Its bark is at its best in the autumn, when the outer layer peels away in bands to reveal rich mahogany-colour new bark.

Shapes of trees

Most varieties of Japanese cherry are small trees, usually around 3-4m (10-12ft) high, with an open, spreading crown (**1**), but a few have radically different habits. The variety 'Cheal's Weeping' (**2**) has a weeping or pendulous habit in which its branches reach almost down to the ground. Another variety goes to the opposite extreme. This is 'Amanogawa', which has an upright, columnar habit (**3**) and is said to be fastigiate. All its branches are short and swept strongly upwards from a central stem, so that the tree resembles a small Lombardy poplar.

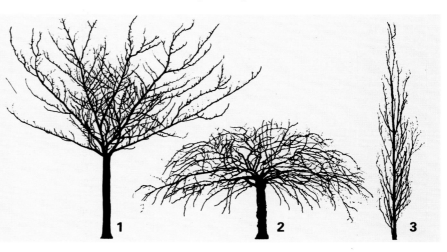

Index

Entries in italics indicate illustrations